McDougal Littell

Geometry

Larson   Boswell   Kanold   Stiff

Notetaking Guide
Teacher's Edition

The Notetaking Guide contains a lesson-by-lesson framework that allows students to take notes on and review the main concepts of each lesson in the textbook. Each Notetaking Guide lesson features worked-out examples and Checkpoint exercises. Each example has a number of write-on lines for students to complete, either in class as the example is discussed or at home as part of a review of the lesson. Each chapter concludes with a review of the main vocabulary of the chapter. Upon completion, each chapter of the Notetaking Guide can be used by students to help review for the test on that particular chapter.

The Teacher's Edition contains annotated overprinted answers for all write-on lines and exercises. In addition, the Notetaking Guide can be used in conjunction with the Notetaking Guide Transparencies which are available separately.

McDougal Littell
A DIVISION OF HOUGHTON MIFFLIN COMPANY
Evanston, Illinois • Boston • Dallas

Contents
Geometry Notetaking Guide

4   Congruent Triangles

5   Relationships within Triangles

6   Similarity

7 Right Triangles and Trigonometry

8 Quadrilaterals

9 Properties of Transformations

10 Properties of Circles

11 Measuring Length and Area

12 Surface Area and Volume of Solids

Identify Points, Lines, and Planes

Goal • Name and sketch geometric figures.

Your Notes

VOCABULARY

Undefined term A word without a formal definition

Point A point has no dimension. It is represented by a dot.

Line A line has one dimension. It is represented by a line with two arrowheads.

Plane A plane has two dimensions. It is represented by a shape that looks like a floor or a wall.

Collinear points Points that lie on the same line

Coplanar points Points that lie in the same plane

Defined Terms Terms that can be described using known words

Line segment, endpoints Part of a line that consists of two points, called endpoints, and all the points on the line between the endpoints

Ray The ray AB consists of the endpoint A and all points on $\overleftrightarrow{AB}$ that lie on the same side of A as B.

Opposite rays If point C lies on $\overleftrightarrow{AB}$ between A and B, then $\overrightarrow{CA}$ and $\overrightarrow{CB}$ are opposite rays.

Intersection The intersection of two or more geometric figures is the set of points that the figures have in common.

UNDEFINED TERMS

Point A point has ___no___ dimension.
It is represented by a ___dot___ .

A
•
point A

Line A line has ___one___ dimension.
It is represented by a ___line___ with
two arrowheads, but it extends
without end.

Through any ___two___ points, there is
exactly ___one___ line. You can use any
___two___ points on a line to name it.

line ℓ, line AB($\overleftrightarrow{AB}$),
or line BA($\overleftrightarrow{BA}$)

Plane A plane has ___two___ dimensions.
It is represented by a shape that
looks like a floor or wall, but it
extends without end.

plane M or plane ABC

Through any ___three___ points not on the same line, there
is exactly ___one___ plane. You can use ___three___ points that
are not all on the same line to name a plane.

> There is a line through points L and Q that is not shown in the diagram. Try to imagine what plane *LMQ* would look like if it were shown.

Example 1   *Name points, lines, and planes*

a. Give two other names for $\overleftrightarrow{LN}$.
Give another name for plane Z.

b. Name three points that are
collinear. Name four points
that are coplanar.

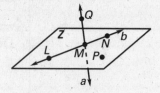

a. Other names for $\overleftrightarrow{LN}$ are ___LM___ and ___line b___. Other
names for plane Z are plane ___LMP___ and ___LNP___.

b. Points ___L, M, and N___ lie on the same line, so they
are collinear. Points ___L, M, N, and P___ lie on the same
plane, so they are coplanar.

✔ *Checkpoint* Use the diagram in Example 1.

1. Give two other names for $\overleftrightarrow{MQ}$. Name a point that is
not coplanar with points *L*, *N*, and *P*.

___$\overleftrightarrow{QM}$ and line a; point Q___

DEFINED TERMS: SEGMENTS AND RAYS

Line *AB* (written as $\overleftrightarrow{AB}$) and points *A* and *B* are used here to define the terms below.

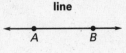
line

Segment The **line segment** *AB*, or segment *AB*, (written as $\overline{AB}$) consists of the endpoints *A* and *B* and all points on $\overleftrightarrow{AB}$ that are ___between___ *A* and *B*.

Note that $\overline{AB}$ can also be named ___BA___.

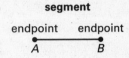
segment
endpoint   endpoint
A   B

Ray The **ray** *AB* (written as $\overrightarrow{AB}$) consists of the endpoint *A* and all points on $\overleftrightarrow{AB}$ that lie on the same side of ___A___ as ___B___.

Note that $\overrightarrow{AB}$ and $\overrightarrow{BA}$ are ___different___ rays.

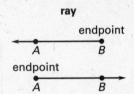
ray
endpoint
A   B
endpoint
A   B

Example 2   *Name segments, rays, and opposite rays*

> In Example 2, $\overrightarrow{WY}$ and $\overrightarrow{WX}$ have a common ___endpoint___, but are *not* ___collinear___. So they are not opposite rays.

a. Give another name for $\overline{VX}$.

b. Name all rays with endpoints *W*. Which of these rays are opposite rays?

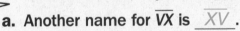

a. Another name for $\overline{VX}$ is ___XV___.

b. The rays with endpoint *W* are ___$\overrightarrow{WV}$, $\overrightarrow{WY}$, $\overrightarrow{WX}$, and $\overrightarrow{WZ}$___.

The opposite rays with endpoint *W* are ___$\overrightarrow{WV}$ and $\overrightarrow{WX}$___, and ___$\overrightarrow{WY}$ and $\overrightarrow{WZ}$___.

✔ *Checkpoint* Use the diagram in Example 2.

2. Give another name for $\overline{YW}$.

___$\overline{WY}$___

---

3. Are $\overrightarrow{VX}$ and $\overrightarrow{XV}$ the same ray? Are $\overrightarrow{VW}$ and $\overrightarrow{VX}$ the same ray? *Explain.*

No, the rays do not have the same endpoint; Yes, the rays have a common endpoint, are collinear, and consist of the same points.

Example 3   *Sketch intersections of lines and planes*

a. Sketch a plane and a line that intersects the plane at more than one point.

b. Sketch a plane and a line that is in the plane. Sketch another line that intersects the line and plane at a point.

a.

b.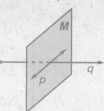

Example 4   *Sketch intersections of planes*

Sketch two planes that intersect in a line.

Step 1 Draw one plane as if you are facing it.

Step 2 Draw a second plane that is __horizontal__. Use dashed lines to show where one plane is hidden.

Step 3 Draw the line of __intersection__.

✔ *Checkpoint* **Complete the following exercises.**

4. Sketch two different lines that intersect a plane at different points.

5. Name the intersection of $\overleftrightarrow{MX}$ and line *a*.

point *M*

Homework

6. Name the intersection of plane *C* and plane *D*.

line *a*

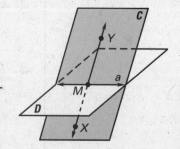

Use Segments and Congruence

Goal • Use segment postulates to identify congruent segments.

Your Notes

VOCABULARY

Postulate, axiom A rule that is accepted without proof

Theorem A rule that can be proved

Coordinate The real number that corresponds to a point

Distance The distance between two points A and B, written as AB, is the absolute value of the difference of the coordinates of A and B.

Between When three points are collinear, you can say that one point is between the other two.

Congruent segments Line segments that have the same length

POSTULATE 1   RULER POSTULATE

The points on a line can be matched one to one with real numbers. The real number that corresponds to a point is the ___coordinate___ of the point.

The ___distance___ between points A and B, written as AB, is the absolute value of the difference of the coordinates of A and B.

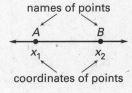

$AB = |x_2 - x_1|$

Example 1 | *Apply the Ruler Postulate*

Measure the length of $\overline{CD}$ to the nearest tenth of a centimeter.

Solution

Align one mark of a metric ruler with *C*. Then estimate the coordinate of *D*. For example, if you align *C* with 1, *D* appears to align with __4.7__ .

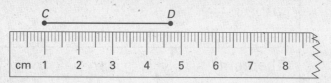

$CD = |\ \underline{4.7}\ -\ \underline{1}\ | = \underline{3.7}$ **Ruler postulate**

The length of $\overline{CD}$ is about __3.7__ centimeters.

POSTULATE 2   SEGMENT ADDITION POSTULATE

If *B* is between *A* and *C*, then
$AB + BC = AC$.

If $AB + BC = AC$, then *B* is between *A* and *C*.

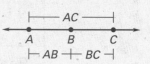

Example 2 | *Apply the Segment Addition Postulate*

Road Trip The locations shown lie in a straight line. Find the distance from the starting point to the destination.

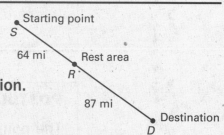

Solution

The rest area lies between the starting point and the destination, so you can apply the Segment Addition Postulate.

$SD = \underline{SR} + \underline{RD}$ **Segment Addition Postulate**

$ = \underline{64} + \underline{87}$ **Substitute for __SR__ and __RD__ .**

$ = \underline{151}$ **Add.**

The distance from the starting point to the destination is __151__ miles.

Example 3 *Find a length*

Use the diagram to find KL.

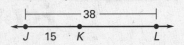

Use the Segment Addition Postulate to write an equation. Then solve the equation to find *KL*.

$\underline{JL}$ = $\underline{JK}$ + *KL*	**Segment Addition Postulate**
$\underline{38}$ = $\underline{15}$ + *KL*	**Substitute for** $\underline{JL}$ **and** $\underline{JK}$.
$\underline{23}$ = *KL*	**Subtract** $\underline{15}$ **from each side.**

Example 4 *Compare segments for congruence*

Plot F(4, 5), G(−1, 5), H(3, 3), and J(3, −2) in a coordinate plane. Then determine whether $\overline{FG}$ and $\overline{HJ}$ are congruent.

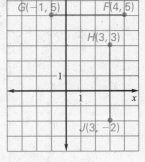

Horizontal segment: Subtract the $\underline{x\text{-coordinates}}$ **of the endpoints.**

$FG = \left|\ \underline{4 - (-1)}\ \right| = \underline{5}$

Vertical segment: Subtract the $\underline{y\text{-coordinates}}$ **of the endpoints.**

$HJ = \left|\ \underline{3 - (-2)}\ \right| = \underline{5}$

$\overline{FG}$ and $\overline{HJ}$ have the $\underline{\text{same}}$ length. So $\overline{FG}\ \underline{\cong}\ \overline{HJ}$.

✔ **Checkpoint** Complete the following exercises.

1. Find the length of $\overline{AB}$ to the nearest $\frac{1}{8}$ inch.

A ●————————————————● B

$1\frac{7}{8}$ inches

Homework

2. Find *QS* and *PQ*.

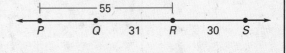

61; 24

3. Consider the points A(−2, −1), B(4, −1), C(3, 0), and D(3, 5). Are $\overline{AB}$ and $\overline{CD}$ congruent?

No

1.3 Use Midpoint and Distance Formulas

Goal • Find lengths of segments in the coordinate plane.

Your Notes

> **VOCABULARY**
>
> **Midpoint** The point that divides a segment into two congruent segments
>
> **Segment bisector** A point, ray, line, line segment, or plane that intersects the segment at its midpoint

---

Example 1 **Find segments lengths**

Find *RS*.

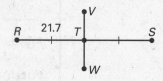

Solution

Point _T_ is the midpoint of $\overline{RS}$. So, $RT =$ _TS_ = 21.7.

$RS =$ _RT_ + _TS_   **Segment Addition Postulate**

   $=$ _21.7_ + _21.7_   **Substitute.**

   $=$ _43.4_   **Add.**

The length of $\overline{RS}$ is _43.4_ .

✔ *Checkpoint* Complete the following exercise.

1. Find *AB*.

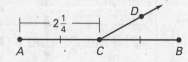

$4\frac{1}{2}$

Example 2   *Use algebra with segment lengths*

Point *C* is the midpoint of $\overline{BD}$.
Find the length of $\overline{BC}$.

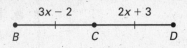

$$
\begin{array}{ccc}
\overset{3x-2}{} & & \overset{2x+3}{} \\
\bullet\!\!\!\!\!-\!\!\!-\!\!\!-\!\!\!|\!\!\!-\!\!\!-\!\!\!\bullet\!\!\!-\!\!\!-\!\!\!|\!\!\!-\!\!\!-\!\!\!-\!\!\!\bullet \\
B & C & D
\end{array}
$$

Solution

Step 1 Write and solve an equation.

$BC = CD$	Write equation.
$\underline{3x-2} = \underline{2x+3}$	Substitute.
$\underline{x-2} = \underline{3}$	Subtract $\underline{2x}$ from each side.
$x = \underline{5}$	Add $\underline{2}$ to each side.

Step 2 Evaluate the expression for BC when $x = \underline{5}$.

$$BC = \underline{3x-2} = \underline{3(5)-2} = \underline{13}$$

So, the length of $\overline{BC}$ is $\underline{13}$.

✔ *Checkpoint* Complete the following exercise.

2. Point *K* is the midpoint of $\overline{JL}$. Find the length of $\overline{KL}$.

$$
\begin{array}{ccc}
\overset{8-3x}{} & & \overset{2x+5}{} \\
\bullet\!\!\!-\!\!\!-\!\!\!-\!\!\!|\!\!\!-\!\!\!-\!\!\!\bullet\!\!\!-\!\!\!-\!\!\!|\!\!\!-\!\!\!-\!\!\!-\!\!\!\bullet \\
J & K & L
\end{array}
$$

$6\dfrac{1}{5}$

THE MIDPOINT FORMULA

The coordinates of the midpoint of a segment are the averages of the *x*-coordinates and of the *y*-coordinates of the endpoints.

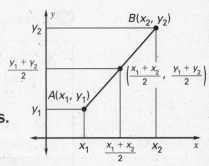

If $A(x_1, y_1)$ and $B(x_2, y_2)$ are points in a coordinate plane, then the midpoint *M* of $\overline{AB}$ has coordinates $\left(\dfrac{x_1+x_2}{2}, \dfrac{y_1+y_2}{2}\right)$.

Example 3   *Use the Midpoint Formula*

a. **Find Midpoint** The endpoints of $\overline{PR}$ are $P(-2, 5)$ and $R(4, 3)$. Find the coordinates of the midpoint M.

b. **Find Endpoint** The midpoint of $\overline{AC}$ is $M(3, 4)$. One endpoint is $A(1, 6)$. Find the coordinates of endpoint C.

Solution

a. Use the Midpoint Formula.

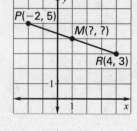

$$M\left(\frac{\boxed{-2} + \boxed{4}}{\boxed{2}}, \frac{\boxed{5} + \boxed{3}}{\boxed{2}} \right)$$

$$= M(\underline{1}, \underline{4})$$

The coordinates of the midpoint of $\overline{PR}$ are $\underline{M(1, 4)}$.

> Multiply each side of the equation by the denominator to clear the fraction.

b. Let (x, y) be the coordinates of endpoint C. Use the Midpoint Formula to find x and y.

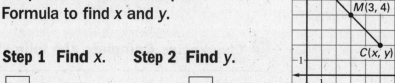

Step 1 Find x.

$$\frac{\boxed{1} + x}{2} = \underline{3}$$

$$\underline{1} + x = \underline{6}$$

$$x = \underline{5}$$

Step 2 Find y.

$$\frac{\boxed{6} + y}{2} = \underline{4}$$

$$\underline{6} + y = \underline{8}$$

$$y = \underline{2}$$

The coordinates of endpoint C are $\underline{(5, 2)}$.

✔ *Checkpoint* **Complete the following exercises.**

3. The endpoints of $\overline{CD}$ are $C(-8, -1)$ and $D(2, 4)$. Find the coordinates of the midpoint M.

$$M\left(-3, \frac{3}{2}\right)$$

4. The midpoint of $\overline{XZ}$ is $M(5, -6)$. One endpoint is $X(-3, 7)$. Find the coordinates of endpoint Z.

$$(13, -19)$$

THE DISTANCE FORMULA

If $A(x_1, y_1)$ and $B(x_2, y_2)$ are points in a coordinate plane, then the distance between A and B is

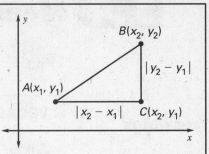

$AB = \sqrt{(\underline{\,x_2 - x_1\,})^2 + (\underline{\,y_2 - y_1\,})^2}$

Example 4   *Use the Distance Formula*

What is the approximate length of $\overline{RT}$, with endpoints $R(3, 2)$ and $T(-4, 3)$?

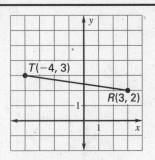

Solution

Use the Distance Formula.

$RT = \sqrt{(\underline{\,x_2 - x_1\,})^2 + (\underline{\,y_2 - y_1\,})^2}$ **Distance Formula**

$= \sqrt{(\underline{\,-4\,} - 3)^2 + (\underline{\,3\,} - \underline{\,2\,})^2}$ **Substitute.**

$= \sqrt{(\underline{\,-7\,})^2 + (\underline{\,1\,})^2}$ **Subtract.**

$= \sqrt{\underline{\,49\,} + \underline{\,1\,}}$ **Evaluate powers.**

$= \sqrt{\underline{\,50\,}}$ **Add.**

$\approx \underline{\,7.07\,}$ **Use a calculator.**

The length of $\overline{RT}$ is about $\underline{\,7.07\,}$.

> The symbol $\approx$ means "is approximately equal to."

✔ *Checkpoint* **Complete the following exercise.**

Homework

5. What is the approximate length of $\overline{GH}$, with endpoints $G(5, -1)$ and $H(-3, 6)$?

   about 10.63

Measure and Classify Angles

Goal • Name, measure, and classify angles.

Your Notes

> **VOCABULARY**
>
> **Angle** An angle consists of two different rays with the same endpoint.
>
> **Sides of an angle** In an angle, the rays are called the sides of the angle.
>
> **Vertex of an angle** In an angle, the endpoint is the vertex of the angle.
>
> **Measure of an angle** In $\angle AOB$, $\overrightarrow{OA}$ and $\overrightarrow{OB}$ can be matched one to one with real numbers from 0 to 180. The measure of $\angle AOB$ is equal to the absolute value of the difference between the real numbers for $\overrightarrow{OA}$ and $\overrightarrow{OB}$.
>
> **Acute angle** An angle that measures between 0° and 90°
>
> **Right angle** An angle that measures 90°
>
> **Obtuse angle** An angle that measures between 90° and 180°
>
> **Straight angle** An angle that measures 180°
>
> **Congruent angles** Angles with the same measure
>
> **Angle bisector** A ray that divides an angle into two angles that are congruent

Example 1 *Name angles*

Name the three angles in the diagram.

> You should not name any of these angles *B* because all three angles have *B* as their _vertex_ .

$\underline{\angle ABC}$, or $\underline{\angle CBA}$

$\underline{\angle CBD}$, or $\underline{\angle DBC}$

$\underline{\angle ABD}$, or $\underline{\angle DBA}$

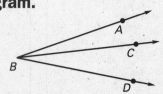

Your Notes

POSTULATE 3: PROTRACTOR POSTULATE

Consider $\overrightarrow{OB}$ and point *A* on one side of $\overrightarrow{OB}$. The rays of the form $\overrightarrow{OA}$ can be matched one to one with the real numbers from 0 to __180__.

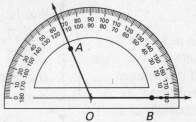

The measure of __∠AOB__ is equal to __the absolute value of the difference__ between the real numbers for $\overrightarrow{OA}$ and $\overrightarrow{OB}$.

Example 2 — *Measure and classify angles*

Use the diagram to find the measure of the indicated angle. Then classify the angle.

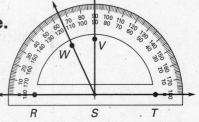

a. ∠WSR   b. ∠TSW

c. ∠RST   d. ∠VST

a. $\overrightarrow{SR}$ is lined up with the 0° on the __outer__ scale of the protractor. $\overrightarrow{SW}$ passes through __65°__ on the __outer__ scale. So, m∠WSR = __65°__. It is __an acute__ angle.

b. $\overrightarrow{ST}$ is lined up with the 0° on the __inner__ scale of the protractor. $\overrightarrow{SW}$ passes through __115°__ on the __inner__ scale. So, m∠TSW = __115°__. It is __an obtuse__ angle.

c. m∠RST = __180°__. It is __a straight__ angle.

d. m∠VST = __90°__. It is __a right__ angle.

✔ **Checkpoint** Complete the following exercises.

1. Name all the angles in the diagram at the right.

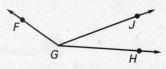

∠FGH or ∠HGF, ∠FGJ or ∠JGF, ∠JGH or ∠HGJ

2. What type of angles do the *x*-axis and *y*-axis form in a coordinate plane?

right angles

POSTULATE 4: ANGLE ADDITION POSTULATE

Words If *P* is in the interior of
∠*RST*, then the measure of
∠*RST* is equal to the sum of
the measures of ∠ _RSP_
and ∠ _PST_ .

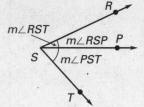

Symbols If *P* is in the interior of ∠*RST*,
then *m*∠*RST* = *m*∠ _RSP_ + *m*∠ _PST_ .

> A point is in the *interior* of an angle if it is between points that lie on each side of the angle.

interior

Example 3 *Find angle measures*

Given that *m*∠*GFJ* = 155°,
find *m*∠*GFH* and *m*∠*HFJ*.

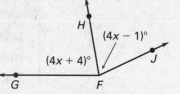

Solution

Step 1 Write and solve an equation to find the value of *x*.

$m\angle GFJ = m\angle \underline{\ GFH\ } + m\angle \underline{\ HFJ\ }$ **Angle Addition Postulate**

$\underline{\ 155°\ } = (\underline{\ 4x+4\ })° + (\underline{\ 4x-1\ })°$ **Substitute.**

$\underline{\ 155\ } = \underline{\ 8x+3\ }$ **Combine like terms.**

$\underline{\ 152\ } = \underline{\ 8x\ }$ **Subtract** _3_ **from each side.**

$\underline{\ 19\ } = x$ **Divide each side by** _8_ .

Step 2 Evaluate the given expressions when *x* = _19_ .

$m\angle GFH = (\underline{\ 4x+4\ })° = (\underline{\ 4 \cdot 19 + 4\ })° = \underline{\ 80°\ }.$

$m\angle HFJ = (\underline{\ 4x-1\ })° = (\underline{\ 4 \cdot 19 - 1\ })° = \underline{\ 75°\ }.$

So, *m*∠*GFH* = _80°_ and *m*∠*HFJ* = _75°_ .

✓ *Checkpoint* Complete the following exercise.

3. Given that ∠*VRS* is a right angle,
find *m*∠*VRT* and ∠*TRS*.

m∠*VRT* = 19°, *m*∠*TRS* = 71°

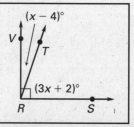

Example 4 *Identify congruent angles*

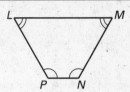

Identify all pairs of congruent angles in the diagram. If $m\angle P = 120°$, what is $m\angle N$?

Solution

There are two pairs of congruent angles:

$\angle P \cong \underline{\ \angle N\ }$ and $\angle L \cong \underline{\ \angle M\ }$

Because $\angle P \cong \underline{\ \angle N\ }$, $m\angle P = \underline{\ m\angle N\ }$.
So, $m\angle N = \underline{\ 120°\ }$.

Example 5 *Double an angle measure*

In the diagram at the right, $\overrightarrow{WY}$ bisects $\angle XWZ$, and $m\angle XWY = 29°$. Find $m\angle XWZ$.

Solution

By the Angle Addition Postulate,
$m\angle XWZ = \underline{\ m\angle XWY\ } + \underline{\ m\angle YWZ\ }$.
Because $\overrightarrow{WY}$ bisects $\angle XWZ$, you know
$\underline{\ \angle XWY\ } \cong \underline{\ \angle YWZ\ }$.

So, $\underline{\ m\angle XWY\ } = \underline{\ m\angle YWZ\ }$, and you can write
$m\angle XWZ = \underline{\ m\angle XWY\ } + \underline{\ m\angle YWZ\ }$
$\qquad\ \ = \underline{\ 29°\ } + \underline{\ 29°\ } = \underline{\ 58°\ }$.

✔ **Checkpoint** Complete the following exercises.

4. Identify all pairs of congruent angles in the diagram. If $m\angle B = 135°$, what is $m\angle D$?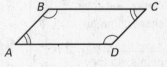

   $\angle B \cong \angle D$ and $\angle A \cong \angle C$; 135°

Homework

5. In the diagram below, $\overrightarrow{KM}$ bisects $\angle LKN$ and $m\angle LKM = 78°$. Find $m\angle LKN$.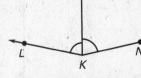

   156°

1.5 Describe Angle Pair Relationships

Goal • Use special angle relationships to find angle measures.

Your Notes

VOCABULARY

Complementary angles Two angles whose sum is 90°

Supplementary angles Two angles whose sum is 180°

Adjacent angles Two angles that share a common vertex or side, but have no common interior points

---

Linear pair Two adjacent angles are a linear pair if their noncommon sides are opposite rays.

Vertical angles Two angles are vertical angles if their sides form two pairs of opposite rays.

Example 1 *Identify complements and supplements*

> In Example 1, ∠BDE and ∠CDE share a common vertex. But they share common __interior__ points, so they are *not* adjacent angles.

In the figure, name a pair of complementary angles, a pair of supplementary angles, and a pair of adjacent angles.

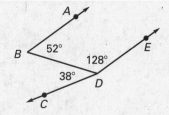

Solution

Because __52°__ + __38°__ = 90°, __∠ABD__ and __∠CDB__ are __complementary__ angles.

Because __52°__ + __128°__ = 180°, __∠ABD__ and __∠EDB__ are __supplementary__ angles.

Because __∠CDB__ and __∠BDE__ share a common vertex and side, they are __adjacent__ angles.

Your Notes

> Angles are sometimes named with numbers. An angle measure in a diagram has a degree symbol. An angle name does not.

Example 2 *Find measures of complements and supplements*

a. Given that $\angle 1$ is a complement of $\angle 2$ and $m\angle 2 = 57°$, find $m\angle 1$.

b. Given that $\angle 3$ is a supplement of $\angle 4$ and $m\angle 4 = 41°$, find $m\angle 3$.

Solution

a. You can draw a diagram with complementary adjacent angles to illustrate the relationship.

$$m\angle 1 = \underline{\ 90°\ } - \underline{\ m\angle 2\ } = \underline{\ 90°\ } - \underline{\ 57°\ } = \underline{\ 33°\ }$$

b. You can draw a diagram with supplementary adjacent angles to illustrate the relationship.

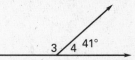

$$m\angle 3 = \underline{\ 180°\ } - \underline{\ m\angle 4\ } = \underline{\ 180°\ } - \underline{\ 41°\ } = \underline{\ 139°\ }$$

✔ **Checkpoint** Complete the following exercises.

1. In the figure, name a pair of complementary angles, a pair of supplementary angles, and a pair of adjacent angles.

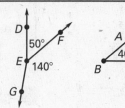

complementary: $\angle DEF$ and $\angle ABC$;
supplementary; $\angle FEG$ and $\angle ABC$;
adjacent: $\angle DEF$ and $\angle FEG$

2. Given that $\angle 1$ is a complement of $\angle 2$ and $m\angle 1 = 73°$, find $m\angle 2$.

17°

3. Given that $\angle 3$ is a supplement of $\angle 4$ and $m\angle 4 = 37°$, find $m\angle 3$.

143°

Your Notes

Example 3   Find angle measures

Basketball The basketball pole forms a pair of supplementary angles with the ground. Find $m\angle BCA$ and $m\angle DCA$.

$(3x + 8)°$ $(4x - 3)°$

B   *C*   *D*

Solution

Step 1 Use the fact that __180°__ is the sum of the measures of supplementary angles.

$$m\angle BCA + m\angle DCA = \underline{180°} \quad \text{Write equation.}$$
$$(\underline{3x + 8})° + (\underline{4x - 3})° = \underline{180°} \quad \text{Substitute.}$$
$$\underline{7x + 5} = \underline{180} \quad \text{Combine like terms.}$$
$$\underline{7x} = \underline{175} \quad \text{Subtract.}$$
$$\underline{x} = \underline{25} \quad \text{Divide.}$$

Step 2 Evaluate the original expressions when $x = \underline{25}$.

$$m\angle BCA = (\underline{3x + 8})° = (\underline{3 \cdot 25 + 8})° = \underline{83°}.$$
$$m\angle DCA = (\underline{4x - 3})° = (\underline{4 \cdot 25 - 3})° = \underline{97°}.$$

The angle measures are __83°__ and __97°__.

✔ **Checkpoint** Complete the following exercise.

4. In Example 3, suppose the angle measures are $(5x + 1)°$ and $(6x + 3)°$. Find $m\angle BCA$ and $m\angle DCA$.

   81° and 99°

Your Notes

> In the diagram, one side of ∠1 and one side of ∠4 are opposite rays. But the angles are not a linear pair because they are not __adjacent__.

Example 4 *Identify angle pairs*

Identify all of the linear pairs and all of the vertical angles in the figure at the right.

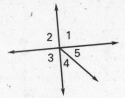

Solution

To find vertical angles, look for angles formed by __intersecting lines__.

__∠1__ and __∠3__ are vertical angles.

To find linear pairs, look for adjacent angles whose noncommon sides are __opposite rays__.

__∠1__ and __∠2__ are a linear pair. __∠2__ and __∠3__ are a linear pair.

✔ **Checkpoint** **Complete the following exercise.**

> 5. Identify all of the linear pairs and all of the vertical angles in the figure.
>
> linear pairs: none; vertical angles: ∠1 and ∠4, ∠2 and ∠5, ∠3 and ∠6

Example 5 *Find angle measures in a linear pair*

Two angles form a linear pair. The measure of one angle is 4 times the measure of the other. Find the measure of each angle.

> You may find it useful to draw a diagram to represent a word problem like the one in Example 5.

Solution

Let $x°$ be the measure of one angle. The measure of the other angle is __$4x°$__. Then use the fact that the angles of a linear pair are __supplementary__ to write an equation.

$x°$ + __$4x°$__ = __180°__		**Write an equation.**
__$5x$__ = __180__		**Combine like terms.**
x = __36__		**Divide each side by** __5__.

The measures of the angles are __36°__ and __4(36°)__ = __144°__.

✔ *Checkpoint* **Complete the following exercise.**

6. Two angles form a linear pair. The measure of one angle is 3 times the measure of the other. Find the meaure of each angle.

45° and 135°

CONCEPT SUMMARY: INTERPRETING A DIAGRAM

There are some things you can conclude from a diagram, and some you cannot. For example, here are some things that you can conclude from the diagram at the right.

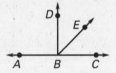

- All points shown are <u>coplanar</u> .

- Points *A*, *B*, and *C* are <u>collinear</u> , and *B* is between *A* and *C*.

- $\overleftrightarrow{AC}$, $\overrightarrow{BD}$, and $\overrightarrow{BE}$ <u>intersect</u> at point *B*.

- ∠*DBE* and ∠*EBC* are <u>adjacent</u> angles, and ∠*ABC* is a <u>straight angle</u> .

- Point *E* lies in the <u>interior</u> of ∠*DBC*.

In the diagram above, you cannot conclude that $\overline{AB} \cong \overline{BC}$, that ∠*DBE* ≅ ∠*EBC*, or that ∠*ABD* is a right angle. This information must be indicated, as shown at the right.

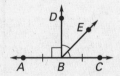

Homework

1.6 Classify Polygons

Goal • Classify polygons.

Your Notes

VOCABULARY

Polygon A polygon is a closed plane figure with the following properties: (1) It is formed by three or more line segments called sides. (2) Each side intersects exactly two sides, one at each endpoint, so that no two sides with a common endpoint are collinear.

Sides The sides of a polygon are the line segments that form the polygon.

Vertex A vertex of a polygon is an endpoint of a side of the polygon.

Convex A polygon is convex if no line that contains a side of the polygon contains a point in the interior of the polygon.

Concave A concave polygon is a polygon that is not convex.

---

n-gon An *n*-gon is a polygon with *n* sides.

Equilateral A polygon is equilateral if all of its sides are congruent.

Equiangular A polygon is equiangular if all of its angles in the interior are congruent.

Regular A polygon is regular if all sides and all angles are congruent.

IDENTIFYING POLYGONS

In geometry, a figure that lies in a plane is called a *plane figure*. A _polygon_ is a closed plane figure with the following properties.

1. It is formed by three or more line segments called _sides_.

2. Each side intersects exactly _two_ sides, one at each endpoint, so that no two sides with a common endpoint are _collinear_.

Each endpoint of a side is a _vertex_ of the polygon. The plural of vertex is *vertices*. A polygon can be named by listing the vertices in consecutive order. For example, *ABCDE* and *CDEAB* are both correct names for the polygon at the right.

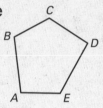

Example 1 *Identify polygons*

> A *plane figure* is two-dimensional. Later, you will study three-dimensional *space figures* such as prisms and cylinders.

Tell whether the figure is a polygon and whether it is *convex* or *concave*.

a.   b.   c.

Solution

a. Some segments intersect more than two segments, so it is _not a polygon_.

b. The figure is _a convex polygon_.

c. The figure is _a concave polygon_.

✔ *Checkpoint* Tell whether the figure is a polygon and whether it is *convex* or *concave*.

1.

convex polygon

2.

not a polygon

Your Notes

Example 2   *Classify polygons*

Classify the polygon by the number of sides. Tell whether the polygon is *equilateral*, *equiangular*, or *regular*.

Solution

The polygon has 8 sides. It is equilateral and equiangular, so it is a regular octagon .

Example 3   *Find side lengths*

(4x + 3) mm

(5x − 1) mm

The head of a bolt is shaped like a regular hexagon. The expressions shown represent side lengths of the hexagonal bolt. Find the length of a side.

> *Hexagonal* means "shaped like a hexagon."

Solution

First, write and solve an equation to find the value of *x*. Use the fact that the sides of a regular hexagon are congruent .

$$4x + 3 = 5x - 1 \qquad \text{Write an equation.}$$
$$4 = x \qquad \text{Simplify.}$$

Then evaluate one of the expressions to find a side length when x = 4 . $4x + 3 = 4(4) + 3 = 19$

The length of a side is 19 millimeters.

✔ *Checkpoint* **Complete the following exercises.**

3. Classify the polygon by the number of sides. Tell whether the polygon is *equilateral*, *equiangular*, or *regular*.

   quadrilateral

4. The expressions (4x + 8)° and (5x − 5)° represent the measures of two of the congruent angles in Example 3. Find the measure of an angle.

   60°

Homework

1.7 Find Perimeter, Circumference, and Area

Goal • Find dimensions of polygons.

Your Notes

FORMULAS FOR PERIMETER P, AREA A, AND CIRCUMFERENCE C

Square
side length s

$P = \underline{4s}$
$A = \underline{s^2}$

Rectangle
length ℓ and width w

$P = \underline{2\ell + 2w}$
$A = \underline{\ell w}$

Triangle
side lengths a, b, and c, base b, and height h.

$P = \underline{a + b + c}$
$A = \underline{\frac{1}{2}bh}$

Circle
radius r

$C = \underline{2\pi r}$
$A = \underline{\pi r^2}$

Pi (π) is the ratio of a circle's circumference to its diameter.

Example 1 *Find the perimeter and area of a rectangle*

Tennis The in-bounds portion of a singles tennis court is shown. Find its perimeter and area.

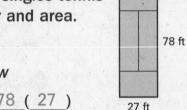

78 ft

27 ft

Perimeter	Area
$P = 2\ell + 2w$	$A = \ell w$
$= 2(\underline{78}) + 2(\underline{27})$	$= \underline{78}(\underline{27})$
$= \underline{210}$	$= \underline{2106}$

The perimeter is __210__ ft and the area is __2106__ ft².

✔ **Checkpoint** Complete the following exercise.

1. In Example 1, the width of the in-bounds rectangle increases to 36 feet for doubles play. Find the perimeter and area of the in-bounds rectangle.

perimeter: 228 ft, area: 2808 ft²

Example 2   *Find the circumference and area of a circle*

Archery The smallest circle on an Olympic target is 12 centimeters in diameter. Find the approximate circumference and area of the smallest circle.

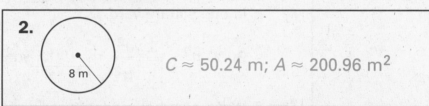

The approximations 3.14 and $\frac{22}{7}$ are commonly used as approximations for the irrational number π. Unless told otherwise, use 3.14 for π.

Solution

First find the radius. The diameter is 12 centimeters, so the radius is $\frac{1}{2}$(_12_) = _6_ centimeters.

Then find the circumference and area. Use 3.14 for π.

$P = 2\pi r \approx 2(\underline{3.14})(\underline{6}) = \underline{37.68\ cm}$

$A = \pi r^2 \approx \underline{3.14}\ (\underline{6})^2 = \underline{113.04\ cm^2}$

✔ *Checkpoint* **Find the approximate circumference and area of the circle.**

2.

8 m

$C \approx 50.24\ m;\ A \approx 200.96\ m^2$

Example 3   *Using a coordinate plane*

Triangle *JKL* has vertices *J*(1, 6), *K*(6, 6), and *L*(3, 2). Find the approximate perimeter of triangle *JKL*.

Solution

First draw triangle *JKL* in a coordinate plane. Then find the side lengths. Because $\overline{JK}$ is horizontal, use the _Ruler Postulate_ to find *JK*. Use the _Distance Formula_ to find *JL* and *LK*.

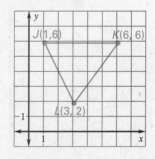

Write down your calculations to make sure you do not make a mistake substituting values in the Distance Formula.

$JK = |\ \underline{6}\ -\ \underline{1}\ | = \underline{5}$ units

$JL = \sqrt{(\underline{3}\ -1)^2 + (2 - \underline{6})^2} = \sqrt{\underline{20}} \approx \underline{4.5}$ units

$LK = \sqrt{(\underline{6}\ -3)^2 + (\underline{6}\ -2)^2} = \sqrt{\underline{25}} = \underline{5}$ units

Then find the perimeter.

$P = JK + JL + LK \approx \underline{5} + \underline{4.5} + \underline{5} = \underline{14.5}$ units.

Example 4 *Solve a multi-step problem*

Lawn care You are using a roller to smooth a lawn. You can roll about 125 square yards in one minute. About how many minutes does it take to roll a lawn that is 120 feet long and 75 feet wide?

Solution

You can roll the lawn at a rate of 125 square yards per minute. So, the amount of time it takes you to roll the lawn depends on its <u>area</u>.

Step 1 Find the area of the rectangular lawn.

$$\text{Area} = \ell w = \underline{\;120\;}(\,\underline{\;75\;}\,) = \underline{\;9000\;}\ \text{ft}^2$$

The rolling rate is in square yards per minute. Rewrite the area of the lawn in square yards. There are <u>3</u> feet in 1 yard, and <u>3</u> $^2 = $ <u>9</u> square feet in one square yard.

$$9000\ \text{ft}^2 \cdot \frac{1\ \text{yd}^2}{\boxed{9}\ \text{ft}^2} = \underline{\;1000\;}\ \text{yd}^2 \quad \textbf{Use unit analysis.}$$

Step 2 Write a verbal model to represent the situation. Then write and solve an equation based on the verbal model.

Let t represent the total time (in minutes) needed to roll the lawn.

Area of lawn (yd²)	=	Rolling rate (yd² per min)	×	Total time (min)

$$\underline{\;1000\;} = \underline{\;125\;} \cdot t \qquad \textbf{Substitute.}$$

$$\underline{\;8\;} = t \qquad \textbf{Divide each side by } \underline{\;125\;}.$$

It takes about <u>8</u> minutes to roll the lawn.

Example 5 *Find unknown length*

The base of a triangle is 24 feet. Its area is 216 square feet. Find the height of the triangle.

Solution

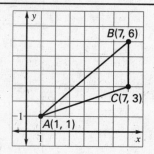

$$A = \frac{1}{2}bh \qquad \text{Area of a triangle}$$

$$\underline{216} = \frac{1}{2}(24)(h) \qquad \text{Substitute.}$$

$$\underline{216} = \underline{12h} \qquad \text{Multiply.}$$

$$\underline{18} = h \qquad \text{Solve for } h.$$

The height is __18__ feet.

✔ **Checkpoint** **Complete the following exercises.**

3. Find the perimeter of the triangle shown at the right.

   about 17.1 units

4. Suppose a lawn is half as long and half as wide as the lawn in Example 4. Will it take half the time to roll the lawn? *Explain.*

   No, it will take a quarter of the time to roll the lawn because it is a quarter of the original area.

Homework

5. The area of a triangle is 96 square inches, and its height is 8 inches. Find the length of its base.

   24 inches

Words to Review

Give an example of the vocabulary word.

Point, line, plane 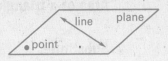	**Collinear points**  A and B are collinear points.
Coplanar points  D and T are coplanar points.	**Line segment, endpoints**  $\overline{CD}$ is a line segment with endpoints C and D.
Ray  $\overrightarrow{XY}$ is a ray with initial point X.	**Opposite rays** 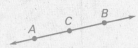 If C is between A and B, then $\overrightarrow{CA}$ and $\overrightarrow{CB}$ are opposite rays.
Intersection  The intersection of two different lines is a point.	**Postulate, axiom** A postulate, or axiom, is a rule that is accepted without proof.
Coordinate  The coordinates of points A and B are x_1 and x_2.	**Distance** $AB = \lvert x_2 - x_1 \rvert$ The distance between points A and B is $\lvert x_2 - x_1 \rvert$.

Between  Point *C* is between Points *A* and *B*.	**Congruent segments** $\overline{AB}$ and $\overline{CD}$ are congruent.
Midpoint 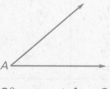 *M* is the midpoint of $\overline{AB}$.	**Segment bisector** 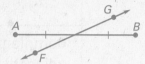 $\overleftrightarrow{FG}$ is a segment bisector of $\overline{AB}$.
Angle, sides, vertex 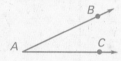 Sides $\overrightarrow{AB}$ and $\overrightarrow{AC}$ form $\angle A$. The vertex is *A*.	**Measure of an angle** 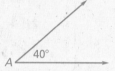 The measure of $\angle A$ is $40°$.
Acute angle 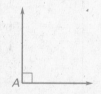 $0° < m\angle A < 90°$	**Right angle** $m\angle A = 90°$
Obtuse angle 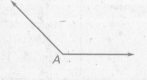 $90° < m\angle A < 180°$	**Straight angle** 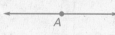 $m\angle A = 180°$

Angle bisector, congruent angles $\vec{BD}$ is an angle bisector of $\angle CBE$. $\angle CBD$ and $\angle DBE$ are congruent.	**Supplementary angles, linear pair** 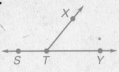 $\angle STX$ and $\angle XTY$ are supplementary. $\angle STX$ and $\angle XTY$ are a linear pair.
Complementary angles, adjacent angles  $\angle QPR$ and $\angle RPS$ are complementary. $\angle QPR$ and $\angle RPS$ are adjacent.	**Vertical angles** $\angle 1$ and $\angle 2$ are vertical angles.
Polygon, side, vertex 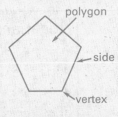	**Concave, convex** $ABCD$ is concave. $FGHJ$ is convex. 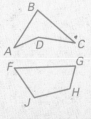
_n_-gon An _n_-gon is a polygon with _n_ sides.	**Equilateral, equiangular, regular** The polygon is equilateral and equiangular, so it is regular.

Review your notes and Chapter 1 by using the Chapter Review on pages 60–63 of your textbook.

2.1 Use Inductive Reasoning

Goal • Describe patterns and use inductive reasoning.

Your Notes

VOCABULARY

Conjecture A conjecture is an unproven statement that is based on observations.

Inductive Reasoning Inductive reasoning is the process of finding a pattern for specific cases and then writing a conjecture for the general case.

Counterexample A counterexample is a specific case for which the conjecture is false.

Example 1 *Describe a visual pattern*

Describe how to sketch the fourth figure in the pattern. Then sketch the fourth figure.

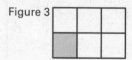

Figure 1   Figure 2   Figure 3

Solution

Each rectangle is divided into <u>twice</u> as many equal regions as the figure number. Sketch the fourth figure by dividing the rectangle into <u>eighths</u>. Shade the section just <u>below</u> the horizontal segment at the <u>left</u>.

Figure 4

✔ *Checkpoint* Complete the following exercise.

1. Sketch the fifth figure in the pattern in Example 1.

Figure 5

> Three dots (. . .) tell you that the pattern continues.

Example 2 *Describe the number pattern*

Describe the pattern in the numbers −1, −4, −16, −64, ... Write the next three numbers in the pattern.

Notice that each number in the pattern is __four__ times the previous number.

−1,   −4,   −16,   −64, . . .

× _4_   × _4_   × _4_   × _4_

The next three numbers are __−256, −1024, and −4096__ .

Example 3 *Make a conjecture*

Given five noncollinear points, make a conjecture about the number of ways to connect different pairs of the points.

Make a table and look for a pattern. Notice the pattern in how the number of connections __increases__ . You can use the pattern to make a conjecture.

Number of points	1	2	3	4	5
Picture	•	•—•	◁	⊠	⬠
Number of connections	_0_	_1_	_3_	_6_	_?_

+ _1_   + _2_   + _3_   + _?_

Conjecture You can connect five noncollinear points __6 + 4__ , or __10__ different ways.

✔ *Checkpoint* **Complete the following exercises.**

2. Describe the pattern in the numbers 1, 2.5, 4, 5.5, . . . and write the next three numbers in the pattern.

The numbers are increasing by 1.5; 7, 8.5, 10.

3. Rework Example 3 if you are given six noncollinear points.

15 different ways

Example 4 *Make and test a conjecture*

Numbers such as 1, 3, and 5 are called consecutive odd numbers. Make and test a conjecture about the sum of any three consecutive odd numbers.

Step 1 Find a pattern using groups of small numbers.

$$1 + 3 + 5 = \underline{9}$$
$$= 3 \cdot 3$$
$$5 + 7 + 9 = \underline{21}$$
$$= \underline{7} \cdot 3$$

$$3 + 5 + 7 = \underline{15}$$
$$= \underline{5} \cdot 3$$
$$7 + 9 + 11 = \underline{27}$$
$$= \underline{9} \cdot 3$$

Conjecture The sum of any three consecutive odd numbers is three times ·the second number .

Step 2 Test your conjecture using other numbers.

$$-1 + 1 + 3 = \underline{3} = \underline{1} \cdot 3 \checkmark$$
$$103 + 105 + 107 = \underline{315} = \underline{105} \cdot 3 \checkmark$$

✔ *Checkpoint* **Complete the following exercise.**

4. Make and test a conjecture about the sign of the product of any four negative numbers.

   The result of the product of four negative numbers is a positive number;
   $(-1)(-2)(-5)(-1) = 10.$

Example 5 *Find a counterexample*

A student makes the following conjecture about the difference of two numbers. Find a counterexample to disprove the student's conjecture.

Conjecture The difference of any two numbers is always smaller than the larger number.

To find a counterexample, you need to find a difference that is __greater__ than the __larger__ number.

$$8 - (-4) = \underline{12}$$

Because $\underline{12} \not< \underline{8}$, a counterexample exists. The conjecture is false.

Example 6 *Making conjectures from data displays*

The scatter plot shows the average salary of players in the National Football League (NFL) since 1999. Make a conjecture based on the graph.

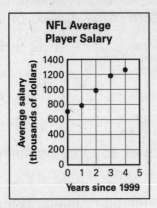

NFL Average Player Salary

Average salary (thousands of dollars) vs. Years since 1999

Solution

The scatter plot shows that the values _increased_ each year. So, one possible conjecture is that the average player in the NFL is earning _more_ money today than in 1999.

✔ **Checkpoint** Complete the following exercises.

5. Find a counterexample to show that the following conjecture is false.

   Conjecture The quotient of two numbers is always smaller than the dividend.

   $$\frac{4}{\frac{1}{2}} = 8$$

6. Use the graph in Example 6 to make a conjecture that *could* be true. Give an explanation that supports your reasoning.

   The average salary of an NFL player in future years will be higher than the previous year; the average salary of an NFL player increased for the 5 years from 1999 to 2003.

Homework

2.2 Analyze Conditional Statements

Goal • Write definitions as conditional statements.

Your Notes

VOCABULARY

Conditional statement A logical statement that has two parts, a hypothesis and a conclusion.

If-then form A form of a conditional statement in which the "if" part contains the hypothesis and the "then" part contains the conclusion.

Hypothesis A hypothesis is the "if" part of a conditional statement.

Conclusion A conclusion is the "then" part of a conditional statement.

Negation The negation of a statement is the opposite of the original statement.

Converse The converse of a conditional statement is formed by switching the hypothesis and conclusion.

Inverse The inverse of a conditional statement is formed by negating both the hypothesis and conclusion.

Contrapositive The contrapositive of a conditional statement is formed by writing the converse and then negating both the hypothesis and conclusion.

Equivalent statements Equivalent statements are two statements that are both true or both false.

Perpendicular lines Two lines that intersect to form a right angle are perpendicular lines.

Biconditional statement A statement that contains the phrase "if and only if."

Your Notes

Example 1 *Rewrite a statement in if-then form*

Rewrite the conditional statement in if-then form.

All vertebrates have a backbone.

Solution

First, identify the hypothesis and the conclusion. When you rewrite the statement in if-then form, you may need to reword the hypothesis or conclusion.

All vertebrates have a backbone.

If _an animal is a vertebrate_ , then _it has a backbone_ .

✔ *Checkpoint* **Write the conditional statement in if-then form.**

1. All triangles have 3 sides.	2. When $x = 2$, $x^2 = 4$.
If a figure is a triangle, then it has 3 sides.	If $x = 2$, then $x^2 = 4$.

Example 2 *Write four related conditional statements*

Write the if-then form, the converse, the inverse, and the contrapositive of the conditional statement "Olympians are athletes." Decide whether each statement is *true* or *false*.

Solution

If-then form _If you are an Olympian, then you are an athlete. *True*, Olympians are athletes._

Converse _If you are an athlete, then you are an Olympian. *False*, not all athletes are Olympians._

Inverse _If you are not an Olympian, then you are not an athlete. *False*, even if you are not an Olympian, you can still be an athlete._

Contrapositive _If you are not an athlete, then you are not an Olympian. *True*, a person who is not an athlete cannot be an Olympian._

PERPENDICULAR LINES

Definition If two lines intersect to form a _right_ angle, then they are perpendicular lines.

The definition can also be written using the converse: If any two lines are perpendicular lines, then they intersect to form a _right_ angle.

You can write "line ℓ is perpendicular to line m" as $\ell \perp m$.

$\ell \perp m$

Example 3 *Use definitions*

Decide whether each statement about the diagram is true. *Explain* your answer using the definitions you have learned.

a. $\overleftrightarrow{AC} \perp \overleftrightarrow{BD}$

b. $\angle AED$ and $\angle BEC$ are a linear pair.

Solution

a. The statement is _true_. The right angle symbol indicates that the lines intersect to form a _right_ angle. So you can say the lines are _perpendicular_.

b. The statement is _false_. Because $\angle AED$ and $\angle BEC$ are not _adjacent_ angles, $\angle AED$ and $\angle BEC$ are not a _linear pair_.

Example 4 *Write a biconditional*

Write the definition of parallel lines as a biconditional.

Definition: If two lines lie in the same plane and do not intersect, then they are parallel.

Solution

Converse: _If two lines are parallel, then they lie in the same plane and do not intersect._

Biconditional: _Two lines are parallel if and only if they lie in the same plane and do not intersect._

✓ **Checkpoint** **Complete the following exercises.**

3. Write the if-then form, the converse, the inverse, and the contrapositive of the conditional statement "Squares are rectangles." Decide whether each statement is *true* or *false*.

If-then form: If a figure is a square, then it is a rectangle. True, squares are rectangles.

Converse: If a figure is a rectangle, then it is a square. False, not all rectangles are squares.

Inverse: If a figure is not a square, then it is not a rectangle. False, even if a figure is not a square, it can still be a rectangle.

Contrapositive: If a figure is not a rectangle, then it is not a square. True, a figure that is not a rectangle cannot be a square.

4. Decide whether each statement about the diagram is true. *Explain* your answer using the definitions you have learned.

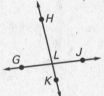

a. ∠GLK and ∠JLK are supplementary.

b. $\overleftrightarrow{GJ} \perp \overleftrightarrow{HK}$

(a) True; linear pairs of angles are supplementary.

(b) False; it is not known that the lines intersect at right angles.

5. Write the statement below as a biconditional.

Statement: If a student is a boy, he will be in group A. If a student is in group A, the student must be a boy.

A student is in group A if and only if the student is a boy.

2.3 Apply Deductive Reasoning

Goal • Form logical arguments using deductive reasoning.

Your Notes

VOCABULARY

Deductive Reasoning Using facts, definitions, accepted properties, and the laws of logic to form a logical argument

LAWS OF LOGIC

Law of Detachment If the hypothesis of a true conditional statement is true, then the <u>conclusion</u> is also true.

Law of Syllogism

> The Law of Detachment is also called a *direct argument*. The Law of Syllogism is sometimes called the *chain rule*.

If hypothesis p, then conclusion q. ⟍
If hypothesis q, then conclusion r. ⟋ **If these statements are true,**

If hypothesis p, then conclusion r. ⟵ **then this statement is true.**

Example 1 *Use the Law of Detachment*

Use the Law of Detachment to make a valid conclusion in the true situation.

a. If two angles have the same measure, then they are congruent. You know that $m\angle A = m\angle B$.

b. Jesse goes to the gym every weekday. Today is Monday.

Solution

a. Because $m\angle A = m\angle B$ satisfies the hypothesis of a true conditional statement, the conclusion is also true. So, <u>$\angle A \cong \angle B$</u>.

b. First, identify the hypothesis and the conclusion of the first statement. The hypothesis is " <u>If it is a weekday</u> ," and the conclusion is " <u>then Jesse goes to the gym</u> ."

"Today is Monday" satisfies the hypothesis of the conditional statement, so you can conclude that <u>Jesse will go to the gym today</u> .

Example 2 *Use the Law of Syllogism*

If possible, use the Law of Syllogism to write the conditional statement that follows from the pair of true statements.

a. If Ron eats lunch today, then he will eat a sandwich. If Ron eats a sandwich, then he will drink a glass of milk.

b. If $x^2 > 36$, then $x^2 > 30$. If $x > 6$, then $x^2 > 36$.

c. If a triangle is equilateral, then all of its sides are congruent. If a triangle is equilateral, then all angles in the interior of the triangle are congruent.

Solution

> The order in which the statements are given does not affect whether you can use the Law of Syllogism.

a. The conclusion of the first statement is the hypothesis of the second statement, so you can write the following.

If Ron eats lunch today, then <u>he will drink a glass of milk</u>.

b. Notice that the conclusion of the second statement is the hypothesis of the first statement, so you can write the following.

If $x > 6$, then <u>$x^2 > 30$</u>.

c. Neither statement's conclusion is the same as the other statement's <u>hypothesis</u>. You cannot use the Law of Syllogism to write a new conditional statement.

✔ **Checkpoint** Complete the following exercises.

1. If $0° < m\angle A < 90°$, then A is acute. The measure of $\angle A$ is 38°. Using the Law of Detachment, what statement can you make?

   $\angle A$ is acute.

2. State the law of logic that is illustrated below.

   If you do your homework, then you can watch TV. If you watch TV, then you can watch your favorite show.

   If you do your homework, then you can watch your favorite show.

   Law of Syllogism

Example 3 *Use inductive and deductive reasoning*

What conclusion can you make about the sum of an odd integer and an odd integer?

Solution

Step 1 Look for a pattern in several examples. Use inductive reasoning to make a conjecture.

$$-3 + 5 = \underline{2}, -1 + 5 = \underline{4}, 3 + 5 = \underline{8}$$
$$-3 + (-5) = \underline{-8}, 1 + (-5) = \underline{-4},$$
$$3 + (-5) = \underline{-2}$$

Conjecture: Odd integer + Odd integer = $\underline{Even}$ integer

Step 2 Let n and m each be any integer. Use deductive reasoning to show the conjecture is true.

$2n$ and $2m$ are $\underline{even}$ integers because any integer multiplied by 2 is $\underline{even}$.

$2n - \underline{1}$ and $2m + \underline{1}$ are $\underline{odd}$ integers because $2n$ and $2m$ are $\underline{even}$ integers.

$(2n - \underline{1}) + (2m + \underline{1})$ represents the sum of an $\underline{odd}$ integer $2n - \underline{1}$ and an $\underline{odd}$ integer $2m + \underline{1}$.

$(2n - \underline{1}) + (2m + \underline{1}) = \underline{2}(n + m)$

The result is the product of $\underline{2}$ and an integer $n + m$. So, $\underline{2}(n + m)$ is an $\underline{even}$ integer.

The sum of an odd integer and an odd integer is an $\underline{even}$ integer.

✔ *Checkpoint* **Complete the following exercise.**

3. Use inductive reasoning to make a conjecture about the sum of a negative integer and itself. Then use deductive reasoning to show the conjecture is true.

The sum of a negative integer and itself is twice the integer; $-n + (-n) = -2n = 2(-n)$.

Example 4   *Reasoning from a graph*

Tell whether the statement is the result of *inductive reasoning* or *deductive reasoning*. *Explain* your choice.

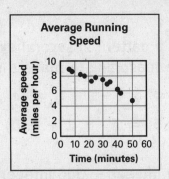

a. The runner's average speed decreases as time spent running increases.

b. The runner's average speed is slower when running for 40 minutes than when running for 10 minutes.

Solution

a.   Inductive   reasoning, because it is based on a pattern in the data

b.   Deductive   reasoning, because you are comparing values that are given on the graph

✔ *Checkpoint* **Complete the following exercises.**

4. Use inductive reasoning to write another statement about the graph in Example 4.

Sample answer: The faster the average speed of the runner, the less time he or she is running.

5. Use deductive reasoning to write another statement about the graph in Example 4.

Sample answer: The runner's average speed is faster when running for 10 minutes than when running for 40 minutes.

Homework

Use Postulates and Diagrams

Goal • Use postulates involving points, lines, and planes.

Your Notes

> **VOCABULARY**
>
> **Line perpendicular to a plane** A line is perpendicular to a plane if and only if the line intersects the plane in a point and is perpendicular to every line in the plane that intersects it at that point.

> **POINT, LINE, AND PLANE POSTULATES**
>
> **Postulate 5** Through any two points there exists exactly one <u>line</u>.
>
> **Postulate 6** A line contains at least two <u>points</u>.
>
> **Postulate 7** If two lines intersect, then their intersection is exactly <u>one point</u>.
>
> **Postulate 8** Through any three <u>noncollinear</u> points there exists exactly one plane.
>
> **Postulate 9** A plane contains at least three <u>noncollinear</u> points.
>
> **Postulate 10** If two points lie in a plane, then the line containing them <u>lies in the plane</u>.
>
> **Postulate 11** If two planes intersect, then their intersection is a <u>line</u>.

Example 1 *Identify a postulate illustrated by a diagram*

State the postulate illustrated by the diagram.

Solution

Postulate <u>8</u> Through any three <u>noncollinear</u> points there exists exactly one plane.

Example 2 *Identify postulates from a diagram*

Use the diagram to write examples of Postulates 9 and 11.

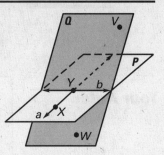

Postulate 9 Plane _Q_ contains at least three noncollinear points, _W, V, and Y_ .

Postulate 11 The intersection of plane *P* and plane *Q* is line *b* .

✓ *Checkpoint* Use the diagram in Example 2 to complete the following exercises.

---

1. Which postulate allows you to say that the intersection of line *a* and line *b* is a point?

   Postulate 7
   _____

2. Write examples of Postulates 5 and 6.

   Line *a* passes through *X* and *Y*; line *a* contains points *X* and *Y*.

CONCEPT SUMMARY: INTERPRETING A DIAGRAM

When you interpret a diagram, you can only assume information about size or measure if it is marked.

YOU CANNOT ASSUME

All points shown are coplanar .

∠*AHB* and ∠*BHD* are a linear pair.

∠*AHF* and ∠*BHD* are vertical angles.

A, H, J, and *D* are collinear .

$\overleftrightarrow{AD}$ and $\overleftrightarrow{BF}$ intersect at *H* .

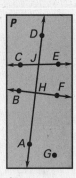

YOU CANNOT ASSUME

G, F, and *E* are collinear.

$\overleftrightarrow{BF}$ and $\overleftrightarrow{CE}$ intersect.

$\overleftrightarrow{BF}$ and $\overleftrightarrow{CE}$ do not intersect.

∠*BHA* ≅ ∠*CJA*

$\overleftrightarrow{AD} \perp \overleftrightarrow{BF}$ or $m\angle AHB = 90°$

Example 3 *Use given information to sketch a diagram*

Sketch a diagram showing $\overline{RS}$ perpendicular to $\overleftrightarrow{TV}$, intersecting at point *X*.

Solution

Step 1 Draw $\overline{RS}$ and label points *R* and *S*.

Step 2 Draw a point *X* <u>between</u> *R* and *S*.

Step 3 Draw $\overleftrightarrow{TV}$ through *X* so that it is <u>perpendicular</u> to $\overline{RS}$.

> Notice that the picture was drawn so that *X* does not look like a midpoint of $\overline{RS}$.

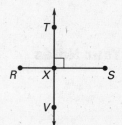

Example 4 *Interpret a diagram in three dimensions*

Which of the following statements *cannot* be assumed from the diagram?

E, *D*, and *C* are collinear.

The intersection of $\overleftrightarrow{BD}$ and $\overleftrightarrow{EC}$ is *D*.

$\overleftrightarrow{BD} \perp \overleftrightarrow{EC}$

$\overleftrightarrow{EC} \perp$ plane *G*

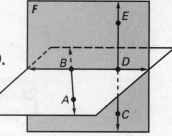

Solution

With no right angles marked, you cannot assume that <u>$\overleftrightarrow{BD} \perp \overleftrightarrow{EC}$</u> or <u>$\overleftrightarrow{EC} \perp$ plane *G*</u> .

✓ **Checkpoint** Complete the following exercises.

3. In Example 3, if the given information indicated that $\overline{RX}$ and $\overline{XS}$ are congruent, how would the diagram change?

   Point *X* would be drawn as the midpoint of $\overline{RS}$ and the congruent segments would be marked.

4. In the diagram for Example 4, can you assume that $\overleftrightarrow{BD}$ is the intersection of plane *F* and plane *G*?

   Yes

Homework

2.5 Reason Using Properties from Algebra

Goal • Use algebraic properties in logical arguments.

Your Notes

ALGEBRAIC PROPERTIES OF EQUALITY

Let a, b, and c be real numbers.

Addition Property   If $a = b$, then $\underline{a + c = b + c}$.

Subtraction Property   If $a = b$, then $\underline{a - c = b - c}$.

Multiplication Property If $a = b$, then $\underline{ac = bc}$.

Division Property   If $a = b$ and $c \neq 0$, then $\underline{\dfrac{a}{c} = \dfrac{b}{c}}$.

Substitution Property   If $a = b$, then $\underline{a \text{ can be}}$ $\underline{\text{substituted for } b \text{ in any}}$ $\underline{\text{equation or expression}}$.

Example 1   Write reasons for each step

Solve $2x + 3 = 9 - x$. Write a reason for each step.

Equation	Explanation	Reason
$2x + 3 = 9 - x$	Write original equation.	Given
$2x + 3 + \underline{x} = 9 - x + \underline{x}$	Add $\underline{x}$ to each side.	$\underline{\text{Addition Property of Equality}}$
$\underline{3x} + 3 = \underline{9}$	Combine like terms.	$\underline{\text{Simplify.}}$
$\underline{3x} = \underline{6}$	Subtract $\underline{3}$ from each side.	$\underline{\text{Subtraction Property of Equality}}$
$x = \underline{2}$	Divide each side by $\underline{3}$.	$\underline{\text{Division Property of Equality}}$

The value of x is $\underline{2}$.

DISTRIBUTIVE PROPERTY

$a(b + c) = \underline{\ ab + ac\ }$, where a, b, and c are real numbers.

Example 2 *Use the Distributive Property*

Solve $-4(6x + 2) = 64$. Write a reason for each step.

Solution

Equation	Explanation	Reason
$-4(6x + 2) = 64$	Write original equation.	**Given**
$\underline{-24x - 8} = 64$	Multiply.	Distributive Property
$\underline{-24x} = \underline{72}$	Add $\underline{8}$ to each side.	Addition **Property of Equality**
$\underline{x} = \underline{-3}$	Divide each side by $\underline{-24}$.	Division **Property of Equality**

✓ *Checkpoint* **Complete the following exercises.**

1. Solve $x - 5 = 7 + 2x$. Write a reason for each step.

$x - 5 = 7 + 2x$	Given
$x - 5 - x = 7 + 2x - x$	Subtraction Property of Equality
$-5 = 7 + x$	Simplify.
$-12 = x$	Subtraction Property of Equality

2. Solve $4(5 - x) = -2x$. Write a reason for each step.

$4(5 - x) = -2x$	Given
$20 - 4x = -2x$	Distributive Property
$20 = 2x$	Addition Property of Equality
$10 = x$	Division Property of Equality

Example 3   *Use properties in the real world*

Speed A motorist travels 5 miles per hour slower than the speed limit s for 3.5 hours. The distance traveled d can be determined by the formula $d = 3.5(s - 5)$. Solve for s.

Equation	Explanation	Reason
$d = 3.5(s - 5)$	Write original equation.	**Given**
$d = \underline{3.5s - 17.5}$	Multiply.	Distributive Property
$d + \underline{17.5} = \underline{3.5s}$	Add $\underline{17.5}$ to each side.	Addition **Property of Equality**
$\dfrac{d + \boxed{17.5}}{\boxed{3.5}} = s$	Divide each side by $\underline{3.5}$.	Division **Property of Equality**

REFLEXIVE PROPERTY OF EQUALITY

Real Numbers   For any real number a, $\underline{a = a}$.

Segment Length   For any segment AB, $\underline{AB = AB}$.

Angle Measure   For any angle A, $\underline{m\angle A = m\angle A}$.

SYMMETRIC PROPERTY OF EQUALITY

Real Numbers   For any real numbers a and b, if $a = b$, then $\underline{b = a}$.

Segment Length   For any segments AB and CD, if $AB = CD$, then $\underline{CD = AB}$.

Angle Measure   For any angles A and B, if $m\angle A = m\angle B$, then $\underline{m\angle B = m\angle A}$.

TRANSITIVE PROPERTY OF EQUALITY

Real Numbers   For any real numbers a, b, and c, if $a = b$ and $b = c$, then $\underline{a = c}$.

Segment Length   For any segments AB, CD, and EF, if $AB = CD$ and $CD = EF$, then $\underline{AB = EF}$.

Angle Measure   For any angles A, B, and C, if $m\angle A = m\angle B$ and $m\angle B = m\angle C$, then $\underline{m\angle A = m\angle C}$.

Your Notes

Example 4 *Use properties of equality*

Show that $CF = AD$.

Equation	Reason
$AB = \underline{EF}$	**Given**
$BC = \underline{DE}$	**Given**
$AC = AB + BC$	<u>Segment Addition Postulate</u>
$DF = \underline{DE} + \underline{EF}$	**Segment Addition Postulate**
$DF = BC + AB$	<u>Substitution</u> **Property of Equality**
$DF = \underline{AC}$	<u>Transitive</u> **Property of Equality**
$DF + CD = \underline{AC} + CD$	<u>Addition</u> **Property of Equality**
$\underline{CF} = \underline{AD}$	**Substitution Property of Equality**

✔ **Checkpoint** **Complete the following exercises. In Exercises 4–6, name the property of equality that the statement illustrates.**

3. **Suppose the equation in Example 3 is $d = 5(s + 3)$. Solve for s. Write a reason for each step.**

$d = 5(s + 3)$	Given
$d = 5s + 15$	Distributive Property
$d - 15 = 5s$	Subtraction Property of Equality
$\dfrac{d - 15}{5} = s$	Division Property of Equality

4. **If $GH = JK$, then $JK = GH$.**

Symmetric Property of Equality for Segment Length

Homework

5. **If $r = s$, and $s = 44$, then $r = 44$.**

Transitive Property of Equality for Real Numbers

6. $m\angle N = m\angle N$

Reflexive Property of Equality for Angle Measure

Prove Statements about Segments and Angles

Goal • Write proofs using geometric theorems.

Your Notes

VOCABULARY

Proof A proof is a logical argument that shows a statement is true.

Two-column proof A two-column proof has numbered statements and corresponding reasons that show an argument in logical order.

Theorem A theorem is a statement that can be proven.

Example 1 *Write a two-column proof*

Use the diagram to prove $m\angle 1 = m\angle 4$.

Given $m\angle 2 = m\angle 3$, $m\angle AXD = m\angle AXC$

Prove $m\angle 1 = m\angle 4$

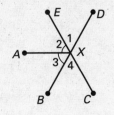

> Writing a two-column proof is a formal way of organizing your reasons to show a statement is true.

Statements	Reasons
1. $m\angle AXC = m\angle AXD$	1. _Given_
2. $m\angle AXD$ $= m\angle \underline{1} + m\angle \underline{2}$	2. Angle Addition Postulate
3. $m\angle AXC$ $= m\angle \underline{3} + m\angle \underline{4}$	3. Angle Addition Postulate
4. $m\angle 1 + m\angle 2$ $= m\angle 3 + m\angle 4$	4. _Substitution Property of Equality_
5. $m\angle 2 = m\angle 3$	5. _Given_
6. $m\angle 1 + m\angle \underline{3}$ $= m\angle 3 + m\angle 4$	6. Substitution Property of Equality
7. $m\angle 1 = m\angle 4$	7. _Subtraction Property of Equality_

THEOREM 2.1 CONGRUENCE OF SEGMENTS

Segment congruence is reflexive, symmetric, and transitive.

Reflexive   For any segment AB, $\underline{\overline{AB} \cong \overline{AB}}$.

Symmetric If $\overline{AB} \cong \overline{CD}$, then $\underline{\overline{CD} \cong \overline{AB}}$.

Transitive If $\overline{AB} \cong \overline{CD}$ and $\overline{CD} \cong \overline{EF}$, then $\underline{\overline{AB} \cong \overline{EF}}$.

THEOREM 2.2 CONGRUENCE OF ANGLES

Angle congruence is reflexive, symmetric, and transitive.

Reflexive   For any angle A, $\underline{\angle A \cong \angle A}$.

Symmetric If $\angle A \cong \angle B$, then $\underline{\angle B \cong \angle A}$.

Transitive If $\angle A \cong \angle B$ and $\angle B \cong \angle C$, then $\underline{\angle A \cong \angle C}$.

Example 2   *Name the property shown*

Name the property illustrated by the statement.

If $\angle 5 \cong \angle 3$, then $\angle 3 \cong \angle 5$.

Symmetric Property of Angle Congruence

✔ **Checkpoint** Complete the following exercises.

1. Three steps of a proof are shown. Give the reasons for the last two steps.

   Given $BC = AB$
   Prove $AC = AB + AB$

Statements	Reasons
1. $BC = AB$	1. Given
2. $AC = AB + BC$	2. Segment Addition Postulate
3. $AC = AB + AB$	3. Substitution Property of Equality

2. Name the property illustrated by the statement.
   If $\angle H \cong \angle T$ and $\angle T \cong \angle B$, then $\angle H \cong \angle B$.

   Transitive Property of Angle Congruence

Example 3   *Use properties of equality*

If you know that $\overrightarrow{BD}$ bisects $\angle ABC$, prove that $m\angle ABC$ is two times $m\angle 1$.

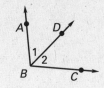

Given $\overrightarrow{BD}$ bisects $\angle ABC$.

Prove $m\angle ABC = 2 \cdot m\angle 1$

Statements	Reasons
1. $\overrightarrow{BD}$ bisects $\angle ABC$.	1. <u>Given</u>
2. <u>$\angle 1 \cong \angle 2$</u>	2. Definition of angle bisector
3. <u>$m\angle 1 = m\angle 2$</u>	3. Definition of congruent angles
4. $m\angle 1 + m\angle 2 = m\angle ABC$	4. <u>Angle Addition Postulate</u>
5. $m\angle 1 + m\angle\underline{\ 1\ } = m\angle ABC$	5. Substitution Property of Equality
6. <u>$2 \cdot m\angle 1 = m\angle ABC$</u>	6. Distributive Property

> Before writing a proof, organize your reasoning by copying or drawing a diagram for the situation described. Then identify the GIVEN and PROVE statements.

CONCEPT SUMMARY: WRITING A TWO-COLUMN PROOF

Proof of the Symmetric Property of Segment Congruence

Given $\overline{AB} \cong \overline{CD}$

Prove $\overline{CD} \cong \overline{AB}$

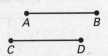

Copy or draw diagrams and label information to help develop proofs.

Statements	Reasons
1. $\overline{AB} \cong \overline{CD}$	1. <u>Given</u>
2. <u>$AB = CD$</u>	2. Definition of congruent segments
3. <u>$CD = AB$</u>	3. Symmetric Property of Equality
4. $\overline{CD} \cong \overline{AB}$	4. Definition of congruent segments

> Statements based on facts that you know or conclusions from deductive reasoning

The number of statements will vary.

Remember to give a reason for the last statement.

Definitions, postulates, or proven theorems that allow you to state the corresponding statement.

Example 4 *Solve a multi-step problem*

Interstate There are two exits between rest areas on a stretch of interstate. The Rice exit is halfway between rest area A and the Mason exit. The distance between rest area B and the Mason exit is the same as the distance between rest area A and the Rice exit. Prove that the Mason exit is halfway between the Rice exit and rest area B.

Solution

Step 1 Draw a diagram.

Step 2 Draw diagrams showing relationships.

Step 3 Write a proof.

Given R is the midpoint of $\overline{AM}$, $MB = AR$.

Prove M is the midpoint of $\overline{RB}$.

Statements	Reasons
1. R is the midpoint of $\overline{AM}$, $MB = AR$.	1. Given
2. $\overline{AR} \cong \overline{RM}$	2. Definition of midpoint
3. $AR = RM$	3. Definition of congruent segments
4. $MB = RM$	4. Transitive Property of Congruence
5. $\overline{MB} \cong \overline{RM}$	5. Definition of congruent segments
6. M is the midpoint of $\overline{RB}$.	6. Definition of midpoint

✔ *Checkpoint* **Complete the following exercise.**

Homework

3. In Example 4, there are rumble strips halfway between the Rice and Mason exits. What other two places are the same distance from the rumble strips?

Rest area A and rest area B

2.7 Prove Angle Pair Relationships

Goal • Use properties of special pairs of angles.

Your Notes

THEOREM 2.3   RIGHT ANGLES CONGRUENCE THEOREM

All right angles are _congruent_ .

Example 1   *Use right angle congruence*

> The given information in Example 1 is about perpendicular lines. You must then use deductive reasoning to show that the angles are right angles.

Write a proof.

Given $\overline{JK} \perp \overline{KL}$, $\overline{ML} \perp \overline{KL}$

Prove $\angle K \cong \angle L$

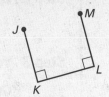

Statements	Reasons
1. $\overline{JK} \perp \overline{KL}$, $\overline{ML} \perp \overline{KL}$	1. _Given_
2. $\angle K$ and $\angle L$ are right angles.	2. Definition of perpendicular lines
3. $\angle K \cong \angle L$	3. _Right Angles Congruence Theorem_

THEOREM 2.4   CONGRUENT SUPPLEMENTS THEOREM

If two angles are supplementary to the same angle (or to congruent angles), then they are _congruent_ .

If $\angle 1$ and $\angle 2$ are supplementary and $\angle 3$ and $\angle 2$ are supplementary, then _$\angle 1 \cong \angle 3$_ .

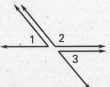

THEOREM 2.5   CONGRUENT COMPLEMENTS THEOREM

If two angles are complementary to the same angle (or to congruent angles), then they are _congruent_ .

If $\angle 4$ and $\angle 5$ are complementary and $\angle 6$ and $\angle 5$ are complementary, then _$\angle 4 \cong \angle 6$_ .

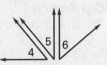

Example 2 *Use the Congruent Supplements Theorem*

Write a proof.

Given ∠1 and ∠2 are supplements.
∠1 and ∠4 are supplements.
m∠2 = 45°

Prove m∠4 = 45°

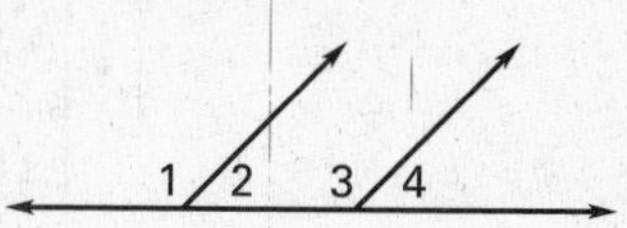

Statements	Reasons
1. ∠1 and ∠2 are supplements. ∠1 and ∠4 are supplements.	1. Given
2. ∠2 ≅ ∠4	2. Congruent Supplements Theorem
3. m∠2 = m∠4	3. Definition of congruent angles
4. m∠2 = 45°	4. Given
5. m∠4 = 45°	5. Substitution Property of Equality

✔ *Checkpoint* **Complete the following exercises.**

1. In Example 1, suppose you are given that ∠K ≅ ∠L. Can you use the Right Angles Congruence Theorem to prove that ∠K and ∠L are right angles? *Explain.*

   No, you cannot prove that ∠K and ∠L are right angles, because the converse of the Right Angles Congruence Theorem is not always true.

2. Suppose ∠A and ∠B are complements, and ∠A and ∠C are complements. Can ∠B and ∠C be supplements? *Explain.*

   No, ∠B and ∠C are complements by the Congruent Complements Theorem, so they cannot be supplements.

POSTULATE 12 LINEAR PAIR POSTULATE

If two angles form a linear pair,
then they are ___supplementary___ .

∠1 and ∠2 form a linear pair, so ∠1 and ∠2 are
supplementary and $m\angle 1 + m\angle 2 =$ ___180°___ .

THEOREM 2.6 VERTICAL ANGLES CONGRUENCE THEOREM

Vertical angles are ___congruent___ .

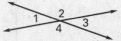

Example 3 *Use the Vertical Angles Congruence Theorem*

Write a proof.

Given ∠4 is a right angle.

Prove ∠2 and ∠4 are supplementary.

> You can use information labeled in a diagram in your proof.

Statements	Reasons
1. ∠4 is a right angle.	1. ___Given___
2. ___$m\angle 4 = 90°$___	2. Definition of a right angle
3. ∠2 ≅ ∠4	3. ___Vertical Angles Congruence Theorem___
4. ___$m\angle 2 = m\angle 4$___	4. Definition of congruent angles
5. $m\angle 2 = 90°$	5. ___Substitution Property of Equality___
6. ___∠2 and ∠4 are supplementary.___	6. $m\angle 2 + m\angle 4 = 180°$

✓ **Checkpoint** In Exercises 3 and 4, use the diagram.

3. If $m\angle 4 = 63°$, find $m\angle 1$ and $m\angle 2$.

    $m\angle 1 = 117°, \ m\angle 2 = 63°$

4. If $m\angle 3 = 121°$, find $m\angle 1$, $m\angle 2$, and $m\angle 4$.

    $m\angle 1 = 121°, \ m\angle 2 = 59°, \ m\angle 4 = 59°$

Example 4 *Find angle measures*

Write and solve an equation to find *x*.
Use *x* to find *m∠FKG*.

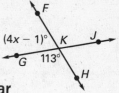

Solution

Because *m∠FKG* and *m∠GKH* form a linear pair, the sum of their measures is __180°__.

$(4x - 1)° + 113° =$ __180°__	Write equation.
$4x +$ __112__ $=$ __180__	Simplify.
$4x =$ __68__	Subtract __112__ from each side.
$x =$ __17__	Divide each side by 4.

Use *x =* __17__ to find *m∠FKG*.

$m∠FKG = (4x - 1)°$	Write equation.
$= [4(\ 17\ ) - 1]°$	Substitute __17__ for *x*.
$= [\ 68\ - 1]°$	Multiply.
$= 67°$	Simplify.

The measure of *∠FKG* is __67°__.

⊘ *Checkpoint* Complete the following exercise.

5. Find *m∠AEB*.

    m∠AEB = 70°

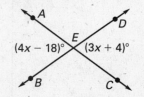

Words to Review

Give an example of the vocabulary word.

Conjecture A conjecture is an unproven statement that is based on observations.	**Inductive reasoning** You use inductive reasoning when you find a pattern in specific cases and then write a conjecture for the general case.
Counterexample A counterexample is a specific case for which the conjecture is false.	**Conditional statement** Leaves change color in fall.
If-then form If leaves are changing color, then it is fall.	**Hypothesis** If leaves are changing color . . .
Conclusion . . . then it is fall.	**Negation** The leaves are not changing color.
Converse If it is fall, then leaves are changing color.	**Inverse** If leaves are not changing color, then it is not fall.

Contrapositive	Equivalent statements
If it is not fall, then leaves are not changing color.	A conditional statement is equivalent to its contrapositive. The inverse and converse of a conditional statement are also equivalent.

Perpendicular lines	Biconditional statement
	The value of x is 5 if and only if $x - 3 = 2$.

Deductive reasoning	Line perpendicular to a plane
Deductive reasoning uses facts, definitions, accepted properties, and the laws of logic to form a logical argument.	

Proof	Theorem
A logical argument that shows a statement is true.	Vertical angles are congruent.

Two-column proof

Given $\angle 1 \cong \angle 2$, $m\angle 1 = 60°$
Prove $m\angle 2 = 60°$

Statements	Reasons
1. $\angle 1 \cong \angle 2$	1. Given
2. $m\angle 1 = m\angle 2$	2. Definition of congruent $\angle$s
3. $m\angle 1 = 60°$	3. Given
4. $m\angle 2 = 60°$	4. Transitive Property of =

Review your notes and Chapter 2 by using the Chapter Review on pages 134–137 of your textbook.

3.1 Identify Pairs of Lines and Angles

Goal • Identify angle pairs formed by three intersecting lines.

Your Notes

VOCABULARY

Parallel lines Two lines are parallel lines if they do not intersect and are coplanar.

Skew lines Two lines are skew lines if they do not intersect and are not coplanar.

Parallel planes Two planes that do not intersect are parallel planes.

Transversal A transversal is a line that intersects two or more coplanar lines at different points.

Corresponding angles Two angles are corresponding angles if they have corresponding positions.

Alternate interior angles Two angles are alternate interior angles if they lie between the two lines and on opposite sides of the transversal.

Alternate exterior angles Two angles are alternate exterior angles if they lie outside the two lines and on opposite sides of the transversal.

Consecutive interior angles Two angles are consecutive interior angles if they lie between the two lines and on the same side of the transversal.

Example 1   *Identify relationships in space*

Think of each segment in the figure as part of a line. Which line(s) or plane(s) in the figure appear to fit the description?

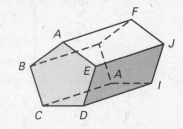

a. Line(s) parallel to $\overleftrightarrow{AF}$ and containing point E

b. Line(s) skew to $\overleftrightarrow{AF}$ and containing point E

c. Line(s) perpendicular to $\overleftrightarrow{AF}$ and containing point E

d. Plane(s) parallel to plane FGH and containing point E

Solution

a. $\underline{\overleftrightarrow{EJ}, \overleftrightarrow{BG}, \overleftrightarrow{CH}, \text{and } \overleftrightarrow{DI}}$ all appear parallel to $\overleftrightarrow{AF}$, but only $\underline{\overleftrightarrow{EJ}}$ contains point E.

b. $\underline{\overleftrightarrow{BC}, \overleftrightarrow{CD}, \overleftrightarrow{DE}, \overleftrightarrow{GH}, \overleftrightarrow{HI}, \text{and } \overleftrightarrow{IJ}}$ all appear skew to $\overleftrightarrow{AF}$, but only $\underline{\overleftrightarrow{DE}}$ contains point E.

c. $\underline{\overleftrightarrow{AB}, \overleftrightarrow{AE}, \overleftrightarrow{FG}, \text{and } \overleftrightarrow{FJ}}$ all appear perpendicular to $\overleftrightarrow{AF}$, but only $\underline{\overleftrightarrow{AE}}$ contains point E.

d. Plane $\underline{ABC}$ appears parallel to plane FGH and contains point E.

 Checkpoint Think of each segment in the figure as part of a line. Which line(s) or plane(s) in the figure appear to fit the description?

1. parallel to $\overleftrightarrow{MN}$ and contains J

$\overleftrightarrow{JL}$

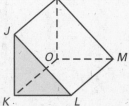

2. skew to $\overleftrightarrow{MN}$ and contains J

$\overleftrightarrow{KJ}$

3. perpendicular to $\overleftrightarrow{MN}$ and contains J

$\overleftrightarrow{JN}$

4. Name the plane that contains J and appears to be parallel to plane MNO.

plane JKL

POSTULATE 13   PARALLEL POSTULATE

If there is a line and a point not on the line, then there is exactly one line through the point parallel to the given line.

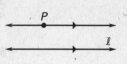

There is exactly one line through P parallel to ℓ.

POSTULATE 14   PERPENDICULAR POSTULATE

If there is a line and a point not on the line, then there is exactly one line through the point perpendicular to the given line.

There is exactly one line through P perpendicular to ℓ.

Example 2   *Identify parallel and perpendicular lines*

Use the diagram at the right to answer each question.

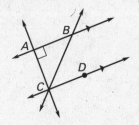

a. Name a pair of parallel lines.

b. Name a pair of perpendicular lines.

c. Is $\overleftrightarrow{AB} \perp \overleftrightarrow{BC}$? *Explain*.

Solution

a. $\overleftrightarrow{AB} \parallel \overleftrightarrow{CD}$

b. $\overleftrightarrow{AB} \perp \overleftrightarrow{AC}$

c. $\overleftrightarrow{AB}$ is not perpendicular to $\overleftrightarrow{BC}$, because $\overleftrightarrow{AB}$ is perpendicular to $\overleftrightarrow{AC}$ and by the Perpendicular Postulate there is exactly one line perpendicular to $\overleftrightarrow{AB}$ through C .

✓ *Checkpoint* **Complete the following exercise.**

5. In Example 2, can you use the Perpendicular Postulate to show that $\overleftrightarrow{AC} \perp \overleftrightarrow{CD}$? *Explain*.

No, there is no right angle symbol at C so you do not know if $\overleftrightarrow{AC} \perp \overleftrightarrow{CD}$.

ANGLES FORMED BY TRANSVERSALS

Two angles are __corresponding__ angles if they have corresponding positions. For example, ∠2 and ∠6 are above the lines and to the right of the transversal t.

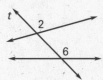

Two angles are __alternate interior__ angles if they lie between the two lines and on opposite sides of the transversal.

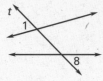

Two angles are __alternate exterior__ angles if they lie outside the two lines and on opposite sides of the transversal.

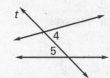

Another name for consecutive interior angles is __same-side__ __interior__ __angles.__

Two angles are __consecutive interior__ angles if they lie between the two lines and on the same side of the transversal.

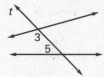

Example 3   *Identify angle relationships*

Identify all pairs of (a) corresponding angles, (b) alternate interior angles, (c) alternate exterior angles, and (d) consecutive interior angles.

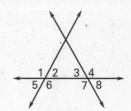

a. ∠1 and __∠3__ , ∠2 and __∠4__ ,
   ∠5 and __∠7__ , ∠6 and __∠8__

b. ∠2 and __∠7__ , ∠6 and __∠3__

c. ∠5 and __∠4__ , ∠1 and __∠8__

d. ∠2 and __∠3__ , ∠6 and __∠7__

✔ *Checkpoint* **Classify the pair of numbered angles.**

Homework

6.

Consecutive interior angles

7.

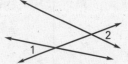

Alternate exterior angles

Use Parallel Lines and Transversals

Goal • Use angles formed by parallel lines and transversals.

Your Notes

> **POSTULATE 15   CORRESPONDING ANGLES POSTULATE**
>
> If two parallel lines are cut by a transversal, then the pairs of corresponding angles are __congruent__ .
>
>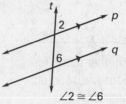
>
> ∠2 ≅ ∠6

Example 1   *Identify congruent angles*

The measure of three of the numbered angles is 125°. Identify the angles. *Explain* your reasoning.

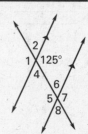

Solution

By the Corresponding Angles Postulate,
__m∠7__ = 125°.

Using the Vertical Angles Congruence Theorem,
__m∠1__ = 125°.

Because ∠1 and ∠5 are corresponding angles, by the __Corresponding Angles Postulate__ , you know that __m∠5__ = 125°.

✓ *Checkpoint* Complete the following exercise using the diagram shown.

> **1.** If *m*∠7 = 75°, find *m*∠1, *m*∠3, and *m*∠5. Tell which postulate or theorem you use in each case.
>
>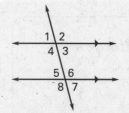
>
> *m*∠3 = 75°,
> Corresponding Angles Postulate;
> *m*∠5 = 75°, Vertical Angles Congruence Theorem;
> *m*∠1 = 75°, Corresponding Angles Postulate

Your Notes

●

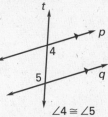

THEOREM 3.1   ALTERNATE INTERIOR ANGLES THEOREM

If two parallel lines are cut by a transversal, then the pairs of alternate interior angles are <u>congruent</u>.

∠4 ≅ ∠5

THEOREM 3.2   ALTERNATE EXTERIOR ANGLES THEOREM

If two parallel lines are cut by a transversal, then the pairs of alternate exterior angles are <u>congruent</u>.

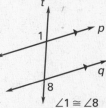

∠1 ≅ ∠8

THEOREM 3.3   CONSECUTIVE INTERIOR ANGLES THEOREM

If two parallel lines are cut by a transversal, then the pairs of consecutive interior angles are <u>supplementary</u>.

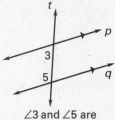

∠3 and ∠5 are supplementary.

●

Example 2   *Use properties of parallel lines*

Find the value of x.

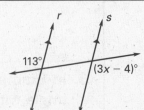

Solution

Lines *r* and *s* are <u>parallel</u>, so you can use the theorems about parallel lines.

$\underline{113°}$ = $(3x - 4)°$ <u>Alternate Exterior Angles Theorem</u>

$\underline{117}$ = $3x$ Add <u>4</u> to each side.

$\underline{39}$ = x Divide each side by <u>3</u>.

The value of *x* is <u>39</u>.

●

Example 3   *Solve a real-world problem*

Runways A taxiway is being constructed that intersects two parallel runways at an airport. You know that $m\angle2 = 98°$. What is $m\angle1$? How do you know?

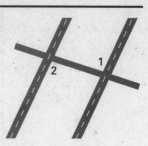

Solution

Because the runways are parallel, $\angle1$ and $\angle2$ are <u>alternate interior angles</u>. By the Alternate Interior Angles Theorem, $\angle1 \cong \underline{\angle2}$. By the definition of congruent angles, $m\angle1 = \underline{m\angle2} = \underline{98°}$.

❷ *Checkpoint* **Complete the following exercises.**

2. Find the value of x.

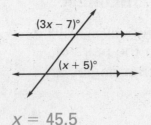

$(3x - 7)°$

$(x + 5)°$

$x = 45.5$

3. In Example 3, suppose $\angle3$ is the consecutive interior angle with $\angle2$. What is $m\angle3$?

$82°$

Homework

3.3 Prove Lines are Parallel

Goal • Use angle relationships to prove that lines are parallel.

Your Notes

VOCABULARY

Paragraph proof A proof can be written in paragraph form, called a paragraph proof.

POSTULATE 16   CORRESPONDING ANGLES CONVERSE

If two lines are cut by a transversal so the corresponding angles are congruent, then the lines are
<u>parallel</u> .

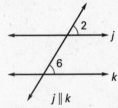

$j \parallel k$

Example 1 *Apply the Corresponding Angles Converse*

Find the value of x that makes $m \parallel n$.

Solution

Lines m and n are parallel if the marked corresponding angles are congruent.

$(2x + 3)° = \underline{\ 71°\ }$ Use Postulate 16 to write an equation.

$2x = \underline{\ 68\ }$ Subtract 3 from each side.

$x = \underline{\ 34\ }$ Divide each side by 2 .

The lines m and n are parallel when $x = \underline{\ 34\ }$.

✔ **Checkpoint** Find the value of x that makes $a \parallel b$.

1.

$(5x - 7)°$ a

$98°$ b

$x = 21$

THEOREM 3.4 ALTERNATE INTERIOR ANGLES CONVERSE

If two lines are cut by a transversal so the alternate interior angles are congruent, then the lines are <u>parallel</u>.

THEOREM 3.5 ALTERNATE EXTERIOR ANGLES CONVERSE

If two lines are cut by a transversal so the alternate exterior angles are congruent, then the lines are <u>parallel</u>.

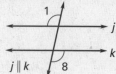

THEOREM 3.6 CONSECUTIVE INTERIOR ANGLES CONVERSE

If two lines are cut by a transversal so the consecutive interior angles are supplementary, then the lines are <u>parallel</u>.

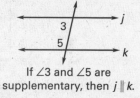

If $\angle 3$ and $\angle 5$ are supplementary, then $j \parallel k$.

Example 2 *Solve a real-world problem*

Flags How can you tell whether the sides of the flag of Nepal are parallel?

Solution

Because the <u>alternate interior angles</u> are congruent, you know that the sides of the flag are <u>parallel</u>.

✔ *Checkpoint* Can you prove that lines *a* and *b* are parallel? *Explain* why or why not.

2. $m\angle 1 + m\angle 2 = 180°$

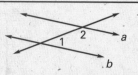

Yes, you can use the Consecutive Interior Angles Converse to prove $a \parallel b$.

Example 3   *Write a paragraph proof*

In the figure, $a \parallel b$ and $\angle 1$ is congruent to $\angle 3$. Prove $x \parallel y$.

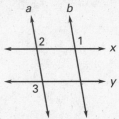

Solution

Look at the diagram to make a plan. The diagram suggests that you look at angles 1, 2, and 3. Also, you may find it helpful to focus on one pair of lines and one transversal at a time.

Plan for Proof

a. Look at $\angle 1$ and $\angle 2$.   **b.** Look at $\angle 2$ and $\angle 3$.

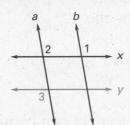   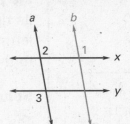

$\underline{\angle 1 \cong \angle 2}$ because $a \parallel b$.   If $\angle 2 \cong \angle 3$ then $\underline{x \parallel y}$.

Plan in Action

> In paragraph proofs, transitional words such as *so, then,* and *therefore* help to make the logic clear.

a. It is given that $a \parallel b$, so by the $\underline{\text{Corresponding}}$ $\underline{\text{Angles Postulate}}$, $\angle 1 \cong \angle 2$.

b. It is also given that $\angle 1 \cong \angle 3$. Then $\underline{\angle 2 \cong \angle 3}$ by the Transitive Property of Congruence for angles. Therefore, by the $\underline{\text{Alternate Exterior Angles Converse}}$, $x \parallel y$.

✓ *Checkpoint* **Complete the following exercise.**

> **3.** In Example 3, suppose it is given that $\angle 1 \cong \angle 3$ and $x \parallel y$. Complete the following paragraph proof showing that $a \parallel b$.
>
> It is given that $x \parallel y$. By the Exterior Angles Postulate, $\underline{\angle 2 \cong \angle 3}$.
>
> It is also given that $\angle 1 \cong \angle 3$. Then $\underline{\angle 1 \cong \angle 2}$. by the Transitive Property of Congruence for angles. Therefore, by the $\underline{\text{Corresponding Angles}}$ $\underline{\text{Converse}}$, $a \parallel b$.

THEOREM 3.7 TRANSITIVE PROPERTY OF PARALLEL LINES

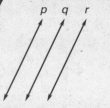

If two lines are parallel to the same line, then they are <u>parallel</u> to each other.

If $p \parallel q$ and $q \parallel r$, then $p \parallel r$.

Example 4   Use the Transitive Property of Parallel Lines

Utility poles Each utility pole shown is parallel to the pole immediately to its right. *Explain* why the leftmost pole is parallel to the rightmost pole.

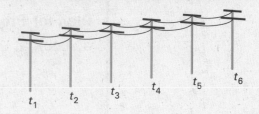

> When you name several similar items, you can use one variable with subscripts to keep track of the items.

Solution

The poles from left to right can be named t_1, t_2, t_3, . . . , t_6. Each pole is parallel to the one to its right, so $t_1 \parallel$ <u>t_2</u> , $t_2 \parallel$ <u>t_3</u> , and so on. Then $t_1 \parallel t_3$ by the <u>Transitive Property of Parallel Lines</u> . Similarly, because $t_3 \parallel t_4$, it follows that $t_1 \parallel$ <u>t_4</u> . By continuing this reasoning, $t_1 \parallel$ <u>t_6</u> . So, the leftmost pole is parallel to the rightmost pole.

✔ *Checkpoint* **Complete the following exercise.**

4. Each horizontal piece of the window blinds shown is called a slat. Each slat is parallel to the slat immediately below it. *Explain* why the top slat is parallel to the bottom slat.

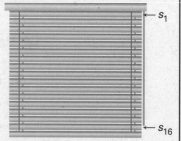

The slats from top to bottom can be named s_1, s_2, s_3, . . . , s_{16}. Each slat is parallel to the one below it, so $s_1 \parallel s_2$, $s_2 \parallel s_3$, and so on. Then $s_1 \parallel s_3$ by the Transitive Property of Parallel Lines. Similarly, because $s_3 \parallel s_4$, it follows that $s_1 \parallel s_4$. By continuing this reasoning, $s_1 \parallel s_{16}$. So, the top slat is parallel to the bottom slat.

Homework

3.4 Find and Use Slopes of Lines

Goal • Find and compare slopes of lines.

Your Notes

VOCABULARY

Slope The slope of a nonvertical line is the ratio of vertical change (rise) to horizontal change (run) between any two points on the line.

SLOPE OF LINES IN THE COORDINATE PLANE

Negative slope: ___falls___ from left to right, as in line j

Positive slope: ___rises___ from left to right, as in line k

Undefined slope: ___vertical___, as in line n

Zero slope (slope of 0): ___horizontal___, as in line ℓ

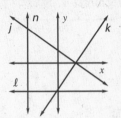

Example 1   *Find slopes of lines in a coordinate plane*

Slope
$$m = \frac{\text{rise}}{\text{run}}$$
$$= \frac{y_2 - y_1}{x_2 - x_1}$$

Find the slope of line a and line c.

Slope of line a:

$$m = \frac{6 - \boxed{2}}{4 - \boxed{0}} = \frac{\boxed{4}}{\boxed{4}} = \underline{1}$$

Slope of line c:

$$m = \frac{6 - \boxed{6}}{4 - \boxed{0}} = \frac{\boxed{0}}{\boxed{4}} = \underline{0}$$

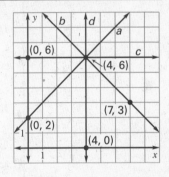

✔ *Checkpoint* Use the graph in Example 1. Find the slope of the line.

1. line b	**2.** line d
−1	undefined

Your Notes

> If the product of two numbers is −1, then the numbers are called *negative reciprocals*.

POSTULATE 17   SLOPES OF PARALLEL LINES

In a coordinate plane, two nonvertical lines are parallel if and only if they have the same <u>slope</u> .

Any two <u>vertical</u> lines are parallel.

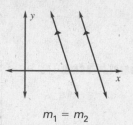

$m_1 = m_2$

POSTULATE 18   SLOPES OF PERPENDICULAR LINES

In a coordinate plane, two nonvertical lines are perpendicular if and only if the product of their slopes is <u>−1</u> .

Horizontal lines are <u>perpendicular</u> to vertical lines.

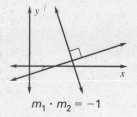

$m_1 \cdot m_2 = -1$

Example 2   *Identify parallel lines*

Find the slope of each line. Which lines are parallel?

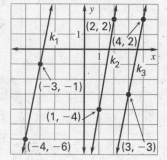

Solution

Find the slope of k_1.

$$m = \frac{-1 - (-6)}{-3 - (-4)} = \frac{5}{1} = \underline{5}$$

Find the slope of k_2.

$$m = \frac{2 - (-4)}{2 - 1} = \underline{6}$$

Find the slope of k_3.

$$m = \frac{2 - (-3)}{4 - 3} = \underline{5}$$

Compare the slopes. Because <u>k_1</u> and <u>k_3</u> have the same slope, they are <u>parallel</u> . The slope of <u>k_3</u> is different, so <u>k_3</u> is <u>not parallel</u> to the other lines.

✔ **Checkpoint** Complete the following exercise.

3. Line *c* passes through (2, −2) and (5, 7). Line *d* passes through (−3, 4) and (1, −8). Are the two lines parallel? *Explain* how you know.

   No; the slope of *c* is not equal to the slope of *d*.

Example 3 *Draw a perpendicular line*

Line *h* passes through (1, −2) and (5, 6). Graph the line perpendicular to *h* that passes through the point (2, 5).

Step 1 Find the slope m_1 of *h* through (1, −2) and (5, 6).

$$m_1 = \frac{6 - (-2)}{5 - 1} = \frac{8}{4} = \underline{2}$$

Step 2 Find the slope m_2 of a line perpendicular to *h*.

$$\underline{2} \cdot m_2 = -1$$

$$m_2 = \underline{-\frac{1}{2}}$$

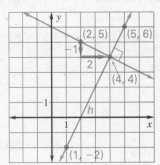

> Given a point on a line and the line's slope, you can use the rise and run to find a second point and draw the line.

Step 3 Use the rise and run to graph the line.

Example 4 *Analyze graphs*

Delivery A trucker made three deliveries. The graph shows the trucker's distance to the destination from the starting time to the arrival time for each delivery. Use slopes to make a statement about the deliveries.

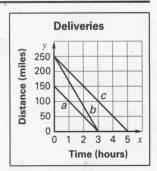

The rate at which the trucker drives is represented by the _slope_ of the segments. Segments _a_ and _c_ have the same slope, so deliveries *a* and *c* were driven at the same _rate_ .

✔ *Checkpoint* **Complete the following exercises.**

4. Line *n* passes through (1, 6) and (8, 4). Line *m* passes through (0, 5) and (2, 12). Is *n* ⊥ *m*? *Explain*.

Yes, the product of the slopes equals −1.

5. In Example 4, which delivery included the fastest rate of travel?

delivery *b*

3.5 Write and Graph Equations of Lines

Goal • Find equations of lines.

VOCABULARY

Slope-intercept form The general form of a linear equation in slope-intercept form is $y = mx + b$, where m is the slope and b is the y-intercept.

Standard form The general form of a linear equation in standard form is $Ax + By = C$, where A and B are not both zero.

Example 1 *Write an equation of a line from a graph*

Write an equation of the line in slope-intercept form.

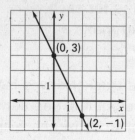

Solution

Step 1 Find the slope. Choose two points on the graph of the line, (0, 3) and (2, −1).

$$m = \frac{3 - (-1)}{0 - 2} = \frac{4}{-2} = \underline{-2}$$

Step 2 Find the y-intercept. The line intersects the y-axis at the point (0, 3) , so the y-intercept is 3 .

Step 3 Write the equation.

$y = mx + b$ Use slope-intercept form.

$y = \underline{-2x + 3}$ Substitute −2 for m and 3 for b.

Example 2 *Write an equation of a parallel line*

Write an equation of the line passing through the point (1, −1) that is parallel to the line with the equation $y = 2x − 1$.

Solution

Step 1 Find the slope m. The slope of a line parallel to $y = 2x − 1$ is the same as the given line, so the slope is __2__ .

> The graph of a linear equation represents all the solutions of the equation. So, the given point must be a solution of the equation.

Step 2 Find the y-intercept b by using $m = $ __2__ and $(x, y) = $ __(1, −1)__ .

$y = mx + b$	Use slope-intercept form.
$\underline{-1} = \underline{2}\,(\,\underline{1}\,) + b$	Substitute for x, y, and m.
$\underline{-3} = b$	Solve for b.

Because $m = $ __2__ and $b = $ __−3__ , an equation of the line is $y = $ __$2x − 3$__ .

✔ **Checkpoint** Complete the following exercises.

1. Write an equation of the line in the graph at the right.

    $y = 3x − 5$

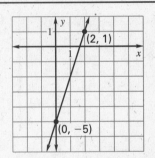

2. Write an equation of the line that passes through the point (−2, 5) and is parallel to the line with the equation $y = −2x + 3$.

    $y = −2x + 1$

Example 3   *Write an equation of a perpendicular line*

Write an equation of the line *j* passing through the point (3, 2) that is perpendicular to the line *k* with the equation $y = -3x + 1$.

Solution

Step 1 Find the slope *m* of line *j*. The slope of *k* is __−3__ .

$$\underline{-3} \cdot m = \underline{-1}$$ The product of the slopes of perpendicular lines is __−1__ .

$$m = \frac{1}{3}$$ Divide each side by __−3__ .

Step 2 Find the *y*-intercept *b* by using $m = \frac{1}{3}$ and $(x, y) = \underline{(3, 2)}$.

$$y = mx + b$$ Use slope-intercept form.

$$\underline{2} = \frac{1}{3}(\underline{3}) + b$$ Substitute for *x*, *y*, and *m*.

$$\underline{1} = b$$ Solve for *b*.

Because $m = \frac{1}{3}$ and $b = \underline{1}$, an equation of line *j* is $y = \underline{\frac{1}{3}x + 1}$.

You can check that the lines *j* and *k* are perpendicular by graphing, then using a protractor to measure one of the angles formed by the lines.

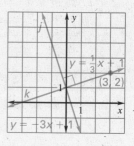

✔ *Checkpoint* **Complete the following exercise.**

3. Write an equation of the line passing through the point (−8, −2) that is perpendicular to the line with the equation $y = 4x - 3$.

$$y = -\frac{1}{4}x - 4$$

Your Notes

Example 4   *Write an equation of a line from a graph*

Rent The graph models the total cost of renting an apartment. Write an equation of the line. *Explain* the meaning of the slope and the *y*-intercept of the line.

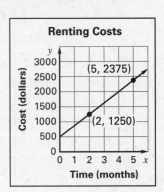

Renting Costs

Step 1 Find the slope.

$$m = \frac{2375 - 1250}{5 - 2}$$

$$= \frac{1125}{3} = \underline{375}$$

Step 2 Find the *y*-intercept. Use a point on the graph.

$y = mx + b$ **Use slope-intercept form.**

$\underline{1250} = \underline{375} \cdot \underline{2} + b$ **Substitute.**

$\underline{500} = b$ **Simplify.**

Step 3 Write the equation. Because $m = \underline{375}$ and $b = \underline{500}$, an equation is $y = \underline{375x + 500}$.

The equation $y = \underline{375x + 500}$ models the cost. The slope is the $\underline{\text{monthly rent}}$, and the $\underline{y\text{-intercept}}$ is the initial cost to rent the apartment.

Example 5   *Graph a line with equation in standard form*

Graph $2x + 3y = 6$.

The equation is in standard form, so use the $\underline{\text{intercepts}}$.

Step 1 Find the intercepts.

To find the *x*-intercept, let $y = \underline{0}$.

$$2x + 3y = 6$$
$$2x + 3(\underline{0}) = 6$$
$$x = \underline{3}$$

To find the *y*-intercept, let $x = \underline{0}$.

$$2x + 3y = 6$$
$$2(\underline{0}) + 3y = 6$$
$$y = \underline{2}$$

Step 2 Graph the line.

The intercepts are $\underline{(3, 0)}$ and $\underline{(0, 2)}$. Graph these points, then draw a line through the points.

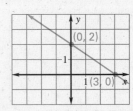

Example 6 *Solve a real-world problem*

Subscriptions You can buy a magazine at a store for $3. You can subscribe yearly to the magazine for a flat fee of $18. After how many magazines is the subscription a better buy?

Solution

Step 1 Model each purchase with an equation.

Cost of yearly subscription: $y =$ __18__

Cost of one magazine: $y =$ __3__ x, where x represents the number of magazines

Step 2 Graph each equation.

The point of intersection is __(6, 18)__ . Using the graph, you can see that it is cheaper to buy magazines individually if you buy less than __6__ magazines per year. If you buy more than __6__ magazines per year, it is cheaper to buy a subscription.

> The point at which the costs are the same is sometimes called the *break-even point*.

Magazine Purchases

✔ *Checkpoint* **Complete the following exercises.**

4. The equation $y = 650x + 425$ models the total cost of joining a health club for x years. What are the meaning of the slope and y-intercept of the line?

   The slope is the cost per year, $650, and the y-intercept is the initiation fee, $425.

5. Graph $y = 3$ and $x = 3$.

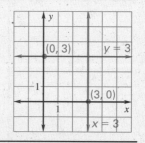

Homework

6. In Example 6, suppose you can buy the magazine at a different store for $2.50. After how many magazines is the subscription the better buy?

   8 magazines

3.6 Prove Theorems About Perpendicular Lines

Goal • Find the distance between a point and a line.

Your Notes

THEOREM 3.8

If two lines intersect to form a linear pair of congruent angles, then the lines are <u>perpendicular</u>.

If ∠1 ≅ ∠2, then *g* <u>⊥</u> *h*.

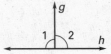

THEOREM 3.9

If two lines are perpendicular, then they intersect to form four <u>right angles</u>.

If *a* ⊥ *b*, then ∠1, ∠2, ∠3, and ∠4 are <u>right angles</u>.

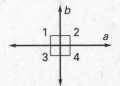

Example 1 *Draw conclusions*

In the diagram at the right, ∠1 ≅ ∠2. What can you conclude about *a* and *b*?

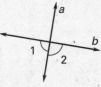

Solution

Lines *a* and *b* intersect to form a <u>linear pair of congruent angles</u>, ∠1 and ∠2. So, by Theorem 3.8, <u>*a* ⊥ *b*</u>.

THEOREM 3.10

If two sides of two adjacent acute angles are perpendicular, then the angles are _complementary_ .

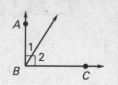

If $\overrightarrow{BA} \perp \overrightarrow{BC}$, then $\angle 1$ and $\angle 2$ are _complementary_ .

Example 2 *Write a proof*

In the diagram at the right, $\angle 1 \cong \angle 2$.
Prove that $\angle 3$ and $\angle 4$ are complementary.

Given $\angle 1 \cong \angle 2$

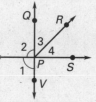

Prove $\angle 3$ and $\angle 4$ are complementary.

Statements	Reasons
1. $\angle 1 \cong \angle 2$	1. _Given_
2. _$\overleftrightarrow{PS} \perp \overleftrightarrow{PQ}$_	2. Theorem 3.8
3. $\angle 3$ and $\angle 4$ are complementary.	3. _Theorem 3.10_

✔ *Checkpoint* **Complete the following exercises.**

1. If $c \perp d$, what do you know about the sum of the measures of $\angle 3$ and $\angle 4$? *Explain*.

Because $c \perp d$, angles 1, 2, 3, and 4 are right angles by Theorem 3.9. So, $m\angle 3 + m\angle 4 = 180°$.

2. Using the diagram in Example 2, complete the following proof that $\angle QPS$ and $\angle 1$ are right angles.

Statements	Reasons
1. $\angle 1 \cong \angle 2$	1. _Given_
2. $\overleftrightarrow{PS} \perp \overleftrightarrow{PQ}$	2. _Theorem 3.8_
3. $\angle QPS$ and $\angle 1$ are right angles.	3. _Theorem 3.9_

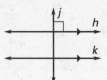

THEOREM 3.11 PERPENDICULAR TRANSVERSAL THEOREM

If a transversal is perpendicular to one of two parallel lines, then it is __perpendicular__ to the other.

If $h \parallel k$ and $j \perp h$, then j __$\perp$__ k.

THEOREM 3.12 LINES PERPENDICULAR TO A TRANSVERSAL THEOREM

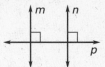

In a plane, if two lines are perpendicular to the same line, then they are __parallel__ to each other.

If $m \perp p$ and $n \perp p$, then m __$\parallel$__ n.

Example 3 *Draw conclusions*

Determine which lines, if any, must be parallel in the diagram. *Explain* your reasoning.

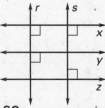

Solution

Lines r and s are both perpendicular to __x__, so by Theorem 3.12, __$r \parallel s$__. Similarly, lines x and y are both perpendicular to r, so __$x \parallel y$__. Also, lines __x__ and __z__ are both perpendicular to s, so __$x \parallel z$__. Finally, because y and z are both parallel to __x__, you know that __$y \parallel z$__ by the Transitive Property of Parallel Lines.

✔ **Checkpoint** Use the diagram to complete the following exercises.

3. Is $c \parallel d$? *Explain.*

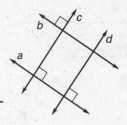

Yes, because c and d are both perpendicular to a, $c \parallel d$ by Theorem 3.12.

---

4. Is $b \perp d$? *Explain.*

Yes, because $b \perp c$, and $c \parallel d$ as explained in Exercise 3, then $b \perp d$ by Theorem 3.11.

Example 4 *Find the distance between two parallel lines*

Railroads The section of broad gauge railroad track at the right are drawn on a graph where units are measured in inches. What is the width of the track?

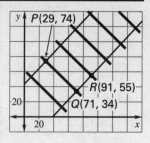

Solution

You need to find the length of a perpendicular segment from one side of the track to the other.

Using $Q(71, 34)$ and $R(91, 55)$, the slope of each rail is

$$\frac{55 - \boxed{34}}{91 - \boxed{71}} = \frac{21}{20}$$

The segment *PQ* has a slope of

$$\frac{74 - \boxed{34}}{29 - \boxed{71}} = \frac{40}{-42} = -\frac{20}{21}$$

The segment *PQ* is perpendicular to the rail so *PQ* is

$$d = \sqrt{(\ \underline{29 - 71}\ )^2 + (\ \underline{74 - 34}\ )^2} = \underline{58}\ .$$

The width of the track is <u>58 inches</u> .

✔ **Checkpoint** Complete the following exercise.

5. What is the approximate distance from line *m* to line *n*?

about 3.2 units

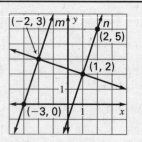

Homework

Words to Review

Give an example of the vocabulary word.

Parallel lines	Skew lines
	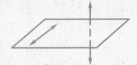
Parallel planes	**Transversal**
	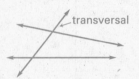
Corresponding angles	**Alternate interior angles**
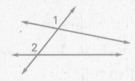	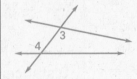
Alternate exterior angles	**Consecutive interior angles**
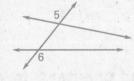	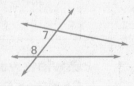

Paragraph proof

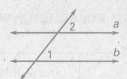

Given: $m\angle 1 = 50°$
$\quad\quad\quad m\angle 2 = 50°$

Prove: $a \parallel b$

You are given that $m\angle 1 = m\angle 2$, so $\angle 1 \cong \angle 2$ by the definition of congruent angles. So, $a \parallel b$ by the Corresponding Angles Converse.

Slope

The slope of $y = 8x - 7$ is 8.

Slope-intercept form

$y = mx + b$, where m is the slope and b is the y-intercept.

Standard form

$Ax + By = C$, where A and B are not both zero.

Distance from a point to a line.

The distance from point A to line b is 5.

Review your notes and Chapter 3 by using the Chapter Review on pages 202–205 of your textbook.

Apply Triangle Sum Properties

Goal • Classsify triangles and find measures of their angles.

Your Notes

VOCABULARY

Triangle A triangle is a polygon with three sides.

Interior angles When the sides of a polygon are extended, the original angles are the interior angles.

Exterior angles When the sides of a polygon are extended, the angles that form linear pairs with the interior angles are the exterior angles.

Corollary to a theorem A corollary to a theorem is a statement that can be proved easily using the theorem.

CLASSIFYING TRIANGLES BY SIDES

Scalene Triangle	Isosceles Triangle	Equilateral Triangle

_No_ congruent sides   At least _2_ congruent sides   _3_ congruent sides

CLASSIFYING TRIANGLES BY ANGLES

Acute Triangle	Right Triangle	Obtuse Triangle	Equiangular Triangle

_3_ acute angles   _1_ right angle   _1_ obtuse angle   _3_ congruent angles

> Notice that an equilateral triangle is also isosceles. An equiangular triangle is also acute.

Example 1   *Classify triangles by sides and by angles*

Shuffleboard Classify the triangular shape of the shuffleboard scoring area in the diagram by its sides and by measuring its angles.

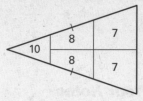

Solution

The triangle has a pair of congruent sides, so it is __isosceles__ . By measuring, the angles are about __72°, 72°, and 36°__ . It is an __acute isosceles__ triangle.

✓ *Checkpoint* **Complete the folowing exercise.**

1. Draw an isosceles right triangle and an obtuse scalene triangle.

Sample Drawings: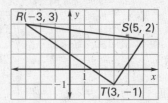

Example 2   *Classify a triangle in a coordinate plane*

Classify △*RST* by its sides. Then determine if the triangle is a right triangle.

Solution

Step 1 Use the distance formula $\sqrt{(x_2 - x_1)^2 + (y_2 - y_1)^2}$ to find the side lengths.

$RT = \sqrt{\underline{(3 - (-3))}^2 + \underline{(-1 - 3)}^2} = \underline{\sqrt{52}}$

$RS = \sqrt{\underline{(5 - (-3))}^2 + \underline{(2 - 3)}^2} = \underline{\sqrt{65}}$

$ST = \sqrt{\underline{(3 - 5)}^2 + \underline{(-1 - 2)}^2} = \underline{\sqrt{13}}$

Step 2 **Check** for right angles. The slope of $\overline{RT}$ is

$\dfrac{-1 - 3}{3 - (-3)} = \underline{-\dfrac{2}{3}}$. The slope of $\overline{ST}$ is

$\dfrac{-1 - 2}{3 - 5} = \underline{\dfrac{3}{2}}$. The product of the slopes is

__−1__ , so $\overline{RT} \perp \overline{ST}$ and $\angle RTS$ is a __right__ angle.

Therefore, △*RST* is a __right scalene__ triangle.

     Copyright © McDougal Littell/Houghton Mifflin Company.

Your Notes

THEOREM 4.1: TRIANGLE SUM THEOREM

The sum of the measures of the interior angles of a triangle is __180°__ .

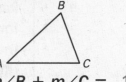

$$m\angle A + m\angle B + m\angle C = \underline{180°}$$

THEOREM 4.2: EXTERIOR ANGLE THEOREM

The measure of an exterior angle of a triangle is equal to the sum of the measures of the two __nonadjacent interior__ angles.

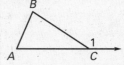

$$m\angle 1 = m\angle\ \underline{A}\ + m\angle\ \underline{B}$$

Example 3 *Find angle measure*

Use the diagram at the right to find the measure of ∠DCB.

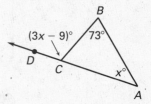

Solution

Step 1 Write and solve an equation to find the value of *x*.

$$(3x - 9)° = \underline{73° + x°}$$ **Exterior Angle Theorem**

$$x = \underline{41°}$$ **Solve for *x*.**

Step 2 Substitute __41__ for *x* in 3*x* − 9 to find *m*∠DCB.

$$3x - 9 = 3 \cdot \underline{41} - 9 = \underline{114}$$

The measure of ∠DCB is __114°__ .

COROLLARY TO THE TRIANGLE SUM THEOREM

The acute angles of a right triangle are __complementary__ .

$$m\angle A + m\angle B = \underline{90°}$$

Example 4 *Find angle measures from a verbal description*

Ramps The front face of the wheelchair ramp shown forms a right triangle. The measure of one acute angle in the triangle is eight times the measure of the other. Find the measure of each acute angle.

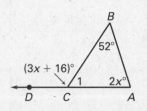

Solution

First, sketch a diagram of the situation. Let the measure of the smaller acute angle be $x°$. Then the measure of the larger acute angle is __$8x°$__ .

Use the Corollary to the Triangle Sum Theorem to set up and solve an equation.

$x° + $ __$8x°$__ $ = $ __$90°$__   **Corollary to the Triangle Sum Theorem**

$x = $ __10__   **Solve for x.**

So, the measures of the acute angles are __$10°$__ and __$80°$__ .

✔ *Checkpoint* **Complete the following exercises.**

2. Triangle *JKL* has vertices $J(-2, -1)$, $K(1, 3)$, and $L(5, 0)$. Classify it by its sides. Then determine if it is a right triangle.

   isosceles triangle; right triangle

3. Find the measure of ∠1 in the diagram shown.

   56°

4. In Example 4, what is the measure of the obtuse angle formed between the ramp and a segment extending from the horizontal leg?

   170°

Homework

4.2 Apply Congruence and Triangles

Goal · Identify congruent figures.

Your Notes

> **VOCABULARY**
>
> **Congruent figures** In two congruent figures, all the parts of one figure are congruent to the corresponding parts of the other figure.
>
> **Corresponding parts** In congruent polygons, the corresponding parts are the corresponding sides and the corresponding angles.

Example 1 *Identify congruent parts*

Write a congruence statement for the triangles. Identify all pairs of congruent corresponding parts.

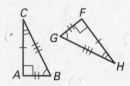

To help you identify corresponding parts, turn △FGH.

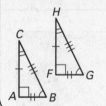

Solution

The diagram indicates that $\triangle ABC \cong \triangle\ \underline{FGH}$.

Corresponding angles $\angle A \cong \underline{\angle F}$, $\angle B \cong \underline{\angle G}$, $\angle C \cong \underline{\angle H}$

Corresponding sides $\overline{AB} \cong \underline{\overline{FG}}$, $\overline{BC} \cong \underline{\overline{GH}}$, $\overline{CA} \cong \underline{\overline{HF}}$

Example 2 *Use properties of congruent figures*

In the diagram, $QRST \cong WXYZ$.

a. Find the value of x.

b. Find the value of y.

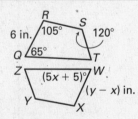

Solution

a. You know $\angle Q \cong \angle W$.

$m\angle Q = \underline{m\angle W}$

$65° = \underline{(5x + 5)°}$

$\underline{60} = \underline{5x}$

$\underline{12} = x$

b. You know $\overline{QR} \cong \overline{WX}$.

$QR = \underline{WX}$

$6 = \underline{y - x}$

$6 = \underline{y - 12}$

$\underline{18} = y$

✓ *Checkpoint* **In Exercises 1 and 2, use the diagram shown in which *FGHJ* ≅ *STUV*.**

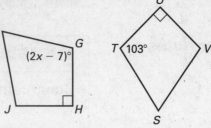

1. Identify all pairs of congruent corresponding parts.

Corresponding angles: ∠F ≅ ∠S, ∠G ≅ ∠T, ∠H ≅ ∠U, ∠J ≅ ∠V

Corresponding sides: $\overline{FG}$ ≅ $\overline{ST}$, $\overline{GH}$ ≅ $\overline{TU}$, $\overline{HJ}$ ≅ $\overline{UV}$, $\overline{JF}$ ≅ $\overline{VS}$

2. Find the value of *x* and find *m∠G*.

x = 55; *m∠G* = 103°

Example 3 *Show that figures are congruent*

Maps If you cut the map in half along $\overline{PR}$, will the sections of the map be the same size and shape? *Explain*.

Solution

From the diagram, ∠S ≅ ∠Q because all right angles are congruent. Also, by the Lines Perpendicular to a Transversal Theorem, $\overline{PQ}$ ∥ $\overline{RS}$. Then ∠1 ≅ ∠4 and ∠2 ≅ ∠3 by the Alternate Interior Angles Theorem. So, all pairs of corresponding angles are congruent.

The diagram shows $\overline{PQ}$ ≅ $\overline{RS}$ and $\overline{QR}$ ≅ $\overline{SP}$. By the Reflexive Property, $\overline{PR}$ ≅ $\overline{RP}$. All corresponding parts are congruent, so △PQR ≅ △RSP.

Yes, the two sections will be the same size and shape.

Your Notes

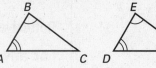

THEOREM 4.3: THIRD ANGLES THEOREM

If two angles of one triangle are congruent to two angles of another triangle, then the third angles are also ___congruent___.

Example 4 *Use the Third Angles Theorem*

Find $m\angle V$.

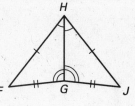

Solution

$\angle SUT \cong \angle VUW$ by the ___Vertical Angles Theorem___.
The diagram shows that $\angle STU \cong$ ___$\angle VWU$___, so by the Third Angles Theorem, $\angle S \cong$ ___$\angle V$___. By the Triangle Sum Theorem, $m\angle S =$ ___$180° - 66° - 44°$___ $=$ ___$70°$___. So, $m\angle S = m\angle V =$ ___$70°$___ by the definition of congruent angles.

Example 5 *Prove that triangles are congruent*

Write a proof.

Given $\overline{FH} \cong \overline{JH}, \overline{FG} \cong \overline{JG},$
$\angle FHG \cong \angle JHG, \angle FGH \cong \angle JGH$

Prove $\triangle FGH \cong \triangle JGH$

Plan for Proof

a. Use the Reflexive Property to show ___$\overline{HG} \cong \overline{HG}$___.

b. Use the Third Angles Theorem to show ___$\angle F \cong \angle J$___.

Plan in Action

Statements	Reasons
1. $\overline{FH} \cong \overline{JH}, \overline{FG} \cong \overline{JG}$	1. ___Given___
a. 2. ___$\overline{HG} \cong \overline{HG}$___	2. Reflexive Property of Congruence
3. $\angle FHG \cong \angle JHG,$ $\angle FGH \cong \angle JGH$	3. ___Given___
b. 4. ___$\angle F \cong \angle J$___	4. Third Angles Theorem
5. $\triangle FGH \cong \triangle JGH$	5. ___Definition of $\cong \triangle$s___

THEOREM 4.4: PROPERTIES OF CONGRUENT TRIANGLES

Reflexive Property of Congruent Triangles

For any triangle ABC, △ABC ≅ △ABC .

Symmetric Property of Congruent Triangles

If △ABC ≅ △DEF, then △DEF ≅ △ABC .

Transitive Property of Congruent Triangles

If △ABC ≅ △DEF and △DEF ≅ △JKL, then
△ABC ≅ △JKL .

✔ *Checkpoint* **Complete the following exercises.**

3. In the diagram at the right, E is the midpoint of $\overline{AC}$ and $\overline{BD}$. Show that △ABE ≅ △CDE.

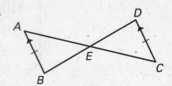

From the diagram, $\overline{AB} ≅ \overline{CD}$. Point E is the midpoint of $\overline{AC}$ and $\overline{BD}$, so $\overline{AE} ≅ \overline{CE}$ and $\overline{BE} ≅ \overline{DE}$ by the definition of midpoint. So all pairs of corresponding sides are congruent.

The diagram shows $\overline{AB} \parallel \overline{CD}$, so ∠A ≅ ∠C and ∠B ≅ ∠D by the Alternate Interior Angles Theorem. Also, ∠AEB ≅ ∠CED by the Vertical Angles Theorem. All corresponding parts are congruent, so △ABE ≅ △CDE.

4. In the diagram, what is the measure of ∠D?

62°

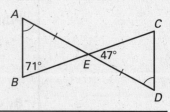

5. By the definition of congruence, what additional information is needed to know that △ABE ≅ △DCE in Exercise 4?

You must know that $\overline{AB} ≅ \overline{DC}$ and $\overline{BE} ≅ \overline{CE}$ to conclude that △ABE ≅ △DCE. The remaining information can be inferred from the graph.

Homework

4.3 Prove Triangles Congruent by SSS

Goal • Use side lengths to prove triangles are congruent.

POSTULATE 19: SIDE-SIDE-SIDE (SSS) CONGRUENCE POSTULATE

If three sides of one triangle are congruent to three sides of a second triangle, then the two triangles are congruent.

If   Side $\overline{AB} \cong$ _RS_ ,

     Side $\overline{BC} \cong$ _ST_ , and

     Side $\overline{CA} \cong$ _TR_ ,

then $\triangle ABC \cong$ _△RST_ .

Example 1   *Use the SSS Congruence Postulate*

Write a proof.

Given $\overline{FJ} \cong \overline{HJ}$,
          G is the midpoint of $\overline{FH}$.

Prove $\triangle FGJ \cong \triangle HGJ$

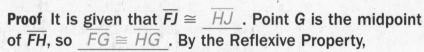

Proof It is given that $\overline{FJ} \cong$ _HJ_ . Point G is the midpoint of $\overline{FH}$, so _FG_ $\cong$ _HG_ . By the Reflexive Property, _GJ_ $\cong$ _JG_ . So, by the _SSS Congruence Postulate_ , $\triangle FGJ \cong \triangle HGJ$.

✔ *Checkpoint* Decide whether the congruence statement is true. *Explain* your reasoning.

1. $\triangle JKL \cong \triangle MKL$	2. $\triangle RST \cong \triangle TVW$
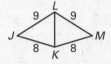	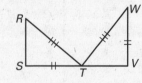
True; all corresponding sides are congruent.	False; $\overline{RS} \ncong \overline{TV}$

Example 2   *Congruence in the coordinate plane*

Determine whether △PQR is congruent to the other triangles shown at the right.

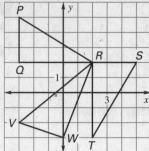

Solution

By counting, PQ = 3 and QR = 5. Use the distance formula to find PR.

$$d = \sqrt{(x_2 - x_1)^2 + (y_2 - y_1)^2}$$

$$PR = \sqrt{(2 - (-3))^2 + (2 - 5)^2} = \sqrt{34}$$

By the SSS Congruence Postulate, any triangle with side lengths _3_ , _5_ , and $\sqrt{34}$ will be congruent to △PQR. The distance from R to S is _3_ . The distance from R to T is _5_ . The distance from S to T is

$$\sqrt{(2 - 5)^2 + (-3 - 2)^2} = \sqrt{34}.\ \text{So,}$$

△PQR ≅ _△SRT_ .

The distance from W to V is

$$\sqrt{(-3 - 0)^2 + (-2 - (-3))^2} = \sqrt{10}.\ \text{No side of}$$

△PQR has a length of $\sqrt{10}$, so △PQR _≇_ △VWR.

✓ *Checkpoint* **Complete the following exercise.**

3. △DFG has vertices D(−2, 4), F(4, 4), and G(−2, 2). △LMN has vertices L(−3, −3), M(−3, 3), and N(−1, −3). Graph the triangles in the same coordinate plane and show that they are congruent.

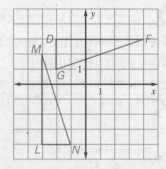

DG = LN = 2, DF = LM = 6, and
FG = MN = √40, so △DFG ≅ △LMN by the
SSS Congruence Postulate.

Your Notes

Example 3   Solve a real-world problem

Stability *Explain* why the table with the diagonal legs is stable, while the one without the diagonal legs can collapse.

Solution

The table with the diagonal legs forms triangles with __fixed__ side lengths. By the SSS Congruence Postulate, these triangles __cannot change shape__, so the table is __stable__. The table without the diagonal legs is __not stable__ because there are many possible quadrilaterals with the given side lengths.

✔ **Checkpoint** Determine whether the figure is stable. *Explain* your reasoning.

4. 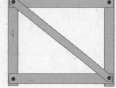	5. 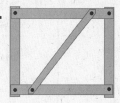
Yes, the figure is stable. By the SSS Congruence Postulate, the triangles formed cannot change shape, so it is stable.	No, the figure is not stable. There are many possible quadrilaterals with the given side lengths.

Homework

4.4 Prove Triangles Congruent by SAS and HL

Goal • Use sides and angles to prove congruence.

Your Notes

> **VOCABULARY**
>
> **Leg of a right triangle** In a right triangle, a side adjacent to the right angle is called a leg.
>
> **Hypotenuse** In a right triangle, the side opposite the right angle is called the hypotenuse.

> **POSTULATE 20: SIDE-ANGLE-SIDE (SAS) CONGRUENCE POSTULATE**
>
> If two sides and the included angle of one triangle are congruent to two sides and the included angle of a second triangle, then the two triangles are congruent.
>
> If   Side $\overline{RS} \cong$ _$\overline{UV}$_ ,
>
>   Angle $\angle R \cong$ _$\angle U$_ , and
>
>   Side $\overline{RT} \cong$ _$\overline{UW}$_ ,
>
> then $\triangle RST \cong$ _$\triangle UVW$_ .

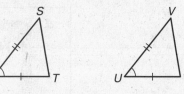

Example 1   *Use the SAS Congruence Postulate*

Write a proof.

Given $\overline{JN} \cong \overline{LN}, \overline{KN} \cong \overline{MN}$

Prove $\triangle JKN \cong \triangle LMN$

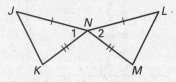

Statements	Reasons
1. $\overline{JN} \cong$ _$\overline{LN}$_ , $\overline{KN} \cong$ _$\overline{MN}$_	1. Given
2. $\angle 1 \cong \angle 2$	2. Vertical Angles Theorem
3. $\triangle JKN \cong \triangle LMN$	3. SAS Congruence Postulate

Your Notes

Example 2   *Use SAS and properties of shapes*

In the diagram, *ABCD* is a rectangle. What can you conclude about △*ABC* and △*CDA*?

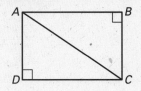

Solution

By the __Right Angles Congruence Theorem__ , ∠*B* ≅ ∠*D*. Opposite sides of a rectangle are congruent, so __$\overline{AB} \cong \overline{CD}$__ and __$\overline{BC} \cong \overline{DA}$__ .

△*ABC* and △*CDA* are congruent by the __SAS Congruence Postulate__ .

✓ *Checkpoint* In the diagram, $\overline{AB}$, $\overline{CD}$, and $\overline{EF}$ pass through the center *M* of the circle. Also, ∠1 ≅ ∠2 ≅ ∠3 ≅ ∠4.

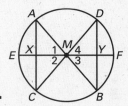

1. Prove that △*DMY* ≅ △*BMY*.

Statements	Reasons
1. ∠3 ≅ ∠4	1. Given
2. $\overline{DM} \cong \overline{BM}$	2. Definition of a circle
3. $\overline{MY} \cong \overline{MY}$	3. Reflexive Property of Congruence
4. △*DMY* ≅ △*BMY*	4. SAS Congruence Postulate

2. What can you conclude about $\overline{AC}$ and $\overline{BD}$?

Because they are vertical angles, ∠*AMC* ≅ ∠*BMD*. All points on a circle are the same distance from the center, so *AM* = *BM* = *CM* = *DM*. By the SAS Congruence Postulate, △*AMC* ≅ △*BMD*. Corresponding parts of congruent triangles are congruent, so you know $\overline{AC} \cong \overline{BD}$.

THEOREM 4.5: HYPOTENUSE-LEG CONGRUENCE THEOREM

If the hypotenuse and a leg of a right triangle are congruent to the hypotenuse and a leg of a second triangle, then the two triangles are __congruent__ .

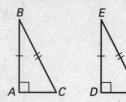

Example 3   *Use the Hypotenuse-Leg Theorem*

Write a proof.

Given $\overline{AC} \cong \overline{EC}$,
    $\overline{AB} \perp \overline{BD}$,
    $\overline{ED} \perp \overline{BD}$,
    $\overline{AC}$ is a bisector of $\overline{BD}$.

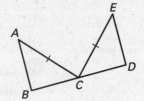

Prove $\triangle ABC \cong \triangle EDC$

	Statements	Reasons
H	1. $\overline{AC} \cong \overline{EC}$	1. __Given__
	2. $\overline{AB} \perp \overline{BD}$, $\overline{ED} \perp \overline{BD}$	2. __Given__
	3. $\angle B$ and $\angle D$ are __right angles__ .	3. Definition of $\perp$ lines
	4. $\triangle ABC$ and $\triangle EDC$ are __right triangles__ .	4. Definition of a __right triangle__
	5. $\overline{AC}$ is a bisector of $\overline{BD}$.	5. __Given__
L	6. $\overline{BC} \cong \overline{DC}$	6. Definition of segment bisector
	7. $\triangle ABC \cong \triangle EDC$	7. __HL Congruence Theorem__

Example 4 *Choose a postulate or theorem*

Gate The entrance to a ranch has a rectangular gate as shown in the diagram. You know that △*AFC* ≅ △*EFC*. What postulate or theorem can you use to conclude that △*ABC* ≅ △*EDC*?

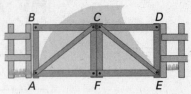

Solution

You are given that *ABDE* is a rectangle, so ∠*B* and ∠*D* are ___right angles___ . Because opposite sides of a rectangle are ___congruent___ , $\overline{AB}$ ≅ ___$\overline{DE}$___ . You are also given that △*AFC* ≅ △*EFC*, so $\overline{AC}$ ≅ ___$\overline{EC}$___ . The hypotenuse and a leg of each triangle is congruent.

You can use the ___HL Congruence Theorem___ to conclude that △*ABC* ≅ △*EDC*.

☑ *Checkpoint* **Complete the following exercises.**

3. *Explain* why a diagonal of a rectangle forms a pair of congruent triangles.

A diagonal of a rectangle will be the hypotenuse of each triangle formed. Because the hypotenuse is congruent to itself, and because opposite sides of a rectangle are congruent, you can use the HL Congruence Theorem to conclude the triangles are congruent.

4. In Example 4, suppose it is given that *ABCF* and *EDCF* are squares. What postulate or theorem can you use to conclude that △*ABC* ≅ △*EDC*? *Explain.*

It is given that *ABCF* and *EDCF* are squares, so ∠*B* and ∠*D* are right angles, $\overline{AB}$ ≅ $\overline{DE}$, and $\overline{BC}$ ≅ $\overline{DC}$. You can use the SAS Congruence Postulate to conclude that △*ABC* ≅ △*EDC*.

Homework

4.5 Prove Triangles Congruent by ASA and AAS

Goal • Use two more methods to prove congruences.

Your Notes

VOCABULARY

Flow proof A flow proof uses arrows to show the flow of a logical argument.

POSTULATE 21: ANGLE-SIDE-ANGLE (ASA) CONGRUENCE POSTULATE

If two angles and the included side of one triangle are congruent to two angles and the included side of a second triangle, then the two triangles are congruent.

If **Angle** $\angle A \cong \underline{\angle D}$,

      Side $\overline{AC} \cong \underline{\overline{DF}}$, and

      Angle $\angle C \cong \underline{\angle F}$,

then $\triangle ABC \cong \underline{\triangle DEF}$.

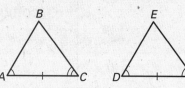

THEOREM 4.6: ANGLE-ANGLE-SIDE (AAS) CONGRUENCE THEOREM

If two angles and a non-included side of one triangle are congruent to two angles and the corresponding non-included side of a second triangle, then the two triangles are congruent.

If **Angle** $\angle A \cong \underline{\angle D}$,

      Angle $\angle C \cong \underline{\angle F}$, and

      Side $\overline{BC} \cong \underline{\overline{EF}}$,

then $\triangle ABC \cong \underline{\triangle DEF}$.

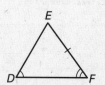

Example 1 *Identify congruent triangles*

Can the triangles be proven congruent with the information given in the diagram? If so, state the postulate or theorem you would use.

a.    b.   c.

Solution

a. There is not enough information to prove the triangles are congruent, because no ___sides___ are known to be congruent.

b. Two pairs of angles and a ___non-included___ pair of sides are congruent. The triangles are congruent by the ___AAS Congruence Theorem___.

c. The vertical angles are congruent, so two pairs of angles and their ___included sides___ are congruent. The triangles are congruent by the ___ASA Congruence Postulate___.

✔ **Checkpoint** Can △STW and △VWT be proven congruent with the information given in the diagram? If so, state the postulate or theorem you would use.

1.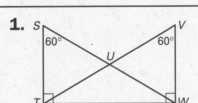

Yes; AAS Congruence Theorem

2.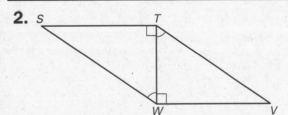

Yes; ASA Congruence Postulate

Your Notes

Example 2   *Write a flow proof*

In the diagram, ∠1 ≅ ∠4 and
$\overline{CF}$ bisects ∠ACE. Write a flow
proof to show △CBF ≅ △CDF.

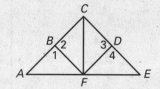

Solution

Given   ∠1 ≅ ∠4, $\overline{CF}$ bisects ∠ACE.

Prove   △CBF ≅ △CDF

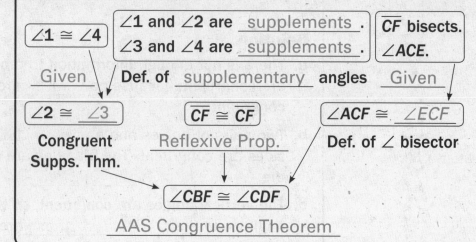

∠1 ≅ ∠4	∠1 and ∠2 are __supplements__.	$\overline{CF}$ bisects.
	∠3 and ∠4 are __supplements__.	∠ACE.

__Given__   Def. of __supplementary__ angles   __Given__

∠2 ≅ __∠3__ $\overline{CF} ≅ \overline{CF}$ ∠ACF ≅ __∠ECF__

Congruent   Reflexive Prop.   Def. of ∠ bisector
Supps. Thm.

∠CBF ≅ ∠CDF

__AAS Congruence Theorem__

✔ *Checkpoint* **Complete the following exercise.**

3. In Example 2, suppose it is given that $\overline{CF}$ bisects
∠ACE and ∠BFD. Write a flow proof to show
△CBF ≅ △CDF.

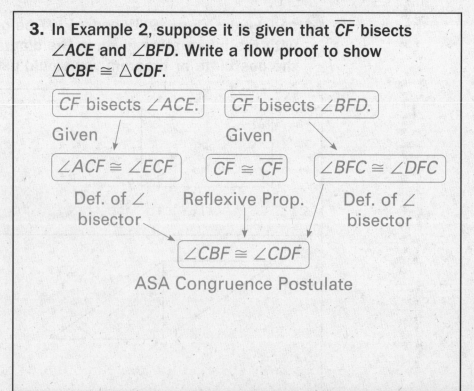

$\overline{CF}$ bisects ∠ACE. $\overline{CF}$ bisects ∠BFD.

Given   Given

∠ACF ≅ ∠ECF $\overline{CF} ≅ \overline{CF}$ ∠BFC ≅ ∠DFC

Def. of ∠   Reflexive Prop.   Def. of ∠
bisector   bisector

∠CBF ≅ ∠CDF

ASA Congruence Postulate

Example 3 *Choose a postulate or theorem*

Games You and a friend are trying to find a flag hidden in the woods. Your friend is standing 75 feet away from you. When facing each other, the angle from you to the flag is 72° and the angle from your friend to the flag is 53°. Is there enough information to locate the flag?

Solution

The locations of you, your friend, and the flag form a triangle. The measures of two angles and an included side of the triangle are known.

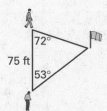

By the ASA Congruence Postulate , all triangles with these measures are congruent. So, the triangle formed is unique and the flag location is given by the third vertex .

✔ *Checkpoint* **Complete the following exercise.**

4. **Theater** You are working two spotlights for a play. Two actors are standing apart from each other on the end of the stage. The spotlights are located and pointed as shown in the diagram. Can one of the actors move without requiring the spotlight to move and without changing the distance between the other actor?

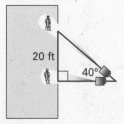

The measures of two angles and a nonincluded side of the triangle are known. By the AAS Congruence Theorem, all triangles with these measures are congruent. So, the triangle formed is unique, and one of the actors cannot move without requiring the spotlight to move and without changing the distance between the other actor.

Homework

4.6 Use Congruent Triangles

Goal • Use congruent triangles to prove corresponding parts congruent.

Your Notes

Example 1   *Use congruent triangles*

Explain how you can use the given information to prove that the triangles are congruent.

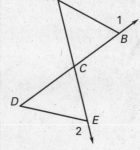

Given $\angle 1 \cong \angle 2, \overline{AB} \cong \overline{DE}$

Prove $\overline{DC} \cong \overline{AC}$

Solution

If you can show that __$\triangle ABC \cong \triangle DEC$__ , you will know that $\overline{DC} \cong \overline{AC}$. First, copy the diagram and mark the given information. Then add the information that you can deduce. In this case, $\angle ABC$ and $\angle DEC$ are __supplementary__ to congruent angles, so $\angle$ _ABC_ $\cong \angle$ _DEC_ . Also, $\angle ACB \cong$ __$\angle DCE$__ .

Mark given information.   **Add deduced information.**

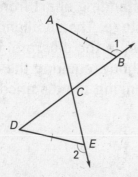 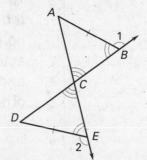

Two angle pairs and a __non-included__ side are congruent, so by the __AAS Congruence Theorem__ , $\triangle ABC \cong \triangle DEC$. Because __corresponding parts__ of congruent triangles are congruent, $\overline{DC} \cong \overline{AC}$.

Your Notes

> When you cannot easily measure a length directly, you can make conclusions about the length *indirectly*, usually by calculations based on known lengths.

Example 2 *Use congruent triangles for measurement*

Boats Use the following method to find the distance between two docked boats, from point *A* to point *B*.

*   Place a marker at *D* so that $\overline{AB} \perp \overline{BD}$.
*   Find *C*, the midpoint of $\overline{BD}$.
*   Locate the point *E* so that $\overline{BD} \perp \overline{DE}$ and *A*, *C*, and *E* are collinear.
*   *Explain* how this plan allows you to find the distance.

Solution

Because $\overline{AB} \perp \overline{BD}$ and $\overline{BD} \perp \overline{DE}$, $\underline{\angle B}$ and $\underline{\angle D}$ are congruent right angles. Because *C* is the midpoint of $\overline{BD}$, $\underline{\overline{BC}} \cong \underline{\overline{DC}}$. The vertical angles $\underline{\angle ACB}$ and $\underline{\angle ECD}$ are congruent. So, $\triangle CBA \cong \underline{\triangle CDE}$ by the $\underline{\text{ASA Congruence Postulate}}$. Then, because corresponding parts of congruent triangles are congruent, $\overline{BA} = \underline{\overline{DE}}$. So, you can find the distance *AB* between the boats by measuring $\underline{\overline{DE}}$.

✔ *Checkpoint* **Complete the following exercises.**

1. *Explain* how you can prove that $\overline{PR} \cong \overline{QS}$.

Use the AAS Congruence Theorem to show $\triangle PTS \cong \triangle QTR$. Because corresponding pairs of congruent triangles are congruent, $\overline{PT} \cong \overline{QT}$. Then $\overline{PR} \cong \overline{QS}$ because $\overline{ST} \cong \overline{RT}$.

2. In Example 2, does it matter how far away from point *B* you place a marker at point *D*? *Explain*.

Point *D* should be placed far enough away from point *B* so that it is on land. This allows $\overline{DE}$ to be easily measured. However, the method will work regardless of how far *D* is from *B*.

Example 3   *Plan a proof involving pairs of triangles*

Use the given information
to write a plan for proof.

Given $\angle 1 \cong \angle 2$, $\angle 3 \cong \angle 4$

Prove $\triangle ABD \cong \triangle ACD$

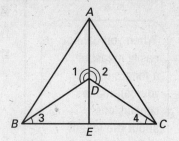

Solution

In $\triangle ABD$ and $\triangle ACD$, you know that $\angle 1 \cong$ __$\angle 2$__ and
$\overline{AD} \cong \overline{AD}$. If you can show that $\overline{BD} \cong \overline{CD}$, you can use
the __SAS Congruence Postulate__.

To prove that $\overline{BD} \cong \overline{CD}$, you can first prove that
$\triangle BED \cong$ __$\triangle CED$__. You are given $\angle 1 \cong \angle 2$ and
$\angle 3 \cong \angle 4$. $\overline{ED} \cong \overline{ED}$ by the Reflexive Property and
$\angle BDE \cong$ __$\angle CDE$__ by the Congruent Supplements
Theorem. You can use the __AAS Congruence Theorem__
to prove that $\triangle BED \cong$ __$\triangle CED$__.

Plan for Proof Use the __AAS Congruence Theorem__ to
prove that $\triangle BED \cong$ __$\triangle CED$__. Then state that $\overline{BD} \cong \overline{CD}$.
Use the __SAS Congruence Postulate__ to prove that
$\triangle ABD \cong \triangle ACD$.

✓ *Checkpoint* Use the given information to write a plan
for proof.

---

3. Given $\overline{GH} \cong \overline{KJ}$, $\overline{FG} \cong \overline{LK}$,
   $\angle FJG$ and $\angle LHK$ are rt. $\angle$s.

   Prove $\triangle FJK \cong \triangle LHG$

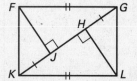

Plan for Proof: Use the HL Congruence Theorem
to prove that $\triangle FJG \cong \triangle LHK$. Then state that
$\overline{FJ} \cong \overline{LH}$. Then show that $\angle FJK \cong \angle LHG$ and
use the SAS Congruence Postulate to prove that
$\triangle FJK \cong \triangle LHG$.

Example 4 *Prove a construction*

Write a proof to verify that the construction for copying an obtuse angle is valid.

Solution

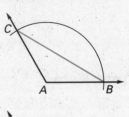

Add $\overline{BC}$ and $\overline{EF}$ to the diagram. In the construction, $\overline{AB}$, $\underline{DE}$, $\underline{AC}$, and $\underline{DF}$ are determined by the same compass setting, as are $\overline{BC}$ and $\underline{EF}$. So, you can assume the following as given statements.

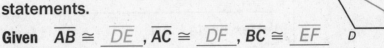

Given $\overline{AB} \cong \underline{DE}$, $\overline{AC} \cong \underline{DF}$, $\overline{BC} \cong \underline{EF}$

Prove $\angle D \cong \underline{\angle A}$

Plan for Proof Show that $\triangle CAB \cong \underline{\triangle FDE}$, so you can conclude that the corresponding parts $\angle D$ and $\underline{\angle A}$ are congruent.

	Statements	Reasons
Plan for Action	1. $\overline{AB} \cong \underline{DE}$, $\overline{AC} \cong \underline{DF}$, $\overline{BC} \cong \underline{EF}$	1. $\underline{\text{Given}}$
	2. $\triangle CAB \cong \underline{\triangle FDE}$	2. SSS Congruence Postulate
	3. $\angle D \cong \underline{\angle A}$	3. Corresp. parts of $\cong$ triangles are $\cong$.

✔ *Checkpoint* **Complete the following exercise.**

4. Write a paragraph proof to verify that the construction for bisecting a right angle is valid.

You know that $\overline{AC} \cong \overline{AB}$ and $\overline{BD} \cong \overline{CD}$ because they are determined by the same compass settings. Also, $\overline{AD} \cong \overline{AD}$ by the Reflexive Property. So, by the SSS Congruence Postulate, $\triangle CAD \cong \triangle BAD$. Thus, $\angle CAD \cong \angle BAD$ because corresponding parts of congruent triangles are congruent.

Homework

4.7 Use Isosceles and Equilateral Triangles

Goal • Use theorems about isosceles and equilateral triangles.

Your Notes

VOCABULARY

Legs The legs of an isosceles triangle are the two congruent sides.

Vertex angle The vertex angle of an isosceles triangle is the angle formed by the legs.

Base The base of an isosceles triangle is the side that is not a leg.

Base angles The base angles of an isosceles triangle are the two angles adjacent to the base.

THEOREM 4.7: BASE ANGLES THEOREM

If two sides of a triangle are congruent, then the angles opposite them are congruent.

If $\overline{AB} \cong \overline{AC}$, then $\angle B \cong \underline{\angle C}$.

THEOREM 4.8: CONVERSE OF BASE ANGLES THEOREM

If two angles of a triangle are congruent, then the sides opposite them are congruent.

If $\angle B \cong \angle C$, then $\overline{AB} \cong \underline{\overline{AC}}$.

Example 1   *Apply the Base Angles Theorem*

In △FGH, $\overline{FH} \cong \overline{GH}$. Name two congruent angles.

Solution

$\overline{FH} \cong \overline{GH}$, so by the Base Angles Theorem,
$\underline{\angle F} \cong \underline{\angle G}$.

The corollaries state that a triangle is *equilateral* if and only if it is *equiangular*.

COROLLARY TO THE BASE ANGLES THEOREM

If a triangle is equilateral, then it is <u>equiangular</u> .

COROLLARY TO THE CONVERSE OF BASE ANGLES THEOREM

If a triangle is equiangular, then it is <u>equilateral</u> .

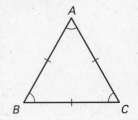

Example 2   *Find measures in a triangle*

Find the measures of ∠R, ∠S, and ∠T.

Solution

The diagram shows that △RST is <u>equilateral</u> . Therefore, by the Corollary to the Base Angles Theorem, △RST is <u>equiangular</u> . So, m∠R = m∠S = m∠T.

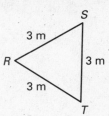

$3(m\angle R) =$ <u>180°</u>   **Triangle Sum Theorem**

$m\angle R =$ <u>60°</u>   **Divide each side by 3.**

The measures of ∠R, ∠S, and ∠T are all <u>60°</u> .

Example 3   *Use isosceles and equilateral triangles*

Find the values of x and y in the diagram.

Solution

You cannot use ∠J to refer to ∠LJM because three angles have J as their vertex.

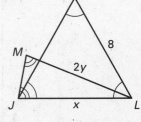

Step 1   Find the value of x. Because △JKL is <u>equiangular</u> , it is also <u>equilateral</u> and $\overline{KL} \cong$ <u>JL</u> . Therefore, x = <u>8</u> .

Step 2   Find the value of y. Because ∠JML ≅ <u>∠LJM</u> , $\overline{LM} \cong$ <u>LJ</u> , and △LMJ is isosceles. You know that LJ = <u>8</u> .

$LM =$ <u>LJ</u>   **Definition of congruent segments**

$2y =$ <u>8</u>   **Substitute 2y for LM and <u>8</u> for LJ.**

$y =$ <u>4</u>   **Divide each side by 2.**

Example 4   *Solve a multi-step problem*

Quilting The pattern at the right is present in a quilt.

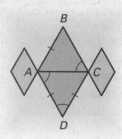

a. *Explain* why △ADC is equilateral.

b. Show that △CBA ≅ △ADC.

Solution

a. By the Base Angles Theorem, ∠DAC ≅ <u>∠DCA</u> . So, △ADC is <u>equiangular</u> . By the <u>Corollary to the Converse of Base Angles Theorem</u> , △ADC is equilateral.

b. By the Base Angles Theorem, ∠ABC ≅ <u>∠ACB</u> . So, △CBA ≅ △ADC by the <u>AAS Congruence Theorem</u> .

✔ *Checkpoint* **Complete the following exercises.**

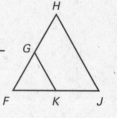

1. Copy and complete the statement:
If $\overline{FH} ≅ \overline{FJ}$, then ∠ _?_ ≅ ∠ _?_ .

  H; J

2. Copy and complete the statement:
If △FGK is equiangular and
FG = 15, then GK = _?_ .

  15

3. Use parts (a) and (b) in Example 4 to show that
m∠BAD = 120°.

  △DCA is equiangular. So,
  m∠ADC = m∠DCA = m∠CAD.

  3(m∠CAD) = 180° Triangle Sum Theorem

    m∠CAD = 60°   Divide each side by 3.

  Because △DCA is equiangular and
  △CBA ≅ △ADC, you know that m∠BAC = 60°.

  m∠BAD = m∠BAC + m∠CAD

         = 60° + 60°

         = 120°

Homework

Perform Congruence Transformations

Goal • Create an image congruent to a given triangle.

Your Notes

VOCABULARY

Transformation A transformation is an operation that moves or changes a geometric figure in some way to produce a new figure.

Image The new figure produced by a transformation is the image.

Translation A translation moves every point of a figure the same distance in the same direction.

Reflection A reflection uses a *line of reflection* to create a mirror image of the original figure.

Rotation A rotation turns a figure about a fixed point, called the *center of rotation*.

Congruence Transformation A congruence transformation changes the position of a figure without changing its size or shape.

Example 1 *Identify transformations*

Name the type of transformation demonstrated in each picture.

a.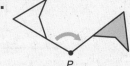

b.

c.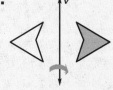

Rotation
about a point

Translation
in a straight path

Reflection
in a vertical
line

Your Notes

COORDINATE NOTATION FOR A TRANSLATION

You can describe a translation
by the notation

$(x, y) \rightarrow (x + a, y + b)$

which shows that each point (x, y)
of the unshaded figure is translated
horizontally a units and vertically b units.

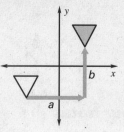

Example 2   *Translate a figure in the coordinate plane*

**Figure ABCD has the vertices A(1, 2), B(3, 3), C(4, −1),
and D(1, −2). Sketch ABCD and its image after the
translation $(x, y) \rightarrow (x − 4, y + 2)$.**

Solution

First draw *ABCD*. Find the translation of each vertex
by subtracting 4 from its *x*-coordinate and adding 2
to its *y*-coordinate. Then draw *ABCD* and its image.

$$(x, y) \rightarrow (x − 4, y + 2)$$

$A(1, 2) \rightarrow \underline{(-3, 4)}$

$B(3, 3) \rightarrow \underline{(-1, 5)}$

$C(4, -1) \rightarrow \underline{(0, 1)}$

$D(1, -2) \rightarrow \underline{(-3, 0)}$

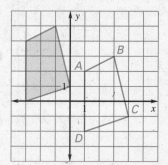

COORDINATE NOTATION FOR A REFLECTION

Reflection in the *x*-axis   Reflection in the *y*-axis

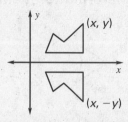   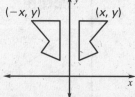

Multiply *y*-coordinate   Multiply *x*-coordinate
by −1.   by −1.

$(x, y) \rightarrow (x, -y)$ $(x, y) \rightarrow (-x, y)$

Example 3   *Reflect a figure in the x-axis*

Shapes You are cutting figures out of paper. Use a reflection in the *x*-axis to draw the other half of the figure.

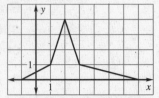

Solution

Multiply the <u>*y*-coordinate</u> of each vertex by −1 to find the corresponding vertex in the image. Then draw the image.

(x, y) → <u>$(x, -y)$</u>

$(-1, 0)$ → <u>$(-1, 0)$</u>

$(1, 1)$ → <u>$(1, -1)$</u>

$(2, 4)$ → <u>$(2, -4)$</u>

$(3, 1)$ → <u>$(3, -1)$</u>

$(7, 0)$ → <u>$(7, 0)$</u>

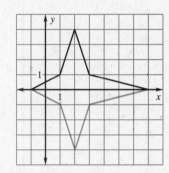

You can check your results by looking to see if each original point and its image are the same distance from the <u>*x*-axis</u>.

⊘ *Checkpoint* **Complete the following exercises.**

1. Name the type of transformation shown.

Translation

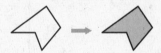

2. Figure *FGHJ* has the vertices *F*(0, 2), *G*(2, 3), *H*(3, 3), and *J*(0, −2). Sketch *FGHJ* and its image after (a) the translation $(x, y) \rightarrow (x - 3, y + 1)$ and (b) a reflection in the *y*-axis.

a.
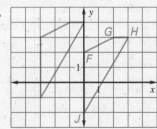

b.
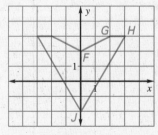

Example 4   *Identify a rotation*

Graph $\overline{JK}$ and $\overline{LM}$. Tell whether $\overline{LM}$ is a rotation of $\overline{JK}$ about the origin. If so, give the angle and direction of rotation.

a. $J(3, 1)$, $K(1, 4)$, $L(-1, 3)$, $M(-4, 1)$

b. $J(-2, 1)$, $K(-1, 5)$, $L(1, 1)$, $M(2, 5)$

Solution

a.

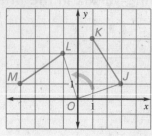

$m\angle JOL = m\angle KOM$

$= \underline{90°}$

$\underline{90° \text{ counterclockwise}}$
$\underline{\text{rotation}}$

b.

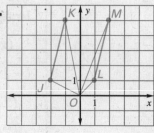

$m\angle JOL > m\angle KOM$

$\underline{\text{not a rotation}}$

✓ *Checkpoint* Graph $\overline{RS}$ and $\overline{TV}$. Tell whether $\overline{TV}$ is a rotation of $\overline{RS}$ about the origin. If so, give the angle of rotation.

3. $R(-3, -2)$, $S(-3, 2)$, $T(-1, 2)$, $V(3, 2)$	4. $R(-1, 1)$, $S(-4, 2)$, $T(1, -1)$, $V(4, -2)$
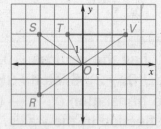	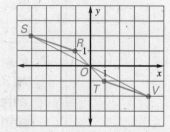
$m\angle ROT < m\angle SOV$	$m\angle ROT = m\angle SOV$
not a rotation	$= 180°$
	180° rotation

Example 5   *Verify congruence*

The vertices of △*PQR* are *P*(2, 2), *Q*(3, 4), and *R*(5, 2). The notation (*x*, *y*) → (*x* + 1, *y* − 6) describes the translation of △*PQR* to △*XYZ*. Show that △*PQR* ≅ △*XYZ* to verify that the translation is a congruence transformation.

Solution

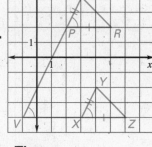

S You can see that
   PR = __*XZ*__ = __3__, so $\overline{PR}$ ≅ __$\overline{XZ}$__.

A Using the slopes, $\overline{PQ}$ ∥ __*XY*__ and
   $\overline{QR}$ ∥ __*YZ*__. If you extend $\overline{PQ}$ and
   $\overline{XZ}$ to form ∠*V*, the Corresponding
   Angles Postulate gives you
   __∠*QPR*__ ≅ ∠*V* and ∠*V* ≅ __∠*YXZ*__. Then,
   __∠*QPR*__ ≅ __∠*YXZ*__ by the Transitive Property
   of Congruence.

S Using the distance formula, *PQ* = __*XY*__ = __$\sqrt{5}$__ so
   $\overline{PQ}$ ≅ __*XY*__. So, △*PQR* ≅ △*XYZ* by the __SAS
   Congruence Postulate__.

Because △*PQR* ≅ △*XYZ*, the translation is a congruence transformation.

✔ *Checkpoint* **Complete the following exercise.**

5. Show that △*ABC* ≅ △*EDC* to verify that the transformation is a congruence transformation.

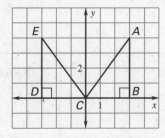

You can see that *AB* = *ED* = 4 and
BC = *DC* = 3. Also, ∠*B* and ∠*D* are congruent
right angles. So, △*ABC* ≅ △*EDC* by the SAS
Congruence Postulate.

Homework

Words to Review

Give an example of the vocabulary word.

Triangle	Scalene triangle
Isosceles triangle	Equilateral triangle
Acute triangle	Right triangle
Obtuse triangle	Equiangular triangle

Interior angles	Exterior angles
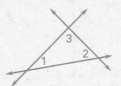 ∠1, ∠2, and ∠3 are interior angles.	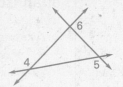 ∠4, ∠5, and ∠6 are exterior angles.
Corollary to a theorem A corollary to a theorem is a statement that can be proved easily using the theorem.	**Congruent figures** 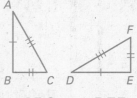 $\triangle ABC \cong \triangle DEF$
Corresponding parts If $\triangle ABC \cong \triangle DEF$, then ∠A and ∠D are corresponding parts.	**Leg of a right triangle, hypotenuse** 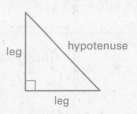
Flow proof 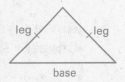	**Legs, base of an isosceles triangle** 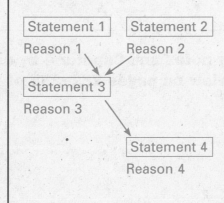

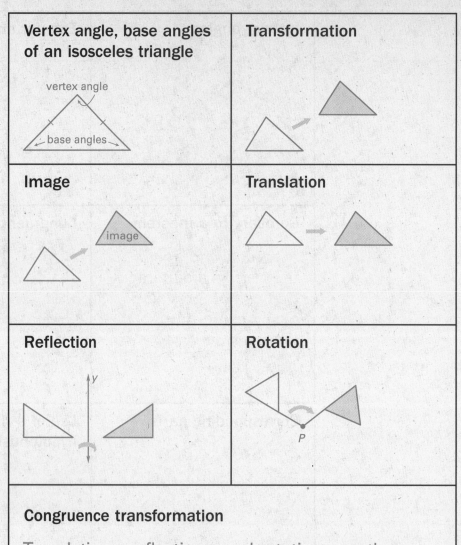

Vertex angle, base angles of an isosceles triangle	Transformation
vertex angle base angles	
Image	**Translation**
image	
Reflection	**Rotation**
y	*P*

Congruence transformation

Translations, reflections, and rotations are three types of congruence transformations. Because they change the position of a figure without changing its size or shape.

Review your notes and Chapter 4 by using the Chapter Review on pages 282–285 of your textbook.

5.1 Midsegment Theorem and Coordinate Proof

Goal • Use properties of midsegments and write coordinate proofs.

Your Notes

> ### VOCABULARY
>
> **Midsegment of a triangle** A midsegment of a triangle is a segment that connects the midpoints of two sides of the triangle.
>
> **Coordinate proof** A coordinate proof involves placing geometric figures in a coordinate plane.

> ### THEOREM 5.1: MIDSEGMENT THEOREM
>
> The segment connecting the midpoints of two sides of a triangle is __parallel__ to the third side and is __half__ as long as that side.
>
>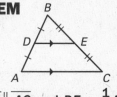
>
> $\overline{DE} \parallel \overline{AC}$ and $DE = \frac{1}{2}AC$

Example 1   *Use the Midsegment Theorem to find lengths*

Windows A large triangular window is segmented as shown. In the diagram, $\overline{DF}$ and $\overline{EF}$ are midsegments of $\triangle ABC$. Find DF and AB.

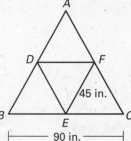

> In the diagram for Example 1, midsegment $\overline{DF}$ can be called "the midsegment opposite $\overline{BC}$."

Solution

$$DF = \frac{1}{2} \cdot BC = \frac{1}{2} (\ \underline{90 \text{ in.}}\ ) = \underline{45 \text{ in.}}$$

$$AB = \underline{2} \cdot FE = \underline{2} (\ \underline{45 \text{ in.}}\ ) = \underline{90 \text{ in.}}$$

✓ *Checkpoint* **Complete the following exercise.**

> **1.** In Example 1, consider $\triangle ADF$. What is the length of the midsegment opposite $\overline{DF}$?
>
> 22.5 in.

Your Notes

Example 2 Use the Midsegment Theorem

In the diagram at the right, QS = SP and PT = TR. Show that $\overline{QR} \parallel \overline{ST}$.

Solution

Because QS = SP and PT = TR, S is the __midpoint__ of $\overline{QP}$ and T is the __midpoint__ of $\overline{PR}$ by definition. Then $\overline{ST}$ is a __midsegment__ of $\triangle PQR$ by definition and $\overline{QR} \parallel \overline{ST}$ by the __Midsegment Theorem__.

✔ *Checkpoint* **Complete the following exercise.**

2. In Example 2, if V is the midpoint of $\overline{QR}$, what do you know about $\overline{SV}$?

   $\overline{SV}$ is a midsegment of $\triangle PQR$ and $\overline{SV} \parallel \overline{PR}$.

Example 3 Place a figure in a coordinate plane

Place each figure in a coordinate plane in a way that is convenient for finding side lengths. Assign coordinates to each vertex.

a. a square   **b.** an acute triangle

Solution

It is easy to find lengths of horizontal and vertical segments and distances from __(0, 0)__, so place one vertex at the __origin__ and one or more sides on an __axis__.

> The square represents a general square because the coordinates are based only on the definition of a square. If you use this square to prove a result, the result will be true for all squares.

a. Let *s* represent the __side length__.

b. You need to use __three__ different variables.

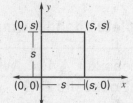

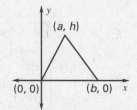

Example 4   *Apply variable coordinates*

In Example 3 part (a), find the length and midpoint of a diagonal of the square.

Solution

Draw a diagonal and its midpoint. Assign letters to the points.

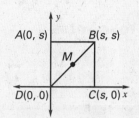

Use the distance formula to find *BD*.

$$BD = \underline{\sqrt{(s-0)^2 + (s-0)^2}}$$
$$= \underline{\sqrt{s^2 + s^2}} = \underline{\sqrt{2s^2}} = \underline{s\sqrt{2}}$$

Use the midpoint formula to find the midpoint *M*.

$$M\left(\underline{\frac{s+0}{2}}, \underline{\frac{s+0}{2}}\right) = M\left(\underline{\frac{s}{2}}, \underline{\frac{s}{2}}\right)$$

✔ *Checkpoint* **Complete the following exercises.**

3. Place an obtuse scalene triangle in a coordinate plane that is convenient for finding side lengths. Assign coordinates to each vertex.

Sample answer:

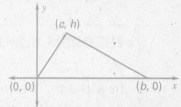

4. In Example 4, find the length and midpoint of diagonal $\overline{AC}$. What do you notice? *Explain* why this is true for all squares.

length: $s\sqrt{2}$; midpoint: $M\left(\frac{s}{2}, \frac{s}{2}\right)$; The lengths of the diagonals are the same, and the midpoints of the diagonals are the same. This is true for all squares because the coordinates are based only on the definition of a square.

Homework

Use Perpendicular Bisectors

Goal • Use perpendicular bisectors to solve problems.

Your Notes

VOCABULARY

Perpendicular bisector A segment, ray, line, or plane that is perpendicular to a segment at its midpoint is called a perpendicular bisector.

Equidistant A point is equidistant from two figures if the point is the *same distance* from each figure.

Concurrent When three or more lines, rays, or segments intersect in the same point, they are called concurrent lines, rays, or segments.

Point of concurrency The point of intersection of concurrent lines, rays, or segments is called the point of concurrency.

Circumcenter The point of concurrency of the three perpendicular bisectors of a triangle is called the circumcenter of the triangle.

THEOREM 5.2: PERPENDICULAR BISECTOR THEOREM

In a plane, if a point is on the perpendicular bisector of a segment, then it is <u>equidistant</u> from the endpoints of the segment.

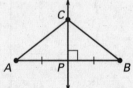

If $\overleftrightarrow{CP}$ is the ⊥ bisector of $\overline{AB}$, then $CA = $ <u>CB</u> .

THEOREM 5.3: CONVERSE OF THE PERPENDICULAR BISECTOR THEOREM

In a plane, if a point is equidistant from the endpoints of a segment, then it is on the <u>perpendicular bisector</u> of the segment.

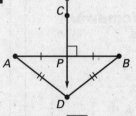

If $DA = DB$, then D lies on the <u>⊥ bisector</u> of $\overline{AB}$.

Example 1   *Use the Perpendicular Bisector Theorem*

$\overleftrightarrow{AC}$ is the perpendicular bisector of $\overline{BD}$. Find AD.

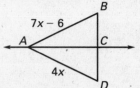

Solution

$AD = \underline{\quad AB \quad}$ Perpendicular Bisector Theorem

$\underline{4x} = \underline{7x - 6}$ Substitute.

$x = \underline{\ 2\ }$ Solve for x.

$AD = \underline{\ 4x\ } = \underline{\ 4(2)\ } = \underline{\ 8\ }$.

Example 2   *Use perpendicular bisectors*

In the diagram, $\overleftrightarrow{KN}$ is the perpendicular bisector of $\overline{JL}$.

a. What segment lengths in the diagram are equal?

b. Is M on $\overleftrightarrow{KN}$?

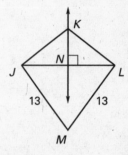

Solution

a. $\overleftrightarrow{KN}$ bisects $\overline{JL}$, so $\underline{\ NJ\ } = \underline{\ NL\ }$. Because K is on the perpendicular bisector of $\overline{JL}$, $\underline{\ KJ\ } = \underline{\ KL\ }$ by Theorem 5.2. The diagram shows that $\underline{\ MJ\ } = \underline{\ ML\ } = 13$.

b. Because $MJ = ML$, M is $\underline{\text{equidistant}}$ from J and L. So, by the $\underline{\text{Converse of the Perpendicular Bisector}}$ $\underline{\text{Theorem}}$, M is on the perpendicular bisector of $\overline{JL}$, which is $\overleftrightarrow{KN}$.

✔ *Checkpoint* In the diagram, $\overleftrightarrow{JK}$ is the perpendicular bisector of $\overline{GH}$.

1. What segment lengths are equal?

$KG = KH, \ JG = JH, \ FG = FH$

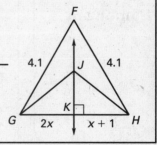

2. Find GH.

$GH = 4$

THEOREM 5.4: CONCURRENCY OF PERPENDICULAR BISECTORS OF A TRIANGLE

The perpendicular bisectors of a triangle intersect at a point that is equidistant from the vertices of the triangle.

If $\overline{PD}$, $\overline{PE}$, and $\overline{PF}$ are perpendicular bisectors, then $PA = \underline{\ PB\ } = \underline{\ PC\ }$.

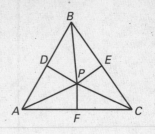

Example 3   *Use the concurrency of perpendicular bisectors*

Football Three friends are playing catch. You want to join and position yourself so that you are the same distance from your friends. Find a location for you to stand.

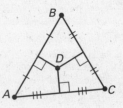

Solution

Theorem 5.4 shows you that you can find a point equidistant from three points by using the _perpendicular bisectors_ of the triangle formed by those points.

Copy the positions of points *A*, *B*, and *C* and connect those points to draw △*ABC*. Then use a ruler and a protractor to draw the three _perpendicular bisectors_ of △*ABC*. The point of concurrency *D* is a location for you to stand.

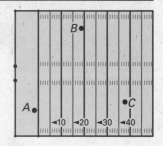

✔ *Checkpoint* Complete the following exercise.

3. In Example 3, your friend at location *A* wants to move to a location that is the same distance from everyone else. Find a new location for *A*.

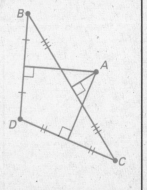

Homework

5.3 Use Angle Bisectors of Triangles

Goal • Use angle bisectors to find distance relationships.

Your Notes

VOCABULARY

Incenter The point of concurrency of the three angle bisectors of a triangle is called the incenter of the triangle.

THEOREM 5.5: ANGLE BISECTOR THEOREM

If a point is on the bisector of an angle, then it is equidistant from the two __sides__ of the angle.

If $\overrightarrow{AD}$ bisects $\angle BAC$ and $\overrightarrow{DB} \perp \overrightarrow{AB}$ and $\overrightarrow{DC} \perp \overrightarrow{AC}$, then $DB =$ __DC__ .

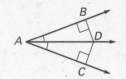

> In Geometry, *distance* means the *shortest* length between two objects.

THEOREM 5.6: CONVERSE OF THE ANGLE BISECTOR THEOREM

If a point is in the interior of an angle and is equidistant from the sides of the angle, then it lies on the __bisector__ of the angle.

If $\overrightarrow{DB} \perp \overrightarrow{AB}$ and $\overrightarrow{DC} \perp \overrightarrow{AC}$ and $DB = DC$, then $\overrightarrow{AD}$ __bisects__ $\angle BAC$.

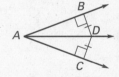

Example 1 *Use the Angle Bisector Theorems*

Find the measure of $\angle CBE$.

Solution

Because $\overrightarrow{EC} \perp \overrightarrow{BC}$ and $\overrightarrow{ED} \perp \overrightarrow{BD}$ and $EC = ED = 21$, $\overrightarrow{BE}$ bisects $\angle CBD$ by the __Converse of the Angle Bisector Theorem__ . So, $m\angle CBE = m\angle$ __DBE__ $=$ __31°__ .

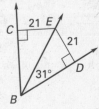

Example 2   *Solve a real-world problem*

Web A spider's position on its web relative to an approaching fly and the opposite sides of the web forms congruent angles, as shown. Will the spider have to move farther to reach a fly toward the right edge or the left edge?

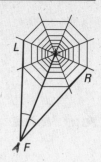

Solution

The congruent angles tell you that the spider is on the __bisector__ of ∠LFR. By the __Angle Bisector Theorem__ , the spider is equidistant from $\overrightarrow{FL}$ and $\overrightarrow{FR}$.

So, the spider must move the __same distance__ to reach each edge.

Example 3   *Use algebra to solve a problem*

For what value of *x* does *P* lie on the bisector of ∠J?

Solution

From the Converse of the Angle Bisector Theorem, you know that *P* lies on the bisector of ∠J if *P* is equidistant from the sides of ∠J, so when __PK__ = __PL__ .

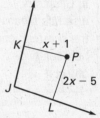

	Set segment lengths equal.
__PK__ = __PL__	Set segment lengths equal.
__x + 1__ = __2x − 5__	Substitute expressions for segment lengths.
__6__ = x	Solve for *x*.

Point *P* lies on the bisector of ∠J when x = __6__ .

THEOREM 5.7: CONCURRENCY OF ANGLE BISECTORS OF A TRIANGLE

The angle bisectors of a triangle intersect at a point that is equidistant from the sides of the triangle.

If $\overline{AP}$, $\overline{BP}$, and $\overline{CP}$ are angle bisectors of △ABC, then
PD = __PE__ = __PF__ .

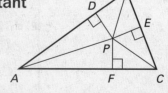

Your Notes

Example 4   *Use the concurrency of angle bisectors*

In the diagram, *L* is the incenter
of △*FHJ*. Find *LK*.

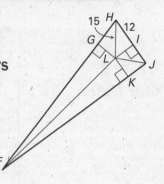

By the Concurrency of Angle Bisectors
of a Triangle Theorem, the incenter
L is *equidistant* from the sides
of △*FHJ*. So, to find *LK*, you can
find *LI* in △*LHI*. Use the
Pythagorean Theorem.

$c^2 = a^2 + b^2$		**Pythagorean Theorem**
$15^2 = LI^2 + 12^2$		**Substitute known values.**
$81 = LI^2$		**Simplify.**
$9 = LI$		**Take the positive square root of each side.**

Because *LI* = *LK*, *LK* = 9 .

✔ *Checkpoint* In Exercises 1 and 2, find the value of *x*.

1.
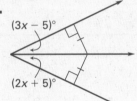
$(3x - 5)°$
$(2x + 5)°$

x = 10

2.
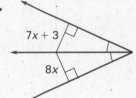
$7x + 3$
$8x$

x = 3

3. Do you have enough information to conclude that $\overrightarrow{AC}$
bisects ∠*DAB*? *Explain.*

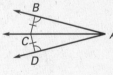

No, you must know that
m∠*ABC* = *m*∠*ADC* = 90° before
you can conclude that $\overrightarrow{AC}$ bisects
∠*DAB*.

Homework

4. In Example 4, suppose you are not given *HL* or *HI*,
but you are given that *JL* = 25 and *JI* = 20. Find *LK*.

LK = 15

5.4 Use Medians and Altitudes

Goal • Use medians and altitudes of triangles.

Your Notes

VOCABULARY

Median of a triangle The median of a triangle is a segment from a vertex to the midpoint of the opposite side.

Centroid The point of concurrency of the three medians of a triangle is the centroid.

Altitude of a triangle An altitude of a triangle is the perpendicular segment from a vertex to the opposite side or to the line that contains the opposite side.

Orthocenter The point at which the lines containing the three altitudes of a triangle intersect is called the orthocenter of the triangle.

THEOREM 5.8: CONCURRENCY OF MEDIANS OF A TRIANGLE

The medians of a triangle intersect at a point that is two thirds of the distance from each vertex to the midpoint of the opposite side.

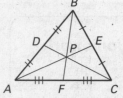

The medians of $\triangle ABC$ meet at P and $AP = \frac{2}{3}\ \underline{AE}$, $BP = \frac{2}{3}\ \underline{BF}$, and $CP = \frac{2}{3}\ \underline{CD}$.

Copyright © McDougal Littell/Houghton Mifflin Company.

Your Notes

Example 1   *Use the centroid of a triangle*

In △*FGH*, *M* is the centroid and *GM* = 6.
Find *ML* and *GL*.

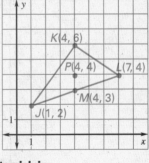

$\underline{GM} = \frac{2}{3}\,GL$ **Concurrency of Medians of a Triangle Theorem**

$\underline{6} = \frac{2}{3}\,GL$ Substitute __6__ for *GM*.

$\underline{9} = GL$ Multiply each side by the reciprocal, $\frac{3}{2}$.

Then *ML* = *GL* − __*GM*__ = __9__ − __6__ = __3__.
So, *ML* = __3__ and *GL* = __9__.

✔ *Checkpoint* **Complete the following exercise.**

1. In Example 1, suppose *FM* = 10. Find *MK* and *FK*.

   MK = 5, *FK* = 15

Example 2   *Find the centroid of a triangle*

The vertices of △*JKL* are *J*(1, 2), *K*(4, 6), and *L*(7, 4).
Find the coordinates of the centroid *P* of △*JKL*.

Sketch △*JKL*. Then use the Midpoint Formula to find the
midpoint *M* of $\overline{JL}$ and sketch median $\overline{KM}$.

> Median $\overline{KM}$ was used in Example 2 because it is easy to find distances on a vertical segment. You can check by finding the centroid using a different median.

$M\left(\dfrac{\boxed{1+7}}{2}, \dfrac{\boxed{2+4}}{2}\right) = \underline{M(4, 3)}$

The centroid is __two thirds__ of the
distance from each vertex to the
midpoint of the opposite side.

The distance from vertex *K* to point
M is 6 − __3__ = __3__ units. So, the centroid is

$\frac{2}{3}$ (__3__) = __2__ units down from *K* on $\overline{KM}$.

The coordinates of the centroid *P* are (4, 6 − __2__),
or (__4, 4__).

THEOREM 5.9: CONCURRENCY OF ALTITUDES OF A TRIANGLE

The lines containing the altitudes of a triangle are __concurrent__ .

The lines containing $\overline{AF}$, $\overline{BE}$, and $\overline{CD}$ meet at G.

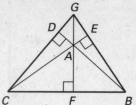

Example 3   *Find the orthocenter*

Find the orthocenter P in the triangle.

Notice that in a right triangle the legs are also altitudes. The altitudes of the obtuse triangle are extended to find the orthocenter.

a.

b.

Solution

a.

b.

✔ *Checkpoint* **Complete the following exercises.**

2. In Example 2, where do you need to move point K so that the centroid is $P(4, 5)$?

   Point K should be moved to $(4, 9)$.

3. Find the orthocenter P in the triangle.

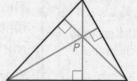

Example 4 *Prove a property of isosceles triangles*

Prove that the altitude to the base of an isosceles triangle is a median.

Solution

Given △ABC is isosceles, with base $\overline{AC}$. $\overline{BD}$ is the altitude to base $\overline{AC}$.

Prove $\overline{BD}$ is a median of △ABC.

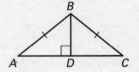

Proof Legs $\overline{AB}$ and $\overline{CD}$ of △ABC are congruent. ∠ADB and ∠CDB are congruent right angles because $\overline{BD}$ is the _altitude_ to $\overline{AC}$. Also, $\overline{BD} \cong \overline{BD}$. Therefore, △ADB ≅ △CDB by the _HL Congruence Theorem_ .

$\overline{AD} \cong \overline{CD}$ because corresponding parts of congruent triangles are congruent. So, *D* is the _midpoint_ of $\overline{AC}$ by definition. Therefore, $\overline{BD}$ intersects $\overline{AC}$ at its _midpoint_ , and $\overline{BD}$ is a median of △ABC.

✔ *Checkpoint* **Complete the following exercise.**

4. Prove that the altitude $\overline{BD}$ in Example 4 is also an angle bisector.

   Proof Legs $\overline{AB}$ and $\overline{CB}$ of △ABC are congruent. ∠ADB and ∠CDB are congruent right angles because $\overline{BD}$ is the altitude to $\overline{AC}$. Also, $\overline{BD} \cong \overline{BD}$. Therefore, △ADB ≅ △CDB by the HL Congruence Theorem. ∠ABD ≅ ∠CBD because corresponding parts of congruent triangles are congruent. Therefore, $\overline{BD}$ bisects ∠ABC, and $\overline{BD}$ is an angle bisector.

Homework

5.5 Use Inequalities in a Triangle

Goal • Find possible side lengths of a triangle.

Your Notes

| Example 1 | *Relate side length and angle measure* |

Mark the largest angle, longest side, smallest angle, and shortest side of the triangle shown at the right. What do you notice?

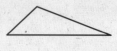

Solution

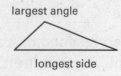

The longest side and largest angle are __opposite__ each other.

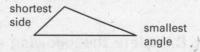

The shortest side and smallest angle are __opposite__ each other.

THEOREM 5.10

If one side of a triangle is longer than another side, then the angle opposite the longer side is __larger__ than the angle opposite the shorter side.

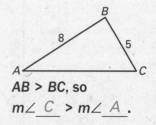

AB > BC, so
m∠ _C_ > m∠ _A_ .

> Be careful not to confuse the symbol ∠ meaning *angle* with the symbol < meaning *is less than*. Notice that the bottom edge of the angle symbol is horizontal.

THEOREM 5.11

If one angle of a triangle is larger than another angle, then the side opposite the larger angle is __longer__ than the side opposite the smaller angle.

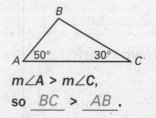

m∠A > m∠C,
so _BC_ > _AB_ .

Example 2   *Find angle measures*

Boating A long-tailed boat leaves a dock and travels 2500 feet to a cave, 5000 feet to a beach, then 6000 feet back to the dock as shown below. One of the angles in the path is about 55° and one is about 24°. What is the angle measure of the path made at the cave?

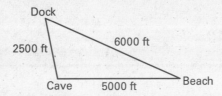

Solution

The cave is opposite the <u>longest</u> side so, by Theorem 5.10, the cave angle is the <u>largest</u> angle.

The angle measures sum to 180°, so the third angle measure is <u>180° − (55° + 24°)</u> = <u>101°</u> .

The angle measure made at the cave is <u>101°</u> .

✔ *Checkpoint* **Complete the following exercises.**

1. List the sides of △*PQR* in order from shortest to longest.

    <u>QR</u>, <u>PQ</u>, <u>PR</u>

    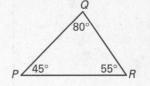

2. Another boat makes a trip whose path has sides of 1.5 miles, 2 miles, and 2.5 miles long and angles of 90°, about 53°, and about 37°. Sketch and label a diagram with the shortest side on the bottom and the right angle at the right.

Your Notes

THEOREM 5.12: TRIANGLE INEQUALITY THEOREM

The sum of the lengths of any two sides of a triangle is greater than the length of the third side.

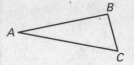

_AB_ + _BC_ > AC

AC + _BC_ > _AB_

_AB_ + AC > _BC_

Example 3 *Find possible side lengths*

A triangle has one side of length 14 and another of length 10. Describe the possible lengths of the third side.

Solution

Let *x* represent the length of the third side. Draw diagrams to help visualize the small and large values of *x*. Then use the Triangle Inequality Theorem to write and solve inequalities.

Small values of *x*   **Large values of *x***

x + _10_ > _14_   _10_ + _14_ > x

x > _4_   _24_ > x, or x < _24_

The length of the third side must be _greater than 4 and less than 24_ .

✔ *Checkpoint* **Complete the following exercise.**

Homework

3. A triangle has one side of 23 meters and another of 17 meters. *Describe* the possible lengths of the third side.

The length of the third side must be greater than 6 meters and less than 40 meters.

Goal • Use inequalities to make comparisons in two triangles.

Your Notes

VOCABULARY

Indirect Proof An indirect proof uses a temporary assumption that the desired conclusion is false. By then showing that this assumption leads to a logical impossibility, the original statement is proven true *by contradiction*.

THEOREM 5.13: HINGE THEOREM

If two sides of one triangle are congruent to two sides of another triangle, and the included angle of the first is larger than the included angle of the second, then the third side of the first is <u>longer</u> than the third side of the second.

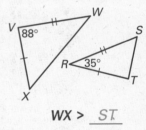

WX > <u>ST</u>

THEOREM 5.14: CONVERSE OF THE HINGE THEOREM

If two sides of one triangle are congruent to two sides of another triangle, and the third side of the first is longer than the third side of the second, then the included angle of the first is <u>larger</u> than the included angle of the second.

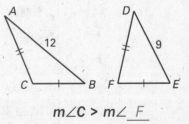

$m\angle C > m\angle \underline{F}$

Example 1   *Use the Converse of the Hinge Theorem*

Given that $\overline{AD} \cong \overline{BC}$, how does ∠1 compare to ∠2?

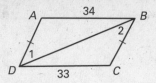

Solution

You are given that $\overline{AD} \cong \overline{BC}$ and you know that $\overline{BD} \cong \overline{BD}$ by the Reflexive Property. Because 34 > 33, __AB__ > __CD__ . So, two sides of △ADB are congruent to two sides of △CBD and the third side in △ADB is __longer__ .

By the Converse of the Hinge Theorem, $m\angle$ __1__ > $m\angle$ __2__ .

Example 2   *Solve a multi-step problem*

Travel Car A leaves a mall, heads due north for 5 mi and then turns due west for 3 mi. Car B leaves the same mall, heads due south for 5 mi and then turns 80° toward east for 3 mi. Which car is farther from the mall?

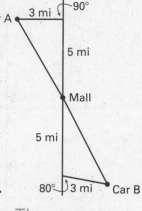

Draw a diagram. The distance driven and the distance back to the mall form two triangles, with __congruent__ 5 mile sides and __congruent__ 3 mile sides. Add the third side to the diagram.

Use linear pairs to find the included angles of __90°__ and __100°__ .

Because 100° > 90°, Car __B__ is farther from the mall than Car A by the __Hinge Theorem__ .

HOW TO WRITE AN INDIRECT PROOF

Step 1 **Identify** the statement you want to prove. **Assume** temporarily that this statement is __false__ by assuming that the opposite is __true__ .

Step 2 **Reason** logically until you reach a contradiction.

Step 3 **Point out** that the desired conclusion must be __true__ because the contradiction proves the temporary assumption __false__ .

Example 3 *Write an indirect proof*

Write an indirect proof to show that an odd number is not divisible by 6.

Given x is an odd number.

Prove x is not divisible by 6.

Solution

Step 1 Assume temporarily that $\underline{x\ is\ divisible\ by\ 6}$.
This means that $\frac{x}{6} = n$ for some whole number n.
So, multiplying both sides by 6 gives $\underline{x} = \underline{6n}$.

You have reached a contradiction when you have two statements that cannot both be true at the same time.

Step 2 If x is odd, then, by definition, x cannot be divided evenly by $\underline{2}$. However, $\underline{x} = \underline{6n}$ so $\frac{x}{2} = \frac{6n}{2} = \underline{3n}$. We know that $\underline{3n}$ is a whole number because n is a whole number, so x can be divided evenly by $\underline{2}$. This contradicts the given statement that $\underline{x\ is\ odd}$.

Step 3 Therefore, the assumption that x is divisible by 6 is $\underline{false}$, which proves that $\underline{x\ is\ not\ divisible}$ $\underline{by\ 6}$.

✓ **Checkpoint** **Complete the following exercises.**

1. If $m\angle ADB > m\angle CDB$ which is longer, $\overline{AB}$ or $\overline{CB}$?

   $\overline{AB}$ is longer.

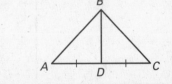

2. In Example 2, car C leaves the mall and goes 5 miles due west, then turns 85° toward south for 3 miles. Write the cars in order from the car closest to the mall to the car farthest from the mall.

   car A, car C, car B

Homework

3. Suppose you wanted to prove the statement "If $x + y \neq 5$ and $y = 2$, then $x \neq 3$." What temporary assumption could you make to prove the conclusion indirectly?

   You can temporarily assume that $x = 3$.

Words to Review

Give an example of the vocabulary word.

Midsegment of a triangle 	**Coordinate proof** A type of proof that involves placing geometric figures in a coordinate plane.
Perpendicular bisector 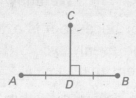 $\overline{CD}$ is a perpendicular bisector of $\overline{AB}$.	**Equidistant** 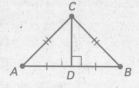 Point C is equidistant from point A and point B.
Concurrent 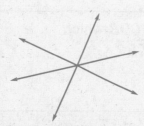 The lines are concurrent.	**Point of concurrency** 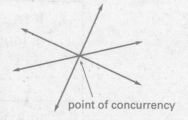
Circumcenter 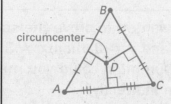	**Incenter** 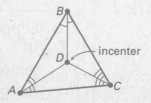

Median of a triangle	Centroid
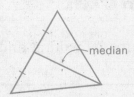	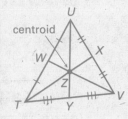

Altitude of a triangle	Orthocenter
	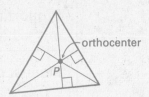

Indirect proof

To use an indirect proof, assume that the original statement is false and that the opposite is true. If this assumption leads to a contradiction, then the assumption must be false and the original statement must be true.

Review your notes and Chapter 5 by using the Chapter Review on pages 344–347 of your textbook.

6.1 Ratios, Proportions, and the Geometric Mean

Goal • Solve problems by writing and solving proportions.

Your Notes

VOCABULARY

Ratio of *a* to *b* If *a* and *b* are two numbers or quantities and $b \neq 0$, then the ratio of *a* to *b* is $\frac{a}{b}$.

Proportion An equation that states that two ratios are equal is a proportion.

Means, extremes In the proportion $\frac{a}{b} = \frac{c}{d}$, *b* and *c* are the means, and *a* and *d* are the extremes.

Geometric mean The geometric mean of two positive numbers *a* and *b* is the positive number *x* that satisfies $\frac{a}{x} = \frac{x}{b}$.

Example 1   Simplify ratios

Simplify the ratio. *(See Table of Measures, p. 921)*

a. 76 cm : 8 cm   b. $\frac{4 \text{ ft}}{24 \text{ in.}}$

Solution

a. Write 76 cm : 8 cm as $\boxed{\dfrac{76 \text{ cm}}{8 \text{ cm}}}$. Then divide out the units and simplify.

$$\frac{76 \text{ cm}}{8 \text{ cm}} = \frac{19}{2} = \underline{19} : \underline{2}$$

> For help with conversion factors, see p. 886.

b. To simplify a ratio with unlike units, multiply by a conversion factor.

$$\frac{4 \text{ ft}}{24 \text{ in.}} = \frac{4 \text{ ft}}{24 \text{ in.}} \cdot \frac{12 \text{ in.}}{1 \text{ ft}} = \frac{48}{24} = \frac{2}{1}$$

Your Notes

Example 2 *Use a ratio to find a dimension*

Painting You are painting barn doors. You know that the perimeter of the doors is 64 feet and that the ratio of the length to the height is 3:5. Find the area of the doors.

Solution

Step 1 **Write** expressions for the length and height. Because the ratio of the length to height is 3:5, you can represent the length by __3__ x and the height by __5__ x.

Step 2 **Solve** an equation to find x.

$$2\ell + 2w = P \quad \text{Formula for perimeter}$$
$$2(\underline{3}\,x) + 2(\underline{5}\,x) = \underline{64} \quad \text{Substitute.}$$
$$\underline{16}\,x = \underline{64} \quad \text{Multiply and combine like terms.}$$
$$x = \underline{4} \quad \text{Divide each side by } \underline{16}.$$

Step 3 **Evaluate** the expressions for the length and height. Substitute the value of x into each expression.

Length: __3__ $x =$ __3__ (__4__) = __12__

Height: __5__ $x =$ __5__ (__4__) = __20__

The doors are __12__ feet long and __20__ feet high, so the area is __12__ · __20__ = __240 ft^2__ .

✔ *Checkpoint* **In Exercises 1 and 2, simplify the ratio.**

1. 4 meters to 18 meters	**2.** 33 yd : 9 ft
2 to 9	11 : 1

3. The perimeter of a rectangular table is 21 feet and the ratio of its length to its width is 5:2. Find the length and width of the table.

length: 7.5 feet, width: 3 feet

Example 3 *Use extended ratios*

The measures of the angles in △*BCD* are in the *extended ratio* of 2:3:4. Find the measures of the angles.

Solution

Begin by sketching the triangle. Then use the extended ratio of 2:3:4 to label the measures as __2__ $x°$, __3__ $x°$, and __4__ $x°$.

$$\underline{2}\ x° + \underline{3}\ x° + \underline{4}\ x° = 180°$$ **Triangle Sum Theorem**

$$\underline{9}\ x = 180$$ **Combine like terms.**

$$x = \underline{20}$$ **Divide each side by __9__ .**

The angle measures are 2(__20°__) = __40°__ , 3(__20°__) = __60°__ , and 4(__20°__) = __80°__ .

✔ *Checkpoint* **Complete the following exercise.**

4. A triangle's angle measures are in the extended ratio of 1:4:5. Find the measures of the angles.

   18°, 72°, 90°

A PROPERTY OF PROPORTIONS

1. **Cross Products Property** In a proportion, the product of the extremes equals the product of the means.

   If $\dfrac{a}{b} = \dfrac{c}{d}$ where $b \neq 0$ and $d \neq 0$, then __ad__ = __bc__ .

   $\dfrac{2}{3} = \dfrac{4}{6}$ 3 • __4__ = __12__

   2 • __6__ = __12__

Example 4 *Solve proportions*

Solve the proportion.

a. $\dfrac{3}{4} = \dfrac{x}{16}$ **Original proportion**

$3 \cdot \underline{16} = \underline{4} \cdot x$ **Cross Products Property**

$\underline{48} = \underline{4}\, x$ **Multiply.**

$\underline{12} = x$ **Divide each side by** $\underline{4}$.

> In part (a), you could multiply each side by the denominator, 16. Then
> $16 \cdot \dfrac{3}{4} = 16 \cdot \dfrac{x}{16}$
> so $\underline{12} = x$.

b. $\dfrac{3}{x+1} = \dfrac{2}{x}$ **Original proportion**

$\underline{3} \cdot x = \underline{2}\,(x+1)$ **Cross Products Property**

$\underline{3}\,x = \underline{2}\,x + \underline{2}$ **Distributive Property**

$x = \underline{2}$ **Subtract** $\underline{2x}$ **from each side.**

Example 5 *Solve a real-world problem*

Bowling You want to find the total number of rows of boards that make up 24 lanes at a bowling alley. You know that there are 117 rows in 3 lanes. Find the total number of rows of boards that make up the 24 lanes.

Solution

Write and solve a proportion involving two ratios that compare the number of rows with the number of lanes.

$\dfrac{117}{3} = \dfrac{n}{24}$ ← number of rows   **Write proportion.**
$\qquad\qquad\quad$ ← number of lanes

$\underline{117} \cdot \underline{24} = \underline{3} \cdot \underline{n}$ **Cross Products Property**

$\underline{936} = n$ **Simplify.**

There are $\underline{936}$ rows of boards that make up the 24 lanes.

GEOMETRIC MEAN

The geometric mean of two positive numbers a and b is the positive number x that satisfies $\dfrac{a}{x} = \dfrac{x}{b}$.

So, $x^2 = \underline{ab}$ and $x = \sqrt{\underline{ab}}$.

Example 6 *Find a geometric mean*

Find the geometric mean of 16 and 48.

Solution

$x = \underline{\sqrt{ab}}$ **Definition of geometric mean**

$= \underline{\sqrt{16 \cdot 48}}$ **Substitute** $\underline{16}$ **for** *a* **and** $\underline{48}$ **for** *b*.

$= \underline{\sqrt{16 \cdot 16 \cdot 3}}$ **Factor.**

$= \underline{16\sqrt{3}}$ **Simplify.**

The geometric mean of 16 and 48 is $\underline{16\sqrt{3}} \approx \underline{27.7}$.

✔ *Checkpoint* **Complete the following exercises.**

5. Solve $\dfrac{8}{y} = \dfrac{2}{5}$.	**6.** Solve $\dfrac{x-3}{3} = \dfrac{2x}{9}$.
$y = 20$	$x = 9$

7. A small gymnasium contains 10 sets of bleachers. You count 192 spectators in 3 sets of bleachers and the spectators seem to be evenly distributed. Estimate the total number of spectators.

about 640 spectators

8. Find the geometric mean of 14 and 16.

$4\sqrt{14} \approx 15.0$

Homework

6.2 Use Proportions to Solve Geometry Problems

Goal • Use proportions to solve geometry problems.

Your Notes

VOCABULARY

Scale drawing A scale drawing is a drawing that is the same shape as the object it represents.

Scale The scale is a ratio that describes how the dimensions in the drawing are related to the actual dimensions of the object.

ADDITIONAL PROPERTIES OF PROPORTIONS

2. **Reciprocal Property** If two ratios are equal, then their reciprocals are also equal.

   If $\frac{a}{b} = \frac{c}{d}$, then $\frac{b}{a} = \frac{d}{c}$.

3. If you interchange the means of a proportion, then you form another true proportion.

   If $\frac{a}{b} = \frac{c}{d}$, then $\frac{a}{c} = \frac{b}{d}$.

4. In a proportion, if you add the value of each ratio's denominator to its numerator, then you form another true proportion.

   If $\frac{a}{b} = \frac{c}{d}$, then $\frac{a+b}{b} = \frac{c+d}{d}$.

Example 1   *Use properties of proportions*

In the diagram, $\frac{AC}{DF} = \frac{BC}{EF}$. Write four true proportions.

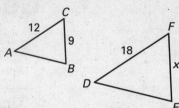

Because $\frac{AC}{DF} = \frac{BC}{EF}$, then $\frac{12}{18} = \frac{9}{x}$.

Reciprocal Property: The reciprocals are equal, so $\frac{18}{12} = \frac{x}{9}$.

Property 3: You can interchange the means, so $\frac{12}{9} = \frac{18}{x}$.

Property 4: You can add the denominators to the numerators, so $\frac{30}{18} = \frac{9 + x}{x}$.

Example 2   *Use proportions with geometric figures*

In the diagram, $\frac{JL}{LH} = \frac{JK}{KG}$.

Find *JH* and *JL*.

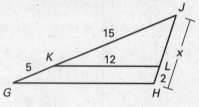

$\frac{JL}{LH} = \frac{JK}{KG}$	**Given**
$\frac{JL + LH}{LH} = \frac{JK + KG}{KG}$	**Property of Proportions (Property 4)**
$\frac{x}{2} = \frac{15 + 5}{5}$	**Substitution Property of Equality**
$5x = 2(15 + 5)$	**Cross Products Property**
$x = \underline{8}$	**Solve for *x*.**

So $JH = \underline{8}$ and $JL = \underline{8 - 2} = \underline{6}$.

✔ *Checkpoint* **Complete the following exercises.**

1. In Example 1, find the value of *x.*	**2.** In Example 2, $\frac{KL}{GH} = \frac{JK}{JG}$. Find *GH*.
$x = 13.5$	$GH = 16$

Example 3   *Find the scale of a drawing*

Keys The length of the key in the scale drawing is 7 centimeters. The length of the actual key is 4 centimeters. What is the scale of the drawing?

Solution

To find the scale, write the ratio of a length in the drawing to _an actual length_ , then rewrite the ratio so that the _denominator_ is 1.

$$\frac{\text{length in drawing}}{\boxed{\text{length of key}}} = \frac{7 \text{ cm}}{4 \text{ cm}} = \frac{7 \div 4}{4 \div 4} = \frac{1.75}{1}$$

The scale of the drawing is _1.75 cm : 1 cm_ .

✔ *Checkpoint* **Complete the following exercise.**

3. In Example 3, suppose the length of the key in the scale drawing is 6 centimeters. Find the new scale of the drawing.

   1.5 cm : 1 cm

Example 4   *Use a scale drawing*

Maps The scale of the map at the right is **1 inch : 8 miles.** Find the actual distance from Westbrook to Cooley.

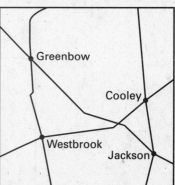

Solution

Use a ruler. The distance from Westbrook to Cooley on the map is about _1.25 inches_ . Let x be the actual distance in miles.

$$\frac{1.25 \text{ in.}}{x \text{ mi}} = \frac{1 \text{ in.}}{8 \text{ mi}} \quad \begin{array}{l} \leftarrow \text{distance on map} \\ \leftarrow \text{actual distance} \end{array}$$

$x =$ _1.25(8)_   **Cross Products Property**

$x =$ _10_   **Simplify.**

The actual distance from Westbrook to Cooley is about _10 miles_ .

| **Example 5** | *Solve a multi-step problem* |

Scale Model You buy a 3-D scale model of the Sunsphere in Knoxville, TN. The actual building is 266 feet tall. Your model is 20 inches tall, and the diameter of the dome on your scale model is about 5.6 inches.

a. What is the diameter of the actual dome?

b. How many times as tall as your model is the actual building?

Solution

a. $\dfrac{20 \text{ in.}}{266 \text{ ft}} = \dfrac{5.6 \text{ in.}}{x \text{ ft}}$ ← measurement on model
← measurement on actual building

$\underline{20}\, x = \underline{1489.6}$ **Cross Products Property**

$x \approx \underline{74.5}$ **Divide each side by** $\underline{20}$.

The diameter of the actual dome is about $\underline{74.5}$ feet.

b. To simplify a ratio with unlike units, multiply by a conversion factor.

$\dfrac{266 \text{ ft}}{20 \text{ in.}} = \dfrac{266 \text{ ft}}{20 \text{ in.}} \cdot \dfrac{12 \text{ in.}}{1 \text{ ft}} = \underline{159.6}$

The actual building is $\underline{159.6}$ times as tall as the model.

✔ *Checkpoint* **Complete the following exercises.**

4. Two landmarks are 130 miles from each other. The landmarks are 6.5 inches apart on a map. Find the scale of the map.

   1 inch : 20 miles

5. Your friend has a model of the Sunsphere that is 5 inches tall. What is the approximate diameter of the dome on your friend's model?

   about 1.4 inches

Homework

6.3 Use Similar Polygons

Goal • Use proportions to identify similar polygons.

Your Notes

VOCABULARY

Similar polygons Two polygons are similar polygons if corresponding angles are congruent and corresponding side lengths are proportional.

Scale factor of two similar polygons If two polygons are similar, then the ratio of the lengths of two corresponding sides is called the scale factor.

Example 1 *Use similarity statements*

In the diagram, $\triangle ABC \sim \triangle DEF$.

a. List all pairs of congruent angles.

b. Check that the ratios of corresponding side lengths are equal.

c. Write the ratios of the corresponding side lengths in a *statement of proportionality*.

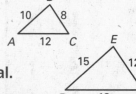

> In a *statement of proportionality*, any pair of ratios forms a true proportion.

Solution

a. $\angle A \cong \angle\ \underline{D}$, $\angle B \cong \angle\ \underline{E}$, $\angle C \cong \angle\ \underline{F}$

b. $\dfrac{AB}{DE} = \dfrac{10}{15} = \dfrac{2}{3}$ $\dfrac{BC}{EF} = \dfrac{8}{12} = \dfrac{2}{3}$

   $\dfrac{CA}{FD} = \dfrac{12}{18} = \dfrac{2}{3}$

c. The ratios in part (b) are equal, so

   $\dfrac{AB}{DE} = \dfrac{BC}{EF} = \dfrac{CA}{FD}$.

✔ *Checkpoint* **Complete the following exercise.**

1. Given $\triangle PQR \sim \triangle XYZ$, list all pairs of congruent angles. Write the ratios of the corresponding side lengths in a statement of proportionality.

   $\angle P \cong \angle X$, $\angle Q \cong \angle Y$, $\angle R \cong \angle Z$; $\dfrac{PQ}{XY} = \dfrac{QR}{YZ} = \dfrac{RP}{ZX}$

Example 2 *Find the scale factor*

Determine whether the polygons are similar. If they are, write a similarity statement and find the scale factor of *ABCD* to *JKLM*.

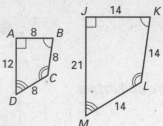

Solution

Step 1 Identify pairs of congruent angles.

From the diagram, you can see that $\angle B \cong \angle\ \underline{K}$, $\angle C \cong \angle\ \underline{L}$, and $\angle D \cong \angle\ \underline{M}$. Angles $\underline{A}$ and $\underline{J}$ are right angles, so $\angle\ \underline{A} \cong \angle\ \underline{J}$. So, the corresponding angles are $\underline{\text{congruent}}$.

Step 2 Show that corresponding side lengths are proportional.

$$\frac{AB}{JK} = \frac{8}{14} = \frac{4}{7} \qquad \frac{BC}{KL} = \frac{8}{14} = \frac{4}{7}$$

$$\frac{CD}{LM} = \frac{8}{14} = \frac{4}{7} \qquad \frac{AD}{JM} = \frac{12}{21} = \frac{4}{7}$$

The ratios are equal, so the corresponding side lengths are $\underline{\text{proportional}}$.

So $ABCD \sim \underline{JKLM}$. The scale factor of *ABCD* to *JKLM* is $\frac{4}{7}$.

Example 3 *Use similar polygons*

In the diagram, $\triangle BCD \sim \triangle RST$. Find the value of *x*.

Solution

The triangles are similar, so the corresponding side lengths are $\underline{\text{proportional}}$.

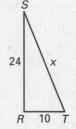

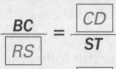
There are several ways to write the proportion. For example, you could write $\frac{BD}{RT} = \frac{CD}{ST}$.

$$\frac{BC}{\boxed{RS}} = \frac{\boxed{CD}}{ST} \qquad \text{Write proportion.}$$

$$\frac{12}{\boxed{24}} = \frac{\boxed{13}}{x} \qquad \text{Substitute.}$$

$$12x = \underline{312} \qquad \text{Cross Products Property}$$

$$x = \underline{26} \qquad \text{Solve for } x.$$

☑ *Checkpoint* In the diagram, *FGHJ* ~ *LMNP*.

2. What is the scale factor of *LMNP* to *FGHJ*?

$\dfrac{4}{5}$

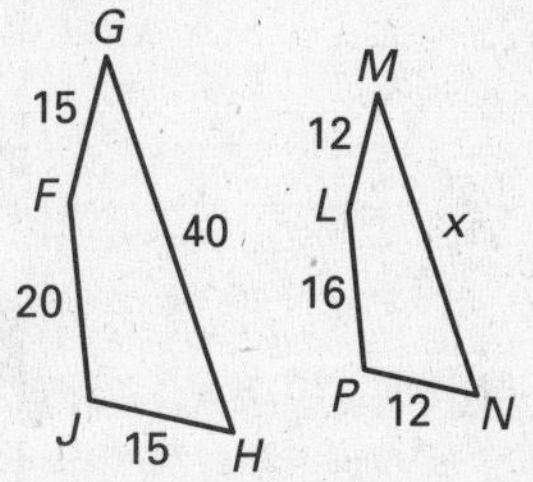

3. Find the value of *x*.

32

[Diagram: triangle FGHJ with G at top, 15 on side GF, F labeled, 40 on side FH, 20 on side FJ, J at bottom with 15 on JH, H at bottom right. Smaller figure LMNP with M at top, 12 on side ML, L labeled, x on side, 16 on side LP, P at bottom with 12 on PN, N at bottom right.]

THEOREM 6.1: PERIMETERS OF SIMILAR POLYGONS

If two polygons are similar, then the ratio of their perimeters is equal to the ratios of their corresponding side lengths.

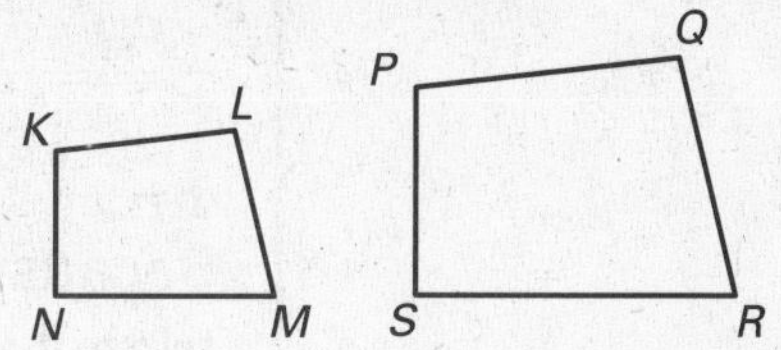

If *KLMN* ~ *PQRS*, then

[Diagram: quadrilateral KLMN and larger quadrilateral PQRS]

$$\dfrac{KL + LM + MN + NK}{PQ + QR + RS + SP} = \underline{\dfrac{KL}{PQ}} = \underline{\dfrac{LM}{QR}} = \underline{\dfrac{MN}{RS}} = \underline{\dfrac{NK}{SP}}.$$

Example 4 *Find perimeters of similar figures*

Basketball A larger cement court is being poured for a basketball hoop in place of a smaller one. The court will be 20 feet wide and 25 feet long. The old court was similar in shape, but only 16 feet wide.

a. Find the scale factor of the new court to the old court.

b. Find the perimeters of the new court and the old court.

Solution

a. Because the new court will be similar to the old court, the scale factor is the ratio of the widths, $\dfrac{20}{16} = \dfrac{5}{4}$.

b. The new court's perimeter is $\underline{2(20) + 2(25)} = \underline{90}$ feet. Use Theorem 6.1 to find the perimeter *x* of the old court.

$\dfrac{90}{x} = \dfrac{5}{4}$ Use Theorem 6.1 to write a proportion.

$x = \underline{72}$ Simplify.

The perimeter of the old court was $\underline{72}$ feet.

CORRESPONDING LENGTHS IN SIMILAR POLYGONS

If two polygons are similar, then the ratio of any two corresponding lengths in the polygons is equal to the _scale factor_ of the similar polygons.

Example 5 *Use a scale factor*

In the diagram, △*FGH* ~ △*JGK*.
Find the length of the altitude $\overline{GL}$.

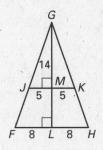

Solution

First, find the scale factor of △*FGH* to △*JGK*.

$$\frac{FH}{\boxed{JK}} = \frac{8+8}{5+5} = \frac{16}{10} = \frac{8}{5}$$

Because the ratio of the lengths of the altitudes in similar triangles is equal to the scale factor, you can write the following proportion.

$$\frac{GL}{GM} = \frac{8}{5} \qquad \text{Write proportion.}$$

$$\frac{GL}{\boxed{14}} = \frac{8}{5} \qquad \text{Substitute } \underline{14} \text{ for } GM.$$

$$GL = \underline{22.4} \qquad \text{Multiply each side by } \underline{14} \text{ and simplify.}$$

The length of altitude $\overline{GL}$ is _22.4_ .

✔ *Checkpoint* In the diagrams, △*PQR* ~ △*WXY*.

4. Find the perimeter of △*WXY*.

The perimeter of △*WXY* is 120.

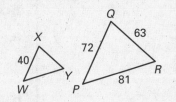

5. Find the length of median $\overline{QS}$.

QS = 26

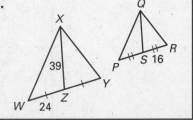

Copyright © McDougal Littell/Houghton Mifflin Company.

6.4 Prove Triangles Similar by AA

Goal • Use the AA Similarity Postulate.

POSTULATE 22: ANGLE-ANGLE (AA) SIMILARITY POSTULATE

If two angles of one triangle are congruent to two angles of another triangle, then the two triangles are similar.

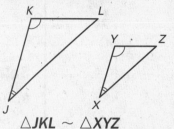

△JKL ~ △XYZ

Example 1 *Use the AA Similarity Postulate*

Determine whether the triangles are similar. If they are, write a similarity statement. *Explain* your reasoning.

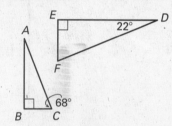

Solution

Because they are both right angles, ∠ _B_ and ∠ _E_ are congruent.

By the Triangle Sum Theorem,
_68°_ + _90°_ + m∠A = 180°, so m∠A = _22°_.
Therefore, ∠A and ∠ _D_ are congruent.

So, △ABC ~ △DEF by the _AA Similarity Postulate_.

✓ **Checkpoint** Determine whether the triangles are similar. If they are, write a similarity statement.

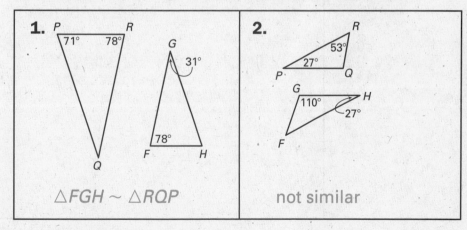

1. △FGH ~ △RQP

2. not similar

Example 2   *Show that triangles are similar*

Show that the two triangles are similar.

a. △RTV and △RQS   **b.** △LMN and △NOP

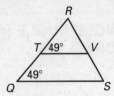   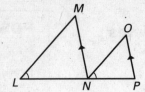

Solution

a. You may find it helpful to redraw the triangles separately.

Because m∠ _RTV_ and m∠ _Q_ both equal 49°, ∠ _RTV_ ≅ ∠ _Q_ . By the Reflexive Property, ∠R ≅ ∠ _R_ .

So, △RTV ~ △RQS by the _AA Similarity Postulate_ .

b. The diagram shows ∠L ≅ ∠ _ONP_ . It also shows that $\overline{MN}$ ∥ _OP_ so ∠ _LNM_ ≅ ∠ _P_ by the Corresponding Angles Postulate.

So, △LMN ~ △NOP by the _AA Similarity Postulate_ .

✔ *Checkpoint* **Complete the following exercise.**

3. Show that △BCD ~ △EFD.

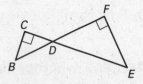

Because they are both right angles, ∠C ≅ ∠F.

You know that ∠CDB ≅ ∠FDE by the Vertical Angles Congruence Theorem.

So, △BCD ~ △EFD by the AA Similarity Postulate.

Example 3 *Using similar triangles*

Height A lifeguard is standing beside the lifeguard chair on a beach. The lifeguard is 6 feet 4 inches tall and casts a shadow that is 48 inches long. The chair casts a shadow that is 6 feet long. How tall is the chair?

Solution

The lifeguard and the chair form sides of two right triangles with the ground, as shown below. The sun's rays hit the lifeguard and the chair at the same angle. You have two pairs of congruent __angles__, so the triangles are similar by the __AA Similarity Postulate__.

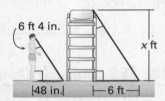

6 ft 4 in.

x ft

48 in.   6 ft

You can use a proportion to find the height *x*. Write 6 feet 4 inches as __76__ inches so you can form two ratios of feet to inches.

$$\frac{x \text{ ft}}{76 \text{ in.}} = \frac{6 \text{ ft}}{48 \text{ in.}}$$ **Write proportion of side lengths.**

$$\underline{48} \; x = \underline{456}$$ **Cross Products Property**

$$x = \underline{9.5}$$ **Solve for *x*.**

The chair is __9.5__ feet tall.

✔ *Checkpoint* **Complete the following exercise.**

4. In Example 3, how long is the shadow of a person that is 4 feet 9 inches tall?

   3 feet

Homework

6.5 Prove Triangles Similar by SSS and SAS

Goal • Use the SSS and SAS Similarity Theorems.

THEOREM 6.2: SIDE-SIDE-SIDE (SSS) SIMILARITY THEOREM

If the corresponding side lengths of two triangles are __proportional__, then the triangles are similar.

If $\dfrac{AB}{RS} = \dfrac{BC}{ST} = \dfrac{CA}{TR}$, then $\triangle ABC \sim \triangle RST$.

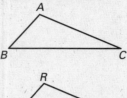

Example 1   Use the SSS Similarity Theorem

Is either $\triangle DEF$ or $\triangle GHJ$ similar to $\triangle ABC$?

  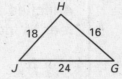

Solution

Compare $\triangle ABC$ and $\triangle DEF$ by finding ratios of corresponding side lengths.

> When using the SSS Similarity Theorem, compare the shortest sides, the longest sides, and then the remaining sides.

Shortest sides	Longest sides	Remaining sides
$\dfrac{AB}{DE} = \dfrac{8}{4} = \underline{2}$	$\dfrac{CA}{FD} = \dfrac{12}{8} = \underline{\dfrac{3}{2}}$	$\dfrac{BC}{EF} = \dfrac{9}{6} = \underline{\dfrac{3}{2}}$

All the ratios are __not equal__, so $\triangle ABC$ and $\triangle DEF$ are __not similar__.

Compare $\triangle ABC$ and $\triangle GHJ$ by finding ratios of corresponding side lengths.

Shortest sides	Longest sides	Remaining sides
$\dfrac{AB}{GH} = \dfrac{8}{16} = \underline{\dfrac{1}{2}}$	$\dfrac{CA}{JG} = \dfrac{12}{24} = \underline{\dfrac{1}{2}}$	$\dfrac{BC}{HJ} = \dfrac{9}{18} = \underline{\dfrac{1}{2}}$

All the ratios are __equal__, so $\triangle \underline{ABC} \sim \triangle \underline{GHJ}$.

Your Notes

Example 2 *Use the SSS Similarity Theorem*

Find the value of *x* that
makes △*ABC* ~ △*DEF*.

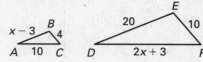

Solution

Step 1 **Find** the value of *x* that makes corresponding side
lengths proportional.

$$\frac{4}{\boxed{10}} = \frac{x-3}{\boxed{20}}$$ 　　**Write proportion.**

$4 \cdot \underline{20} = \underline{10}\,(x-3)$ 　　**Cross Products Property**

$\underline{80} = \underline{10}\,x - \underline{30}$ 　　**Simplify.**

$\underline{11} = x$ 　　**Solve for *x*.**

Step 2 **Check** that the side lengths are proportional when
x = __11__ .

$AB = x - 3 = \underline{8}$ 　　　　$DF = 2x + 3 = \underline{25}$

$\frac{BC}{EF} \overset{?}{=} \frac{AB}{DE}$ 　　$\frac{4}{10} = \frac{8}{20}$ ✓ 　　$\frac{BC}{EF} \overset{?}{=} \frac{AC}{DF}$ 　　$\frac{4}{10} = \frac{10}{25}$ ✓

When *x* = __11__ , the triangles are similar by the
__SSS Similarity Theorem__ .

✔ *Checkpoint* **Complete the following exercises.**

1. Which of the three triangles
are similar?

△*PQR* ~ △*ZXY*

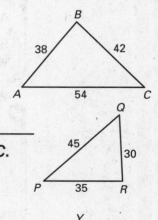

2. Suppose *AB* is not given in △*ABC*.
What length for *AB* would make
△*ABC* similar to △*QRP*?

AB = 36

THEOREM 6.3: SIDE-ANGLE-SIDE (SAS) SIMILARITY THEOREM

If an angle of one triangle is congruent to an angle of a second triangle and the lengths of the sides including these angles are __proportional__, then the triangles are similar.

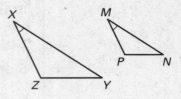

If $\angle X \cong \angle M$, and $\dfrac{ZX}{PM} = \dfrac{XY}{MN}$, then $\triangle XYZ \sim \triangle MNP$.

Example 3   *Use the SAS Similarity Theorem*

Birdfeeder You are drawing a design for a birdfeeder. Can you construct the top so it is similar to the bottom using the angle measure and lengths shown?

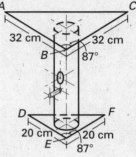

Solution

Both $m\angle$ __B__ and $m\angle$ __E__ equal 87°, so $\angle$ __B__ $\cong \angle$ __E__. Next, compare the ratios of the lengths of the sides that include $\angle B$ and $\angle E$.

$$\dfrac{AB}{\boxed{DE}} = \dfrac{\boxed{BC}}{EF} = \dfrac{32}{20} = \dfrac{8}{5}$$

The lengths of the sides that include $\angle B$ and $\angle E$ are __proportional__.

So, by the __SAS Similarity Theorem__, $\triangle ABC \sim \triangle DEF$. Yes, you can make the top similar to the bottom.

✔ *Checkpoint* **Complete the following exercise.**

3. In Example 3, suppose you use equilateral triangles on the top and bottom. Are the top and bottom similar? *Explain.*

   Yes, the top and bottom are similar. If the side length of the top is *a* and the side length of the bottom is *b*, the ratios of the side lengths are $\dfrac{a}{b}$ and the angles are all 60°. The triangles are similar by SAS or SSS.

TRIANGLE SIMILARITY POSTULATE AND THEOREMS

AA Similarity Postulate If $\angle A \cong \angle D$ and $\angle B \cong \angle E$, then $\triangle ABC \sim \triangle DEF$.

SSS Similarity Theorem If $\dfrac{AB}{DE} = \dfrac{BC}{EF} = \dfrac{AC}{DF}$, then $\triangle ABC \sim \triangle DEF$.

SAS Similarity Theorem If $\angle A \cong \angle D$ and $\dfrac{AB}{DE} = \dfrac{AC}{DF}$, then $\triangle ABC \sim \triangle DEF$.

To identify corresponding parts, redraw the triangles so that the corresponding parts have the same orientation.

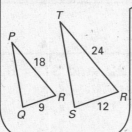

Example 4   *Choose a method*

Tell what method you would use to show that the triangles are similar.

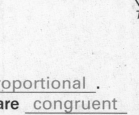

Solution

Find the ratios of the lengths of the corresponding sides.

Shorter sides $\dfrac{QR}{RS} = \dfrac{9}{12} = \dfrac{3}{4}$

Longer sides $\dfrac{PR}{RT} = \dfrac{18}{24} = \dfrac{3}{4}$

The corresponding side lengths are __proportional__. The included angles $\angle PRQ$ and $\angle TRS$ are __congruent__ because they are __vertical__ angles. So, $\triangle PQR \sim \triangle TSR$ by the __SAS Similarity Theorem__.

✔ *Checkpoint* **Complete the following exercise.**

4. *Explain* how to show $\triangle JKL \sim \triangle LKM$.

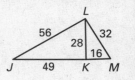

Show that the corresponding side lengths are proportional, then use the SSS Similarity Theorem to show $\triangle JKL \sim \triangle LKM$.

Homework

6.6 Use Proportionality Theorems

Goal • Use proportions with a triangle or parallel lines.

Your Notes

THEOREM 6.4: TRIANGLE PROPORTIONALITY THEOREM

If a line parallel to one side of a triangle intersects the other two sides, then it divides the two sides <u>proportionally</u>.

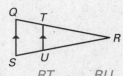

If $\overline{TU} \parallel \overline{QS}$, then $\dfrac{RT}{TQ} = \dfrac{RU}{US}$.

THEOREM 6.5: CONVERSE OF THE TRIANGLE PROPORTIONALITY THEOREM

If a line divides two sides of a triangle proportionally, then it is parallel to the <u>third side</u>.

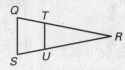

If $\dfrac{RT}{TQ} = \dfrac{RU}{US}$, then <u>$\overline{TU}$</u> $\parallel$ <u>$\overline{QS}$</u>.

Example 1 *Find the length of a segment*

In the diagram, $\overline{QS} \parallel \overline{UT}$, $RQ = 10$, $RS = 12$, and $ST = 6$. What is the length of $\overline{QU}$?

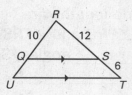

Solution

$\dfrac{RQ}{QU} = \dfrac{RS}{ST}$ Triangle Proportionality Theorem

$\dfrac{\boxed{10}}{QU} = \dfrac{\boxed{12}}{\boxed{6}}$ Substitute.

$\underline{60} = \underline{12} \cdot QU$ **Cross Products Property**

$\underline{5} = QU$ **Divide each side by** $\underline{12}$.

Your Notes

Example 2   *Solve a real-world problem*

Aerodynamics A spoiler for a remote controlled car is shown where $AB = 31$ mm, $BC = 19$ mm, $CD = 27$ mm, and $DE = 23$ mm. *Explain* why $\overline{BD}$ is not parallel to $\overline{AE}$.

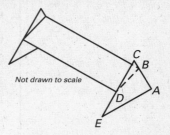

Not drawn to scale

Solution

Find and simplify the ratios of lengths determined by $\overline{BD}$.

$$\frac{CD}{DE} = \frac{27}{23} \qquad \frac{CB}{BA} = \frac{31}{19}$$

Because $\frac{27}{23} \neq \frac{31}{19}$, $\overline{BD}$ is not parallel to $\overline{AE}$.

✔ *Checkpoint* **Complete the following exercises.**

1. Find the length of $\overline{KL}$.

$KL = 33$

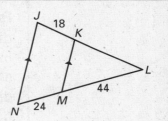

2. Determine whether $\overline{QT} \parallel \overline{RS}$.

No; $\overline{QT}$ is not parallel to $\overline{RS}$.

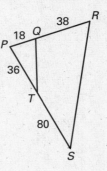

Your Notes

THEOREM 6.6

If three parallel lines intersect two transversals, then they divide the transversals <u>proportionally</u>.

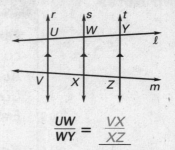

$$\frac{UW}{WY} = \frac{VX}{XZ}$$

THEOREM 6.7

If a ray bisects an angle of a triangle, then it divides the opposite side into segments whose lengths are <u>proportional</u> to the lengths of the other two sides.

$$\frac{AD}{DB} = \frac{CA}{CB}$$

Example 3   *Use Theorem 6.6*

Farming A farmer's land is divided by a newly constructed interstate. The distances shown are in meters. Find the distance *CA* between the north border and the south border of the farmer's land.

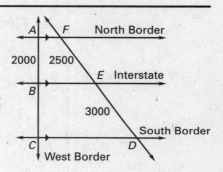

Use Theorem 6.6.

$$\frac{CB}{BA} = \frac{DE}{EF}$$ **Parallel lines divide transversals proportionally.**

$$\frac{\boxed{CB + BA}}{BA} = \frac{\boxed{DE + EF}}{EF}$$ **Property of proportions (Property 4)**

$$\frac{CA}{\boxed{2000}} = \frac{3000 + 2500}{2500}$$ **Substitute.**

$$\frac{CA}{\boxed{2000}} = \frac{5500}{2500}$$ **Simplify.**

$$CA = \underline{4400}$$ **Multiply each side by <u>2000</u> and simplify.**

The distance between the north border and the south border is <u>4400</u> meters.

Example 4   *Use Theorem 6.7*

In the diagram, $\angle DEG \cong \angle GEF$.
Use the given side lengths to
find the length of $\overline{DG}$.

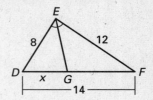

Solution

Because $\overrightarrow{EG}$ is an angle bisector of $\angle DEF$, you can apply
Theorem 6.7. Let $GD = x$. Then $GF = \underline{\ 14 - x\ }$.

$$\frac{GF}{GD} = \frac{EF}{ED}$$ Angle bisector divides opposite side proportionally.

$$\frac{\boxed{14 - x}}{x} = \frac{12}{8}$$ Substitute.

$$\underline{\ 12\ }x = \underline{\ 112\ } - \underline{\ 8\ }x$$ Cross Products Property

$$x = \underline{\ 5.6\ }$$ Solve for x.

✓ **Checkpoint**   Find the length of $\overline{AB}$.

3.

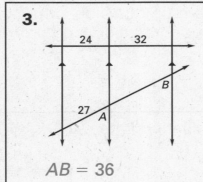

$AB = 36$

4.

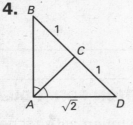

$AB = \sqrt{2}$

Homework

Perform Similarity Transformations

Goal • Perform dilations.

Your Notes

VOCABULARY

Dilation A dilation is a transformation that stretches or shrinks a figure to create a similar figure.

Center of dilation In a dilation, a figure is enlarged or reduced with respect to a fixed point called the center of dilation.

Scale factor of a dilation The scale factor k of a dilation is the ratio of a side length of the image to the corresponding side length of the original figure.

Reduction A dilation where $0 < k < 1$ is a reduction.

Enlargement A dilation where $k > 1$ is an enlargement.

COORDINATE NOTATION FOR A DILATION

You can describe a dilation with respect to the origin with the notation $(x, y) \rightarrow (kx, ky)$, where k is the scale factor.

If $0 < k < 1$, the dilation is a _reduction_ . If $k > 1$, the dilation is an _enlargement_ .

> All of the dilations in this lesson are in the coordinate plane and each center of dilation is the origin.

Example 1 — Draw a dilation with a scale factor greater than 1

Draw a dilation of quadrilateral *ABCD* with vertices *A*(2, 0), *B*(6, −4), *C*(8, 2), and *D*(6, 4). Use a scale factor of $\frac{1}{2}$.

First draw *ABCD*. Find the dilation of each vertex by multiplying its coordinates by $\frac{1}{2}$. Then draw the dilation.

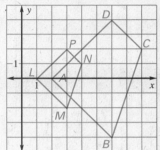

$$(x, y) \rightarrow \left(\frac{1}{2}\,x,\ \frac{1}{2}\,y \right)$$

$A(2, 0) \rightarrow L\ \underline{(1, 0)}$

$B(6, -4) \rightarrow M\ \underline{(3, -2)}$

$C(8, 2) \rightarrow N\ \underline{(4, 1)}$

$D(6, 4) \rightarrow P\ \underline{(3, 2)}$

Example 2 — Verify that a figure is similar to its dilation

A triangle has the vertices *A*(2, −1), *B*(4, −1), and *C*(4, 2). The image of △*ABC* after a dilation with a scale factor of 2 is △*DEF*.

a. Sketch △*ABC* and △*DEF*.

b. Verify that △*ABC* and △*DEF* are similar.

Solution

a. The scale factor is greater than 1, so the dilation is an __enlargement__ .

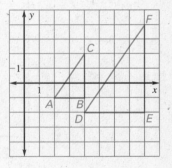

$$(x, y) \rightarrow (\ \underline{2}\ x,\ \underline{2}\ y)$$

$A(2, -1) \rightarrow \underline{D(4, -2)}$

$B(4, -1) \rightarrow \underline{E(8, -2)}$

$C(4, 2) \rightarrow \underline{F(8, 4)}$

b. Because ∠ _B_ and ∠ _E_ are both right angles, ∠ _B_ ≅ ∠ _E_ . Show that the lengths of the sides that include ∠ _B_ and ∠ _E_ are proportional.

$$\frac{AB}{\boxed{DE}} \overset{?}{=} \frac{BC}{\boxed{EF}} \qquad \frac{2}{\boxed{4}} = \frac{3}{\boxed{6}} \ \checkmark$$

The lengths are proportional. So, △*ABC* ~ △*DEF* by the __SAS Similarity Theorem__ .

Example 3 *Find a scale factor*

Magnets You are making your own photo magnets. Your photo is 8 inches by 10 inches. The image on the magnet is 2.8 inches by 3.5 inches. What is the scale factor of the reduction?

Solution

The scale factor is the ratio of a side length of the
___magnet image___ to a side length of the

___original photo___ , or $\dfrac{2.8 \text{ in.}}{8 \text{ in.}}$. In simplest form,

the scale factor is $\dfrac{7}{20}$.

✔ *Checkpoint* **Complete the following exercises.**

1. A triangle has the vertices $B(-1, -1)$, $C(0, 1)$, and $D(1, 0)$. Find the coordinates of L, M, and N so that $\triangle LMN$ is a dilation of $\triangle BCD$ with a scale factor of 4. Sketch $\triangle BCD$ and $\triangle LMN$.

   $L(-4, -4)$,
   $M(0, 4)$,
   $N(4, 0)$

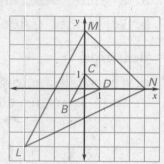

2. In Example 3, what is the scale factor of the reduction if your photo is 4 inches by 5 inches?

   $\dfrac{7}{10}$

Your Notes

Example 4 *Find missing coordinates*

You want to create a quadrilateral *JKLM* that is similar to quadrilateral *PQRS*. What are the coordinates of *M*?

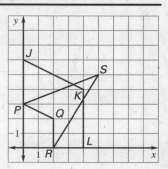

Solution

Determine if *JKLM* is a dilation of *PQRS* by checking whether the same scale factor can be used to obtain *J*, *K*, and *L* from *P*, *Q*, and *R*.

$(x, y) \rightarrow (kx, ky)$

P(_0, 3_) → J(_0, 6_)   *k* = _2_

Q(_2, 2_) → K(_4, 4_)   *k* = _2_

R(_2, 0_) → L(_4, 0_)   *k* = _2_

Because *k* is the same in each case, the image is a _dilation_ with a scale factor of _2_. So, you can use the scale factor to find the image *M* of point *S*.

S(_5, 5_) → M(_2_ · _5_ , _2_ · _5_) = M(_10, 10_)

✔ *Checkpoint* Complete the following exercise.

3. You want to create a quadrilateral *QRST* that is similar to quadrilateral *WXYZ*. What are the coordinates of *T*?

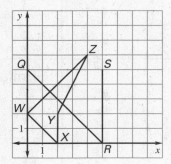

T(10, 15)

Homework

Words to Review

Give an example of the vocabulary word.

Ratio $\frac{4}{3}$ or $4:3$	**Proportion** $\frac{x}{4} = \frac{3}{12}$
Means The means of $\frac{a}{b} = \frac{c}{d}$ are b and c.	**Extremes** The extremes of $\frac{a}{b} = \frac{c}{d}$ are a and d.
Geometric mean The geometric mean of two positive numbers a and b is the positive number x that satisfies $\frac{a}{x} = \frac{x}{b}$.	**Scale drawings** A scale drawing is a drawing that is the same shape as the object it represents. A map is an example of a scale drawing.
Scale The scale of a map is 1 inch to 25 miles.	**Similar polygons** 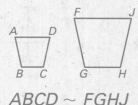 $ABCD \sim FGHJ$

Scale factor of two similar polygons	Dilation
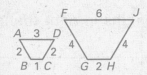 The scale factor of *ABCD* to *FGHJ* is $\frac{1}{2}$.	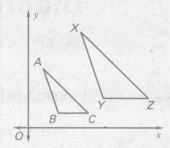

Center of dilation	Scale factor of a dilation
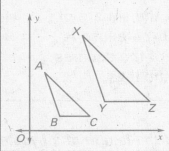 The center of dilation is (0, 0).	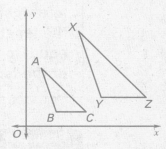 The scale factor of the dilation is $\frac{XY}{AB}$.

Reduction	Enlargement
A dilation with a scale factor greater than 0 and less than 1 is a reduction.	A dilation with a scale factor greater than 1 is an enlargement.

Review your notes and Chapter 6 by using the Chapter Review on pages 418–421 of your textbook.

7.1 Apply the Pythagorean Theorem

Goal • Find side lengths in right triangles.

VOCABULARY

Pythagorean triple A Pythagorean triple is a set of three positive integers a, b, and c that satisfy the equation $c^2 = a^2 + b^2$.

THEOREM 7.1: PYTHAGOREAN THEOREM

In a right triangle, the square of the length of the hypotenuse is equal to the sum of the squares of the lengths of the legs.

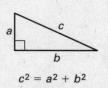

$c^2 = a^2 + b^2$

Example 1 *Find the length of a hypotenuse*

Find the length of the hypotenuse of the right triangle.

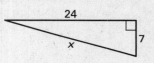

> In the equation for the Pythagorean Theorem, "length of hypotenuse" and "length of leg" was shortened to "hypotenuse" and "leg".

Solution

$(\text{hypotenuse})^2 = (\text{leg})^2 + (\text{leg})^2$ **Pythagorean Theorem**

$x^2 = \underline{\ 7\ }^2 + \underline{\ 24\ }^2$ **Substitute.**

$x^2 = \underline{\ 49\ } + \underline{\ 576\ }$ **Multiply.**

$x^2 = \underline{\ 625\ }$ **Add.**

$x = \underline{\ 25\ }$ **Find the positive square root.**

✔ *Checkpoint* **Complete the following exercise.**

1. Find the length of the hypotenuse of the right triangle.

$x = 15$

Your Notes

| Example 2 | *Find the length of a leg* |

Door A 6 foot board rests under a doorknob and the base of the board is 5 feet away from the bottom of the door. Approximately how high above the ground is the doorknob?

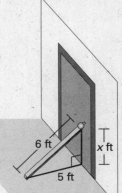

6 ft

x ft

5 ft

Solution

$$\left(\begin{array}{c}\text{Length}\\\text{of board}\end{array}\right)^2 = \left(\begin{array}{c}\text{Distance}\\\text{from door}\end{array}\right)^2 + \left(\begin{array}{c}\text{Height of}\\\text{doorknob}\end{array}\right)^2$$

$\underline{6}^2 = \underline{5}^2 + x^2$ **Substitute.**

$\underline{36} = \underline{25} + x^2$ **Multiply.**

$\underline{11} = x^2$ **Subtract** $\underline{25}$ **from each side.**

$\underline{\sqrt{11}} = x$ **Find positive square root.**

$\underline{3.3} \approx x$ **Approximate with a calculator.**

The board is resting against the doorknob at about $\underline{3.3}$ feet above the ground.

> In real-world applications, it is usually appropriate to use a calculator to approximate the square root of a number. Round your answer to the nearest tenth.

✔ **Checkpoint** Complete the following exercise.

2. A 5 foot board rests under a doorknob and the base of the board is 3.5 feet away from the bottom of the door. Approximately how high above the ground is the doorknob?

about 3.6 feet

Example 3   *Find the area of an isosceles triangle*

Find the area of the isosceles triangle with side lengths 16 meters, 17 meters, and 17 meters.

Solution

Step 1 **Draw** a sketch. By definition, the length of an altitude is the _height_ of the triangle. In an isosceles triangle, the altitude to the base is also a perpendicular bisector. So, the altitude divides the triangle into two _right_ triangles with the dimensions shown.

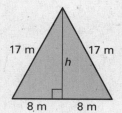

Step 2 **Use** the Pythagorean Theorem to find the height of the triangle.

$c^2 = a^2 + b^2$	**Pythagorean Theorem**
$\underline{17}^2 = \underline{8}^2 + h^2$	**Substitute.**
$\underline{289} = \underline{64} + h^2$	**Multiply.**
$\underline{225} = h^2$	**Subtract** _64_ **from each side.**
$\underline{15} = h$	**Find the positive square root.**

Step 3 **Find** the area.

$$\text{Area} = \frac{1}{2}(\text{base})(\text{height}) = \frac{1}{2}(\ \underline{16}\ )(\ \underline{15}\ ) = \underline{120}$$

The area of the triangle is _120_ square meters.

> You may find it helpful to memorize the basic Pythagorean triples, shown in **bold**, for standardized tests.

COMMON PYTHAGOREAN TRIPLES AND SOME OF THEIR MULTIPLES

3, 4, 5	**5, 12, 13**	**8, 15, 17**	**7, 24, 25**
6, 8, 10	10, 24, 26	16, 30, 34	14, 48, 50
9, 12, 15	15, 36, 39	24, 45, 51	21, 72, 75
30, 40, 50	50, 120, 130	80, 150, 170	70, 240, 250
$3x, 4x, 5x$	$5x, 12x, 13x$	$8x, 15x, 17x$	$7x, 24x, 25x$

The most common Pythagorean triples are in bold. The other triples are the result of multiplying each integer in a bold face triple by the same factor.

Example 4   *Find length of a hypotenuse using two methods*

Find the length of the hypotenuse of the right triangle.

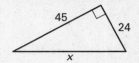

Solution

Method 1: Use a Pythagorean triple.

A common Pythagorean triple is 8, 15, __17__. Notice that if you multiply the lengths of the legs of the Pythagorean triple by __3__, you get the lengths of the legs of this triangle: 8 • __3__ = 24 and 15 • __3__ = 45. So, the length of the hypotenuse is __17__ • __3__ = __51__.

Method 2: Use the Pythagorean Theorem.

$x^2 = 24^2 + 45^2$	**Pythagorean Theorem**
$x^2 = \underline{576} + \underline{2025}$	**Multiply.**
$x^2 = \underline{2601}$	**Add.**
$x = \underline{51}$	**Find the positive square root.**

✔ *Checkpoint* **Complete the following exercises.**

3. Find the area of the triangle.

672 ft²

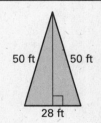

4. Use a Pythagorean triple to find the unknown side length of the right triangle.

50

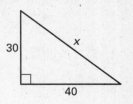

Use the Converse of the Pythagorean Theorem

Goal • Use the Converse of the Pythagorean Theorem to determine if a triangle is a right triangle.

Your Notes

THEOREM 7.2: CONVERSE OF THE PYTHAGOREAN THEOREM

If the square of the length of the longest side of a triangle is equal to the sum of the squares of the lengths of the other two sides, then the triangle is a <u>right</u> triangle.

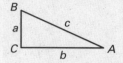

If $c^2 = a^2 + b^2$, then $\triangle ABC$ is a <u>right</u> triangle.

Example 1 *Verify right triangles*

Tell whether the given triangle is a right triangle.

a.

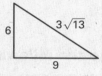

b.

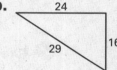

Solution

Let c represent the length of the longest side of the triangle. Check to see whether the side lengths satisfy the equation $c^2 = a^2 + b^2$.

a. $(\underline{3\sqrt{13}})^2 \overset{?}{=} \underline{6}^2 + \underline{9}^2$

$\underline{9} \cdot \underline{13} \overset{?}{=} \underline{36} + \underline{81}$

$\underline{117} = \underline{117}$ ✓

The triangle <u>is</u> a right triangle.

b. $\underline{29}^2 \overset{?}{=} \underline{24}^2 + \underline{16}^2$

$\underline{841} \overset{?}{=} \underline{576} + \underline{256}$

$\underline{841} \neq \underline{832}$

The triangle <u>is not</u> a right triangle.

Your Notes

THEOREM 7.3

If the square of the length of the longest side of a triangle is less than the sum of the squares of the lengths of the other two sides, then the triangle *ABC* is an <u>acute</u> triangle.

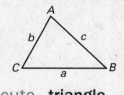

If $c^2 < a^2 + b^2$, then the triangle *ABC* is <u>acute</u>.

THEOREM 7.4

If the square of the length of the longest side of a triangle is greater than the sum of the squares of the lengths of the other two sides, then the triangle *ABC* is an <u>obtuse</u> triangle.

If $c^2 > a^2 + b^2$, then the triangle *ABC* is <u>obtuse</u>.

Example 2   *Classify triangles*

Can segments with lengths of 2.8 feet, 3.2 feet, and 4.2 feet form a triangle? If so, would the triangle be *acute*, *right*, or *obtuse*?

Solution

Step 1 Use the Triangle Inequality Theorem to check that the segments can make a triangle.

> The Triangle Inequality Theorem states that the sum of the lengths of any two sides of a triangle is greater than the length of the third side.

2.8 + 3.2 = <u>6</u>	2.8 + 4.2 = <u>7</u>	3.2 + 4.2 = <u>7.4</u>
<u>6</u> > 4.2	<u>7</u> > 3.2	<u>7.4</u> > 2.8

Step 2 Classify the triangle by comparing the square of the length of the longest side with the sum of squares of the lengths of the shorter sides.

$$c^2 \;\underline{?}\; a^2 + b^2$$ Compare c^2 with $a^2 + b^2$.

$$\underline{4.2}^{\,2} \;\underline{?}\; \underline{2.8}^{\,2} + \underline{3.2}^{\,2}$$ Substitute.

$$\underline{17.64} \;\underline{?}\; \underline{7.84} + \underline{10.24}$$ Simplify.

$$\underline{17.64} \;\underline{<}\; \underline{18.08}$$ c^2 is <u>less</u> than $a^2 + b^2$.

The side lengths 2.8 feet, 3.2 feet, and 4.2 feet form an <u>acute</u> triangle.

Example 3   *Use the Converse of the Pythagorean Theorem*

Lights You are helping install a light pole in a parking lot. When the pole is positioned properly, it is perpendicular to the pavement. How can you check that the pole is perpendicular using a tape measure?

Solution

To show a line is perpendicular to a plane you must show that the line is perpendicular to _two lines_ in the plane.

Think of the pole as a line and the pavement as a plane. Use a 3-4-5 right triangle and the Converse of the Pythagorean Theorem to show that the pole is perpendicular to different lines on the pavement.

First mark 3 feet up the pole and mark on the pavement 4 feet from the pole.

Use the tape measure to check that the distance between the two marks is _5_ feet. The pole makes _a right_ angle with the line on the pavement.

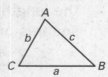

Finally, repeat the procedure to show that the pole is _perpendicular_ to another line on the pavement.

METHODS FOR CLASSIFYING A TRIANGLE BY ANGLES USING ITS SIDE LENGTHS

Theorem 7.2	**Theorem 7.3**	**Theorem 7.4**
If $c^2 = a^2 + b^2$, then $m\angle C = 90°$ and $\triangle ABC$ is a _right_ triangle.	If $c^2 < a^2 + b^2$, then $m\angle C < 90°$ and $\triangle ABC$ is an _acute_ triangle.	If $c^2 > a^2 + b^2$, then $m\angle C > 90°$ and $\triangle ABC$ is an _obtuse_ triangle.

✓ *Checkpoint* **In Exercises 1 and 2, tell whether the triangle is a right triangle.**

1.

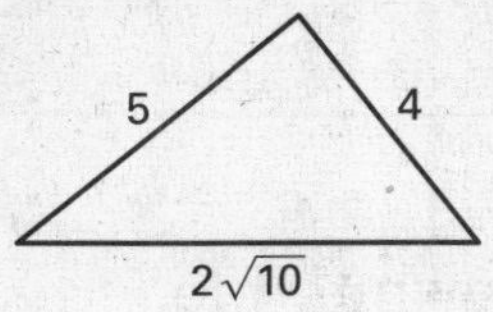

not a right triangle

2.

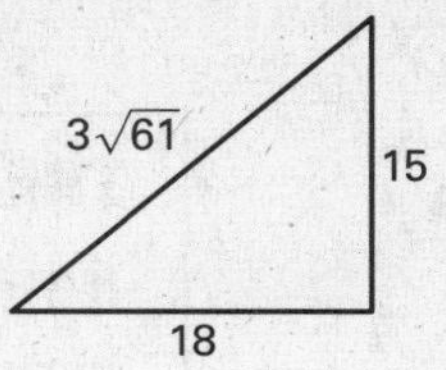

right triangle

3. Can segments with lengths of 6.1 inches, 9.4 inches, and 11.3 inches form a triangle? If so, would the triangle be *acute*, *right*, or *obtuse*?

Yes; obtuse

4. In Example 3, could you use triangles with side lengths 50 inches, 120 inches, and 130 inches to verify that you have perpendicular lines? *Explain*.

Yes; A triangle with side lengths 50 inches, 120 inches, and 130 inches is a right triangle. The right triangle shows that you have perpendicular lines.

Homework

7.3 Use Similar Right Triangles

Goal • Use properties of the altitude of a right triangle.

Your Notes

THEOREM 7.5

If the altitude is drawn to the hypotenuse of a right triangle, then the two triangles formed are __similar__ to the original triangle and to each other.

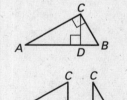

△CBD __~__ △ABC, △ACD __~__ △ABC, and △CBD __~__ △ACD.

Example 1 — *Identify similar triangles*

Identify the similar triangles in the diagram.

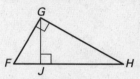

Solution

Sketch the three similar right triangles so that the corresponding angles and sides have the same orientation.

 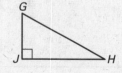 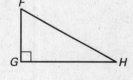

△ __FJG__ ~ △ __GJH__ ~ △ __FGH__

✔ *Checkpoint* Complete the following exercise.

1. Identify the similar triangles in the diagram.

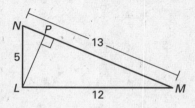

△NPL ~ △LPM ~ △NLM

Copyright © McDougal Littell/Houghton Mifflin Company.

Example 2 *Find the length of the altitude to the hypotenuse*

Stadium A cross section of a group of seats at a stadium shows a drainage pipe $\overline{BD}$ that leads from the seats to the inside of the stadium. What is the length of the pipe?

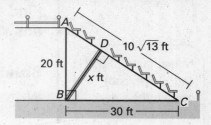

Solution

Step 1 Identify the similar triangles and sketch them.

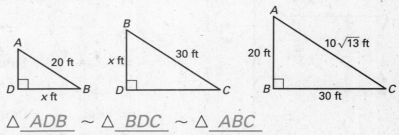

$\triangle\underline{\ ADB\ } \sim \triangle\underline{\ BDC\ } \sim \triangle\underline{\ ABC\ }$

Step 2 Find the value of x. Use the fact that $\triangle BDC \sim \triangle ABC$ to write a proportion.

> Notice that if you tried to write a proportion using $\triangle ADB$ and $\triangle BDC$, there would be two unknowns, so you would not be able to solve for x.

$$\frac{BD}{\boxed{AB}} = \frac{\boxed{BC}}{AC}$$ Corresponding side lengths of similar triangles are in proportion.

$$\frac{x}{\boxed{20}} = \frac{30}{10\sqrt{13}}$$ Substitute.

$$(10\sqrt{13})\,x = \underline{\ 20(30)\ }$$ Cross Products Property

$$x \approx \underline{\ 16.6\ }$$ Approximate.

The length of the pipe is about __16.6__ feet.

✔ **Checkpoint Complete the following exercise.**

2. Identify the similar triangles. Then find the value of x.

$\triangle GFD \sim \triangle DFE \sim \triangle GDE$;
$x = 4.8$

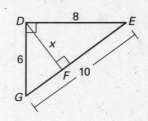

Example 3   *Use a geometric mean*

Find the value of y. Write your answer in simplest radical form.

> Notice that △FEG and △FDE both contain the side with length y, so these are the similar pair of triangles to use to solve for y.

Solution

Write a proportion.

$$\frac{\boxed{\text{length of hyp. of } \triangle FDE}}{\text{length of hyp. of } \triangle FEG}$$

$$= \frac{\text{length of shorter leg of } \triangle FDE}{\boxed{\text{length of shorter leg of } \triangle FEG}}$$

$$\frac{\boxed{15}}{y} = \frac{y}{\boxed{4}} \qquad \textbf{Substitute.}$$

$$\underline{60} = y^2 \qquad \textbf{Cross Products Property}$$

$$\sqrt{\underline{60}} = y \qquad \textbf{Take positive square roots.}$$

$$\underline{2}\sqrt{\underline{15}} = y \qquad \textbf{Simplify.}$$

THEOREM 7.6: GEOMETRIC MEAN (ALTITUDE) THEOREM

In a right triangle, the altitude from the right angle to the hypotenuse divides the hypotenuse into two segments.

The length of the altitude is the ___geometric mean___ of the lengths of the two segments.

$$\frac{BD}{\boxed{CD}} = \frac{\boxed{CD}}{AD}$$

THEOREM 7.7: GEOMETRIC MEAN (LEG) THEOREM

In a right triangle, the altitude from the right angle to the hypotenuse divides the hypotenuse into two segments.

The length of each leg of the right triangle is the geometric mean of the lengths of the hypotenuse and the segment of the hypotenuse that is ___adjacent___ to the leg.

$$\frac{AB}{CB} = \frac{CB}{\boxed{DB}} \text{ and}$$

$$\frac{AB}{AC} = \frac{AC}{\boxed{AD}}$$

Your Notes

Example 4 *Find a height using indirect measurement*

Overpass To find the clearance under an overpass, you need to find the height of a concrete support beam.

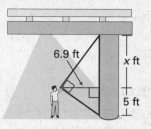

You use a cardboard square to line up the top and bottom of the beam. Your friend measures the vertical distance from the ground to your eye and the distance from you to the beam. Approximate the height of the beam.

Solution

By Theorem 7.6, you know that __6.9__ is the geometric mean of __x__ and __5__.

$$\frac{x}{6.9} = \frac{6.9}{5}$$ Write a proportion.

$x \approx$ __9.5__   Solve for x.

So, the clearance under the overpass is
$5 + x \approx 5 +$ __9.5__ $=$ __14.5__ feet.

✔ **Checkpoint** Complete the following exercises.

3. Find the value of y. Write your answer in simplest radical form.

   $y = 6\sqrt{6}$

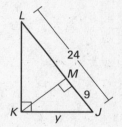

4. The distance from the ground to Larry's eyes is 4.5 feet. How far from the beam in Example 4 would he have to stand in order to measure its height?

   about 6.7 feet

Homework

7.4 Special Right Triangles

Goal • Use the relationships among the sides in special right triangles.

Your Notes

> The extended ratio of the side lengths of a 45°-45°-90° triangle is $1:1:\sqrt{2}$.

THEOREM 7.8: 45°-45°-90° TRIANGLE THEOREM

In a 45°-45°-90° triangle, the hypotenuse is $\underline{\sqrt{2}}$ times as long as each leg.

hypotenuse = leg • $\underline{\sqrt{2}}$

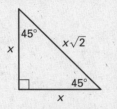

Example 1   *Find hypotenuse length in a 45°-45°-90° triangle*

Find the length of the hypotenuse.

a.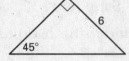

b.

Solution

a. By the Triangle Sum Theorem, the measure of the third angle must be $\underline{45°}$. Then the triangle is a $\underline{45°}$ - $\underline{45°}$ -90° triangle, so by Theorem 7.8, the hypotenuse is $\underline{\sqrt{2}}$ times as long as each leg.

   hypotenuse = leg • $\underline{\sqrt{2}}$ 45° - 45° -90° Triangle Theorem

             = $\underline{6\sqrt{2}}$ **Substitute.**

b. By the Base Angles Theorem and the Corollary to the Triangle Sum Theorem, the triangle is a 45°-45°-90° triangle.

> Remember the following properties of radicals:
> $\sqrt{a} \cdot \sqrt{b}$
> $= \sqrt{a \cdot b}$;
> $\sqrt{a \cdot a} = a$

   hypotenuse = leg • $\underline{\sqrt{2}}$ 45°-45°-90° Triangle Theorem

             = $\underline{4\sqrt{2}}$ • $\underline{\sqrt{2}}$ **Substitute.**

             = $\underline{4}$ • $\underline{2}$ **Product of square roots**

             = $\underline{8}$ **Simplify.**

Example 2 *Find leg lengths in a 45°-45°-90° triangle*

Find the lengths of the legs in the triangle.

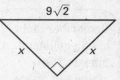

Solution

By the Base Angles Theorem and the Corollary to the Triangle Sum Theorem, the triangle is a 45°-45°-90° triangle.

hypotenuse = leg · $\underline{\sqrt{2}}$		45°-45°-90° Triangle Theorem
$\underline{9\sqrt{2}}$ = x · $\underline{\sqrt{2}}$		Substitute.
$\dfrac{9\sqrt{2}}{\sqrt{2}} = \dfrac{x\boxed{\sqrt{2}}}{\boxed{\sqrt{2}}}$		Divide each side by $\underline{\sqrt{2}}$.
$\underline{9}$ = x		Simplify.

✔ **Checkpoint** **Find the value of the variable.**

1.

$x = 4$

2.

$x = 12$

THEOREM 7.9: 30°-60°-90° TRIANGLE THEOREM

> The extended ratio of the side lengths of a 30°-60°-90° triangle is 1:$\sqrt{3}$:2.

In a 30°-60°-90° triangle, the hypotenuse is $\underline{\text{twice}}$ as long as the shorter leg, and the longer leg is $\underline{\sqrt{3}}$ times as long as the shorter leg.

hypotenuse = $\underline{2}$ · shorter leg

longer leg = shorter leg · $\underline{\sqrt{3}}$

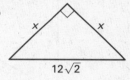

Example 3   *Find the height of an equilateral triangle*

Music You make a guitar pick that resembles an equilateral triangle with side lengths of 32 millimeters. What is the approximate height of the pick?

> Remember that in an equilateral triangle, the altitude to a side is also the median to that side. So, altitude $\overline{BD}$ __bisects__ $\overline{AC}$.

Solution

Draw the equilateral triangle described. Its altitude forms the longer leg of two __30°__ - __60°__ -90° triangles. The length h of the altitude is approximately the height of the pick.

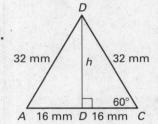

longer leg = shorter leg · __$\sqrt{3}$__

$$h = \underline{16} \cdot \underline{\sqrt{3}} \approx \underline{27.7} \text{ mm}$$

Example 4   *Find lengths in a 30°-60°-90° triangle*

Find the values of x and y. Write your answer in simplest radical form.

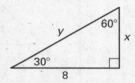

Solution

Step 1 Find the value of x.

longer leg = shorter leg · __$\sqrt{3}$__

$\underline{8} = x \underline{\sqrt{3}}$ **Substitute.**

$\dfrac{8}{\sqrt{3}} = x$ **Divide each side by __$\sqrt{3}$__.**

$\dfrac{8}{\sqrt{3}} \cdot \dfrac{\sqrt{3}}{\sqrt{3}} = x$ **Multiply numerator and denominator by __$\sqrt{3}$__.**

$\dfrac{8\sqrt{3}}{3} = x$ **Multiply fractions.**

Step 2 Find the value of y.

hypotenuse = __2__ · shorter leg

$$y = \underline{2} \cdot \underline{\dfrac{8\sqrt{3}}{3}} = \underline{\dfrac{16\sqrt{3}}{3}}$$

Example 5   *Find a height*

Windshield wipers A car is turned off while the windshield wipers are moving. The 24 inch wipers stop, making a 60° angle with the bottom of the windshield. How far from the bottom of the windshield are the ends of the wipers?

Solution

The distance *d* is the length of the longer leg of a <u>30°</u> - <u>60°</u> -**90°** triangle.

The length of the hypotenuse is <u>24</u> inches.

hypotenuse = <u>2</u> • shorter leg   <u>30°</u> - <u>60°</u> -**90°**
Triangle Theorem

    <u>24</u> = <u>2</u> • *s*   **Substitute.**

    <u>12</u> = *s*   **Divide each side by** <u>2</u> **.**

longer leg = shorter leg • <u>$\sqrt{3}$</u>   <u>30°</u> - <u>60°</u> -**90°**
Triangle Theorem

    d = <u>$12\sqrt{3}$</u>   **Substitute.**

    d ≈ <u>20.8</u>   **Approximate.**

The ends of the wipers are about <u>20.8</u> inches from the bottom of the windshield.

✔ *Checkpoint* **In Exercises 3 and 4, find the value of the variable.**

3.

60°
$2\sqrt{3}$
30°
x

x = 6

4.

12 *h* 12

6 6

h = $6\sqrt{3}$

5. In Example 5, how far from the bottom of the windshield are the ends of the wipers if they make a 30° angle with the bottom of the windshield?

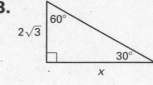

12 inches

7.5 Apply the Tangent Ratio

Goal • Use the tangent ratio for indirect measurement.

Your Notes

VOCABULARY

Trigonometric ratio A trigonometric ratio is a ratio of the lengths of two sides in a right triangle.

Tangent The ratio of the lengths of the legs in a right triangle is called the tangent of the angle.

TANGENT RATIO

> Remember these abbreviations:
> tangent → tan
> opposite → opp.
> adjacent → adj.

Let $\triangle ABC$ be a right triangle with acute $\angle A$. The tangent of $\angle A$ (written as tan A) is defined as follows:

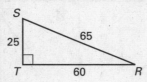

$$\tan A = \frac{\text{length of leg opposite } \angle A}{\text{length of leg adjacent to } \angle A} = \boxed{\frac{BC}{AC}}$$

Example 1 Find tangent ratios

Find tan S and tan R. Write each answer as a fraction and as a decimal rounded to four places, if necessary.

> Unless told otherwise, round values of trigonometric ratios to the ten-thousandths' place and round lengths to the tenths' place.

Solution

$$\tan S = \frac{\text{opp. } \angle S}{\text{adj. to } \angle S} = \boxed{\frac{RT}{ST}} = \boxed{\frac{60}{25}} = \boxed{\frac{12}{5}} = \underline{2.4}$$

$$\tan R = \frac{\text{opp. } \angle R}{\text{adj. to } \angle R} = \boxed{\frac{ST}{RT}} = \boxed{\frac{25}{60}} = \boxed{\frac{5}{12}} \approx \underline{0.4167}$$

Your Notes

✓ **Checkpoint** Find tan *B* and tan *C*. Write each answer as a fraction and as a decimal rounded to four places.

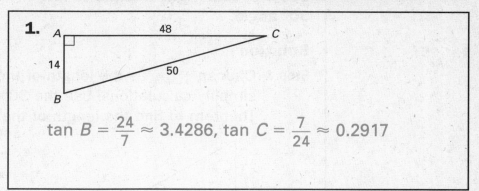

1.

$$\tan B = \frac{24}{7} \approx 3.4286, \tan C = \frac{7}{24} \approx 0.2917$$

Example 2   *Find a leg length*

Find the value of *x*.

Use the tangent of an acute angle to find a leg length.

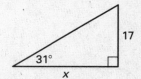

$\tan 31° = \dfrac{\text{opp.}}{\text{adj.}}$	**Write ratio for tangent of 31°.**
$\tan 31° = \dfrac{17}{x}$	**Substitute.**
$\underline{x} \cdot \tan 31° = \underline{17}$	**Multiply each side by __x__ .**
$x = \dfrac{17}{\tan 31°}$	**Divide each side by __tan 31°__ .**
$x \approx \dfrac{17}{0.6009}$	**Use a calculator to find __tan 31°__ .**
$x \approx \underline{28.3}$	**Simplify.**

Example 3   *Estimate height using tangent*

Lighthouse Find the height *h* of the lighthouse to the nearest foot.

$\underline{\tan 62°} = \dfrac{\text{opp.}}{\text{adj.}}$	**Write ratio for __tan 62°__ .**
$\underline{\tan 62°} = \dfrac{h}{\underline{100}}$	**Substitute.**
$\underline{100} \cdot \underline{\tan 62°} = h$	**Multiply each side by __100__ .**
$\underline{188} \approx h$	**Use a calculator and simplify.**

Example 4   *Use a special right triangle to find a tangent*

Use a special right triangle to find the tangent of a 30° angle.

Solution

Step 1 **Choose** $\underline{\sqrt{3}}$ as the length of the shorter leg to simplify calculations. Use the 30°-60°-90° Triangle Theorem to find the length of the longer leg.

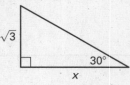

longer leg = $\underline{\text{shorter leg} \cdot \sqrt{3}}$

$x = \underline{\sqrt{3} \cdot \sqrt{3}} = \underline{3}$

Step 2 **Find** tan 30°.

$\tan 30° = \dfrac{\text{opp.}}{\text{adj.}}$ **Write ratio for tangent of 30°.**

$\tan 30° = \dfrac{\sqrt{3}}{3}$ **Substitute.**

> The tangents of all 30° angles are the same constant ratio. Any right triangle with a 30° angle can be used to determine this value.

The tangent of any 30° angle is $\dfrac{\sqrt{3}}{3} \approx \underline{0.5774}$.

✓ *Checkpoint* In Exercises 2 and 3, find the value of *x*. Round to the nearest tenth.

2. 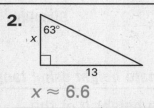 $x \approx 6.6$	3. 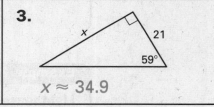 $x \approx 34.9$

4. In Example 4, suppose the length of the shorter leg is 1 instead of $\sqrt{3}$. Show that the tangent of 30° is still equal to $\dfrac{\sqrt{3}}{3}$.

longer leg = shorter leg · $\sqrt{3}$

$x = 1 \cdot \sqrt{3} = \sqrt{3}$

$\tan 30° = \dfrac{\text{opp.}}{\text{adj.}} = \dfrac{1}{\sqrt{3}} = \dfrac{1}{\sqrt{3}} \cdot \dfrac{\sqrt{3}}{\sqrt{3}} = \dfrac{\sqrt{3}}{3}$

Homework

7.6 Apply the Sine and Cosine Ratios

Goal • Use the sine and cosine ratios.

Your Notes

VOCABULARY

Sine, cosine Sine and cosine are trigonometric ratios for acute angles that involve the lengths of a leg and the hypotenuse of a right triangle.

Angle of elevation When looking up at an object, the angle your line of sight makes with a horizontal line is called the angle of elevation.

Angle of depression When looking down at an object, the angle your line of sight makes with a horizontal line is called the angle of depression.

SINE AND COSINE RATIOS

Let $\triangle ABC$ be a right triangle with acute $\angle A$. The sine of $\angle A$ and cosine of $\angle A$ (written sin *A* and cos *A*) are defined as follows:

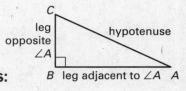

> Remember these abbreviations:
> sine → sin
> cosine → cos
> hypotenuse → hyp

$$\sin A = \frac{\text{length of leg opposite } \angle A}{\text{length of hypotenuse}} = \boxed{\frac{BC}{AC}}$$

$$\cos A = \frac{\text{length of leg adjacent to } \angle A}{\text{length of hypotenuse}} = \boxed{\frac{AB}{AC}}$$

Example 1   *Find sine ratios*

Find sin *U* and sin *W*. Write each answer as a fraction and as a decimal rounded to four places.

Solution

$$\sin U = \frac{\text{opp. } \angle U}{\text{hyp.}} = \frac{\boxed{WV}}{\boxed{UW}} = \frac{\boxed{16}}{\boxed{34}} = \frac{\boxed{8}}{\boxed{17}} \approx \underline{0.4706}$$

$$\sin W = \frac{\text{opp. } \angle W}{\text{hyp.}} = \frac{\boxed{UV}}{\boxed{UW}} = \frac{\boxed{30}}{\boxed{34}} = \frac{\boxed{15}}{\boxed{17}} \approx \underline{0.8824}$$

Example 2   *Find cosine ratios*

Find cos *S* and cos *R*. Write each answer as a fraction and as a decimal rounded to four places.

Solution

$$\cos S = \frac{\text{adj. to } \angle S}{\text{hyp.}} \frac{\boxed{ST}}{\boxed{SR}} = \frac{\boxed{45}}{\boxed{53}} \approx \underline{0.8491}$$

$$\cos R = \frac{\text{adj. to } \angle R}{\text{hyp.}} \frac{\boxed{RT}}{\boxed{SR}} = \frac{\boxed{28}}{\boxed{53}} \approx \underline{0.5283}$$

✔ *Checkpoint* Find sin *B*, sin *C*, cos *B*, and cos *C*. Write each answer as a fraction and as a decimal rounded to four places.

1.

$$\sin B = \frac{21}{29} \approx 0.7241, \ \sin C = \frac{20}{29} \approx 0.6897,$$

$$\cos B = \frac{20}{29} \approx 0.6897, \ \cos C = \frac{21}{29} \approx 0.7241$$

Example 3   *Use a trigonometric ratio to find a hypotenuse*

Basketball You walk from one corner of a basketball court to the opposite corner. Write and solve a proportion using a trigonometric ratio to approximate the distance of the walk.

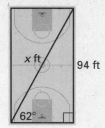

Solution

$\sin 62° = \dfrac{\text{opp.}}{\text{hyp.}}$ Write ratio for sine of 62°.

$\sin 62° = \dfrac{94}{x}$ Substitute.

$\underline{\ x\ } \cdot \sin 62° = 94$ Multiply each side by $\underline{\ x\ }$.

$x = \dfrac{94}{\sin 62°}$ Divide each side by $\underline{\sin 62°}$.

$x \approx \dfrac{94}{0.8829}$ Use a calculator to find $\underline{\sin 62°}$.

$x \approx \underline{106.5}$ Simplify.

The distance of the walk is about $\underline{106.5}$ feet.

Example 4   *Find a hypotenuse using an angle of depression*

Roller Coaster You are at the top of a roller coaster 100 feet above the ground. The angle of depression is 44°. About how far do you ride down the hill?

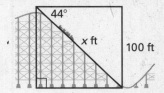

$\sin 44° = \dfrac{\text{opp.}}{\text{hyp.}}$ Write ratio for sine of 44°.

$\sin 44° = \dfrac{100}{x}$ Substitute.

$x \cdot \underline{\sin 44°} = \underline{100}$ Multiply each side by $\underline{\ x\ }$.

$x = \dfrac{100}{\sin 44°}$ Divide each side by $\underline{\sin 44°}$.

$x \approx \dfrac{100}{0.6947}$ Use a calculator to find $\underline{\sin 44°}$.

$x \approx \underline{143.9}$ Simplify.

You ride about $\underline{144}$ feet down the hill.

✓ *Checkpoint* **Complete the following exercises.**

2. In Example 3, use the cosine ratio to approximate the width of the basketball court.

about 50 feet

3. Suppose the angle of depression in Example 4 is 72°. About how far would you ride down the hill?

about 105 feet

Example 5   *Find leg lengths using an angle of elevation*

Railroad A railroad crossing arm that is 20 feet long is stuck with an angle of elevation of 35°. Find the lengths *x* and *y*.

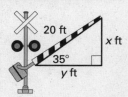

Solution

Step 1 Find *x*.

$$\underline{\sin 35°} = \frac{\text{opp.}}{\text{hyp.}}$$ Write ratio for __sine__ of _35°_ .

$$\underline{\sin 35°} = \frac{x}{20}$$ Substitute.

$$\underline{20 \cdot \sin 35°} = x$$ Multiply each side by _20_ .

$$\underline{11.5} \approx x$$ Use a calculator to simplify.

Step 2 Find *y*.

$$\underline{\cos 35°} = \frac{\text{adj.}}{\text{hyp.}}$$ Write ratio for __cosine__ of _35°_ .

$$\underline{\cos 35°} = \frac{y}{20}$$ Substitute.

$$\underline{20 \cdot \cos 35°} = y$$ Multiply each side by _20_ .

$$\underline{16.4} \approx y$$ Use a calculator to simplify.

Your Notes

Example 6 — *Use a special right triangle to find a sin and cos*

Use a special right triangle to find the sine and cosine of a 30° angle.

Solution

Use the 30°-60°-90° Triangle Theorem to draw a right triangle with side lengths of 1, $\sqrt{3}$, and __2__. Then set up sine and cosine ratios for the 30° angle.

$\sin 30° = \dfrac{\text{opp.}}{\text{hyp.}} = \dfrac{1}{2} = \underline{0.5000}$

$\cos 30° = \dfrac{\text{adj.}}{\text{hyp.}} = \dfrac{\sqrt{3}}{2} \approx \underline{0.8660}$

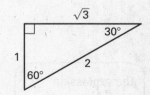

✓ **Checkpoint** Complete the following exercises.

4. In Example 5, suppose the angle of elevation is 40°. What are the new lengths x and y?

   $x \approx 12.9,\ y \approx 15.3$

5. Use a special right triangle to find the sine and cosine of a 60° angle.

   $\sin 60° \approx 0.8660$

   $\cos 60° = 0.5000$

Homework

Solve Right Triangles

Goal • Use inverse tangent, sine, and cosine ratios.

Your Notes

VOCABULARY

Solve a right triangle To solve a right triangle is to find the measures of all of its sides and angles.

> The expression "tan⁻¹ x" is read as "the inverse tangent of x."

INVERSE TRIGONOMETRIC RATIOS

Let ∠A be an acute angle.

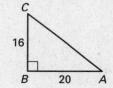

Inverse Tangent If tan $A = x$, then
$\tan^{-1} x = m\angle A$.

$\tan^{-1} \frac{BC}{AC} = m\angle A$

Inverse Sine If sin $A = y$, then
$\sin^{-1} y = m\angle A$.

$\sin^{-1} \frac{BC}{AB} = m\angle A$

Inverse Cosine If cos $A = z$, then
$\cos^{-1} z = m\angle A$.

$\cos^{-1} \frac{AC}{AB} = m\angle A$

Example 1 *Use an inverse tangent to find an angle measure*

Use a calculator to approximate the measure of ∠A to the nearest tenth of a degree.

Because tan $A = \dfrac{16}{20} = \dfrac{4}{5} = \underline{0.8}$,

$\tan^{-1}\underline{\ 0.8\ } = m\angle A$. Using a calculator,
$\tan^{-1}\underline{\ 0.8\ } \approx \underline{38.65980825\ \dots}$.

So, the measure of ∠A is approximately $\underline{38.7°}$.

✔ *Checkpoint* **Complete the following exercise.**

1. In Example 1, use a calculator and an inverse tangent to approximate $m\angle C$ to the nearest tenth of a degree.

$m\angle C \approx 51.3$

Example 2   *Use an inverse sine and an inverse cosine*

Let $\angle A$ and $\angle B$ be acute angles in two right triangles. Use a calculator to approximate the measures of $\angle A$ and $\angle B$ to the nearest tenth of a degree.

a. $\sin A = 0.76$ **b.** $\cos B = 0.17$

Solution

a. $m\angle A = \underline{\sin^{-1} 0.76}$ **b.** $m\angle B = \underline{\cos^{-1} 0.17}$

         $\approx \underline{49.5°}$ $\approx \underline{80.2°}$

Example 3   *Solve a right triangle*

Solve the right triangle. Round decimal answers to the nearest tenth.

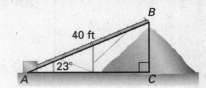

Solution

Step 1 Find $m\angle B$ by using the Triangle Sum Theorem.

$\underline{180°} = 90° + 23° + m\angle B$

$\underline{67°} = m\angle B$

Step 2 Approximate BC using a $\underline{\text{sine}}$ ratio.

$\underline{\sin 23°} = \dfrac{BC}{40}$ Write ratio for $\underline{\sin 23°}$.

$\underline{40 \cdot \sin 23°} = BC$ Multiply each side by $\underline{40}$.

$\underline{40 \cdot 0.3907} \approx BC$ Approximate $\underline{\sin 23°}$.

$\underline{15.6} \approx BC$ Simplify and round answer.

Step 3 Approximate AC using a $\underline{\text{cosine}}$ ratio.

$\underline{\cos 23°} = \dfrac{AC}{40}$ Write ratio for $\underline{\cos 23°}$.

$\underline{40 \cdot \cos 23°} = AC$ Multiply each side by $\underline{40}$.

$\underline{40 \cdot 0.9205} \approx AC$ Approximate $\underline{\cos 23°}$.

$\underline{36.8} \approx AC$ Simplify and round answer.

The angle measures are $\underline{23°}$, $\underline{67°}$, and $\underline{90°}$. The side lengths are $\underline{40}$ feet, about $\underline{15.6}$ feet, and about $\underline{36.8}$ feet.

Example 4 *Solve a real-world problem*

Model Train You are building a track for a model train. You want the track to incline from the first level to the second level, 4 inches higher, in 96 inches. Is the angle of elevation less than 3°?

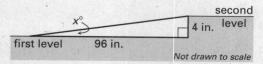

first level   96 in.   4 in.   second level

Not drawn to scale

Solution

Use the tangent and inverse tangent ratios to find the degree measure x of the incline.

$$\tan x° = \frac{\text{opp.}}{\text{adj.}} = \frac{4}{96} \approx \underline{\ 0.0417\ }$$

$$x \approx \underline{\ \tan^{-1} 0.0417\ } \approx \underline{\ 2.4\ }$$

The incline is about __2.4°__, so it __is less than__ 3°.

✔ **Checkpoint** Complete the following exercises.

2. Find $m\angle D$ to the nearest tenth of a degree if sin D = 0.48.

   $m\angle D \approx 28.7°$

3. Solve a right triangle that has a 50° angle and a 15 inch hypotenuse.

   Angles: 90°, 50°, and 40°; Side lengths: 15 in., about 9.6 in., and about 11.5 in.

Homework

4. In Example 4, suppose another incline rises 8 inches in 120 inches. Is the incline less than 3°?

   No, the incline is about 3.8°.

Words to Review

Give an example of the vocabulary word.

Pythagorean triple	Trigonometric ratio
3, 4, 5	sine, cosine, tangent
Tangent $\tan A = \dfrac{\text{opp. } \angle A}{\text{adj. to } \angle A}$	**Sine** $\sin A = \dfrac{\text{opp. } \angle A}{\text{hyp.}}$
Cosine $\cos A = \dfrac{\text{adj. to } \angle A}{\text{hyp.}}$	**Angle of elevation, Angle of depression**
Solve a right triangle To solve $\triangle ABC$, find a, b, c, $m\angle A$, $m\angle B$, and $m\angle C$. 	**Inverse tangent** $\tan^{-1} 0.5 \approx 26.6°$
Inverse sine $\sin^{-1} 0.5 = 30°$	**Inverse cosine** $\tan^{-1} 0.5 = 60°$

Review your notes and Chapter 7 by using the Chapter Review on pages 494–497 of your textbook.

8.1 Find Angle Measures in Polygons

Goal • Find angle measures in polygons.

Your Notes

> **VOCABULARY**
>
> **Diagonal** A diagonal of a polygon is a segment that joins two *nonconsecutive vertices*.

> **THEOREM 8.1: POLYGON INTERIOR ANGLES THEOREM**
>
> The sum of the measures of the interior angles of a convex *n*-gon is $(n - \underline{\;2\;}) \cdot \underline{\;180°\;}$.
>
>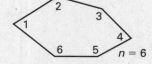
>
> $m\angle 1 + m\angle 2 + \cdots + m\angle n = (n - \underline{\;2\;}) \cdot \underline{\;180°\;}$
>
> **COROLLARY TO THEOREM 8.1: INTERIOR ANGLES OF A QUADRILATERAL**
>
> The sum of the measures of the interior angles of a quadrilateral is $\underline{\;360°\;}$.

> **Example 1** *Find the sum of angle measures in a polygon*
>
> Find the sum of the measures of the interior angles of a convex hexagon.
>
>
>
> **Solution**
>
> A hexagon has $\underline{\;6\;}$ sides. Use the Polygon Interior Angles Theorem.
>
> $(n - \underline{\;2\;}) \cdot \underline{\;180°\;} = (\underline{\;6\;} - \underline{\;2\;}) \cdot \underline{\;180°\;}$ **Substitute** $\underline{\;6\;}$ **for** *n.*
>
> $\qquad\qquad\qquad = \underline{\;4\;} \cdot \underline{\;180°\;}$ **Subtract.**
>
> $\qquad\qquad\qquad = \underline{\;720°\;}$ **Multiply.**
>
> The sum of the measures of the interior angles of a hexagon is $\underline{\;720°\;}$.

Your Notes

Example 2 *Find the number of sides of a polygon*

The sum of the measures of the interior angles of a convex polygon is 1260°. Classify the polygon by the number of sides.

Solution

Use the Polygon Interior Angles Theorem to write an equation involving the number of sides n. Then solve the equation to find the number of sides.

$(n - \underline{2}) \cdot \underline{180°} = \underline{1260°}$ **Polygon Interior Angles Theorem**

$n - \underline{2} = \underline{7}$ **Divide each side by** $\underline{180°}$.

$n = \underline{9}$ **Add** $\underline{2}$ **to each side.**

The polygon has $\underline{9}$ sides. It is a $\underline{nonagon}$.

Example 3 *Find an unknown interior angle measure*

Find the value of x in the diagram shown.

Solution

The polygon is a quadrilateral. Use the Corollary to the Polygon Interior Angles Theorem to write an equation involving x. Then solve the equation.

$x° + \underline{135°} + \underline{112°} + \underline{71°} = \underline{360°}$ **Corollary to Theorem 8.1**

$x + \underline{318} = \underline{360}$ **Combine like terms.**

$x = \underline{42}$ **Subtract** $\underline{318}$ **from each side.**

✓ *Checkpoint* **Complete the following exercise.**

1. Find the sum of the measures of the interior angles of the convex decagon.

   1440°

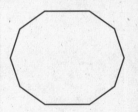

✔ *Checkpoint* Complete the following exercises.

2. The sum of the measures of the interior angles of a convex polygon is 1620°. Classify the polygon by the number of sides.

   11-gon

3. Use the diagram at the right. Find $m\angle K$ and $m\angle L$.

   $m\angle K = m\angle L = 129°$

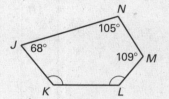

THEOREM 8.2: POLYGON EXTERIOR ANGLES THEOREM

The sum of the measures of the exterior angles of a convex polygon, one angle at each vertex, is ___360°___.

$m\angle1 + m\angle2 + \cdots + m\angle n =$ ___360°___

$n = 5$

Example 4 *Find unknown exterior angle measures*

Find the value of x in the diagram shown.

Solution

Use the Polygon Exterior Angles Theorem to write and solve an equation.

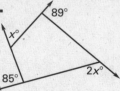

$x° +$ ___$2x°$___ $+$ ___$85°$___ $+$ ___$89°$___ $=$ ___$360°$___   **Polygon Exterior Angles Theorem.**

___3___ $x +$ ___174___ $=$ ___360___   **Combine like terms.**

$x =$ ___62___   **Solve for x.**

Example 5   *Find angle measures in regular polygons*

Lamps The base of a lamp is in the shape of a regular 15-gon. Find (a) the measure of each interior angle and (b) the measure of each exterior angle.

Solution

a. Use the Polygon Interior Angles Theorem to find the sum of the measures of the interior angles.

$$(n - \underline{2}) \cdot \underline{180°} = (\underline{15} - \underline{2}) \cdot \underline{180°}$$
$$= \underline{2340°}$$

Then find the measure of one interior angle. A regular 15-gon has 15 congruent interior angles.
Divide 2340° by 15 : 2340° ÷ 15 = 156° .

The measure of each interior angle in the 15-gon is 156° .

b. By the Polygon Exterior Angles Theorem, the sum of the measures of the exterior angles, one angle at each vertex, is 360° . Divide 360° by 15 :
 360° ÷ 15 = 24° .

The measure of each exterior angle in the 15-gon is 24° .

✔ *Checkpoint* **Complete the following exercises.**

4. A convex pentagon has exterior angles with measures 66°, 77°, 82°, and 62°. What is the measure of an exterior angle at the fifth vertex?

73°

5. Find the measure of (a) each interior angle and (b) each exterior angle of a regular nonagon.

a. 140°

b. 40°

Homework

8.2 Use Properties of Parallelograms

Goal • Find angle and side measures in parallelograms.

Your Notes

VOCABULARY

Parallelogram A parallelogram is a quadrilateral with both pairs of opposite sides parallel.

THEOREM 8.3

If a quadrilateral is a parallelogram, then its opposite sides are congruent.

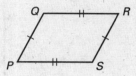

If *PQRS* is a parallelogram, then
$\overline{PQ} \cong \overline{RS}$ and $\overline{QR} \cong \overline{PS}$.

THEOREM 8.4

If a quadrilateral is a parallelogram, then its opposite angles are congruent.

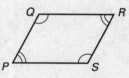

If *PQRS* is a parallelogram, then
$\angle P \cong \underline{\angle R}$ and $\underline{\angle Q} \cong \angle S$.

Example 1 *Use properties of parallelograms*

Find the values of *x* and *y*.

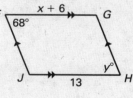

Solution

FGHJ is a parallelogram by the definition of a parallelogram. Use Theorem 8.3 to find the value of *x*.

$FG = \underline{HJ}$ Opposite sides of a ▱ are ≅.

$x + 6 = \underline{13}$ Substitute *x* + 6 for *FG* and _13_ for _HJ_.

$x = \underline{7}$ Subtract 6 from each side.

By Theorem 8.4, $\angle F \cong \underline{\angle H}$, or $m\angle F = \underline{m\angle H}$. So,
$y° = \underline{68°}$.

In ▱*FGHJ*, $x = \underline{7}$ and $y = \underline{68}$.

THEOREM 8.5

If a quadrilateral is a parallelogram, then its consecutive angles are ___supplementary___ .

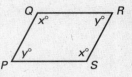

If *PQRS* is a parallelogram, then $x° + y° =$ ___180°___ .

Example 2 *Use properties of a parallelogram*

Gates As shown, a gate contains several parallelograms. Find $m\angle ADC$ when $m\angle DAB = 65°$.

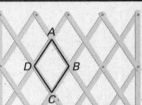

Solution

By Theorem 8.5, the consecutive angle pairs in ▱*ABCD* are ___supplementary___ . So, $m\angle ADC + m\angle DAB =$ ___180°___ . Because $m\angle DAB = 65°$, $m\angle ADC =$ ___180°___ $-$ ___65°___ $=$ ___115°___ .

✓ **Checkpoint** Find the indicated measure in ▱*KLMN* shown at the right.

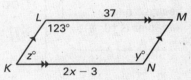

1. *x*	2. *y*
$x = 20$	$y = 123$

3. *z*

$z = 57$

THEOREM 8.6

If a quadrilateral is a parallelogram, then its diagonals __bisect__ each other.

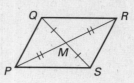

$\overline{QM} \cong \underline{\overline{SM}}$ and
$\overline{PM} \cong \underline{\overline{RM}}$

Example 3 *Use properties of a parallelogram*

The diagonals of □*STUV* intersect at point *W*. Find the coordinates of *W*.

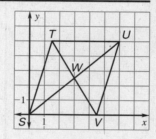

Solution

By Theorem 8.6, the diagonals of a parallelogram __bisect__ each other.
So, *W* is the __midpoint__ of the diagonals $\overline{TV}$ and $\overline{SU}$.
Use the __Midpoint Formula__ .

Coordinates of midpoint *W* of

$$\overline{SU} = \left(\frac{6+0}{2}, \frac{5+0}{2} \right) = \left(3, \frac{5}{2} \right)$$

In Example 3, you can use either diagonal to find the coordinates of *W*. Using $\overline{SU}$ simplifies calculations because one endpoint is (0, 0).

✔ *Checkpoint* **Complete the following exercises.**

4. The diagonals of □*VWXY* intersect at point *Z*. Find the coordinates of *Z*.

   $Z\left(\frac{7}{2}, 3\right)$

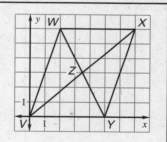

Homework

5. Given that □*FGHJ* is a parallelogram, find *MH* and *FH*.

   MH = 5, *FH* = 10

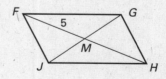

8.3 Show that a Quadrilateral is a Parallelogram

Goal • Use properties to identify parallelograms.

Your Notes

THEOREM 8.7

If both pairs of opposite __sides__ of a quadrilateral are congruent, then the quadrilateral is a parallelogram.

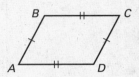

If $\overline{AB} \cong$ __$\overline{CD}$__ and $\overline{BC} \cong$ __$\overline{AD}$__ , then *ABCD* is a parallelogram.

THEOREM 8.8

If both pairs of opposite __angles__ of a quadrilateral are congruent, then the quadrilateral is a parallelogram.

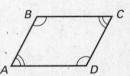

If $\angle A \cong$ __$\angle C$__ and $\angle B \cong$ __$\angle D$__ , then *ABCD* is a parallelogram.

Example 1 *Solve a real-world problem*

Basketball In the diagram at the right, $\overline{AB}$ and $\overline{DC}$ represent adjustable supports of a basketball hoop. *Explain* why $\overline{AD}$ is always parallel to $\overline{BC}$.

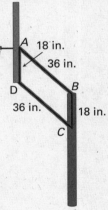

Solution

The shape of quadrilateral *ABCD* changes as the adjustable supports move, but its __side lengths__ do not change. Both pairs of opposite __sides__ are congruent, so *ABCD* is a parallelogram by __Theorem 8.7__ .

By the definition of a parallelogram, $\overline{AD} \parallel$ __$\overline{BC}$__ .

THEOREM 8.9

If one pair of opposite sides of a quadrilateral are __congruent__ and __parallel__, then the quadrilateral is a parallelogram.

If $\overline{BC}$ ∥ $\overline{AD}$ and $\overline{BC}$ ≅ $\overline{AD}$, then ABCD is a parallelogram.

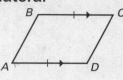

THEOREM 8.10

If the diagonals of a quadrilateral __bisect__ each other, then the quadrilateral is a parallelogram.

If $\overline{BD}$ and $\overline{AC}$ __bisect__ each other, then ABCD is a parallelogram.

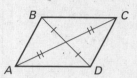

Example 2 *Identify a parallelogram*

Lights The headlights of a car have the shape shown at the right. *Explain* how you know that ∠B ≅ ∠D.

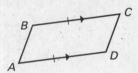

Solution

In the diagram, $\overline{BC}$ ∥ __$\overline{AD}$__ and $\overline{BC}$ ≅ __$\overline{AD}$__. By __Theorem 8.9__, quadrilateral ABCD is a parallelogram. By __Theorem 8.4__, you know that opposite angles of a parallelogram are congruent. So, ∠B ≅ __∠D__.

✔ *Checkpoint* **Complete the following exercises.**

1. In quadrilateral GHJK, m∠G = 55°, m∠H = 125°, and m∠J = 55°. Find m∠K. What theorem can you use to show that GHJK is a parallelogram?

   m∠K = 125°; Theorem 8.8

2. What theorem can you use to show that the quadrilateral is a parallelogram?

   Theorem 8.10

Example 3   *Use algebra with parallelograms*

For what value of *x* is quadrilateral
PQRS a parallelogram?

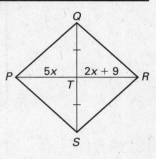

Solution

By Theorem 8.10, if the diagonals of
PQRS _bisect_ each other, then it is
a parallelogram. You are given that
$\overline{QT} \cong$ _$\overline{ST}$_ . Find *x* so that $\overline{PT} \cong$ _$\overline{RT}$_ .

$$PT = \underline{RT}$$ **Set the segment lengths equal.**

$$5x = \underline{2x + 9}$$ **Substitute 5x for *PT* and** _2x + 9_
                               for _RT_ .

$$\underline{3}\,x = \underline{9}$$ **Subtract** _2x_ **from each side.**

$$x = \underline{3}$$ **Divide each side by** _3_ .

When *x* = _3_ , *PT* = 5(_3_) = _15_ and
RT = 2(_3_) + 9 = _15_ .

Quadrilateral *PQRS* is a parallelogram when *x* = _3_ .

**CONCEPT SUMMARY: WAYS TO PROVE A
QUADRILATERAL IS A PARALLELOGRAM**

1. Show both pairs of opposite sides are
parallel. (**Definition**)

2. Show both pairs of opposite sides are
congruent. (**Theorem 8.7**)

3. Show both pairs of opposite angles are
congruent. (**Theorem 8.8**)

4. Show one pair of opposite sides are
congruent and parallel. (**Theorem 8.9**)

5. Show the diagonals bisect each other.
(**Theorem 8.10**)

Example 4   *Use coordinate geometry*

Show that quadrilateral *KLMN* is a parallelogram.

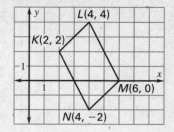

Solution

One way is to show that a pair of sides are congruent and parallel. Then apply <u>Theorem 8.9</u>.

First use the Distance Formula to show that $\overline{KL}$ and $\overline{MN}$ are <u>congruent</u>.

$KL = \sqrt{(4-2)^2 + (4-2)^2} = \sqrt{8}$

$MN = \sqrt{(6-4)^2 + [0-(-2)]^2} = \sqrt{8}$

Because $KL = MN = \sqrt{8}$, $\overline{KL} \cong \overline{MN}$.

Then use the slope formula to show that $\overline{KL} \parallel \overline{MN}$.

Slope of $\overline{KL} = \dfrac{\boxed{4-2}}{\boxed{4-2}} = \underline{1}$

Slope of $\overline{MN} = \dfrac{\boxed{0-(-2)}}{\boxed{6-4}} = \underline{1}$

$\overline{KL}$ and $\overline{MN}$ have the same slope, so they are <u>parallel</u>.

$\overline{KL}$ and $\overline{MN}$ are congruent and parallel. So, *KLMN* is a parallelogram by <u>Theorem 8.9</u>.

✓ *Checkpoint* **Complete the following exercises.**

3. For what value of *x* is quadrilateral *DFGH* a parallelogram?

<u>*x* = 3.5</u>

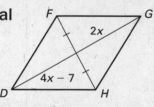

Homework

4. *Explain* another method that can be used to show that quadrilateral *KLMN* in Example 4 is a parallelogram.

Sample Answer: Draw the diagonals and find the point of intersection. Show the diagonals bisect each other and apply Theorem 8.10.

8.4 Properties of Rhombuses, Rectangles, and Squares

Goal • Use properties of rhombuses, rectangles, and squares.

VOCABULARY

Rhombus A rhombus is a parallelogram with four congruent sides.

Rectangle A rectangle is a parallelogram with four right angles.

Square A square is a parallelogram with four congruent sides and four right angles.

RHOMBUS COROLLARY

A quadrilateral is a rhombus if and only if it has four congruent <u>sides</u>.

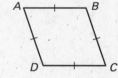

ABCD is a rhombus if and only if $\overline{AB} \cong \overline{BC} \cong \overline{CD} \cong \overline{AD}$.

RECTANGLE COROLLARY

A quadrilateral is a rectangle if and only if it has four <u>right angles</u>.

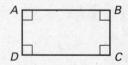

ABCD is a rectangle if and only if $\angle A$, $\angle B$, $\angle C$, and $\angle D$ are right angles.

SQUARE COROLLARY

A quadrilateral is a square if and only if it is a <u>rhombus</u> and a <u>rectangle</u>.

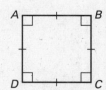

ABCD is a square if and only if $\overline{AB} \cong \overline{BC} \cong \overline{CD} \cong \overline{AD}$ and $\angle A$, $\angle B$, $\angle C$, and $\angle D$ are right angles.

Example 1   *Use properties of special quadrilaterals*

For any rhombus *RSTV*, decide whether the statement is always or sometimes true. Draw a sketch and explain your reasoning.

a. $\angle S \cong \angle V$ **b.** $\angle T \cong \angle V$

Solution

a. By definition, a rhombus is a parallelogram with four congruent _sides_. By Theorem 8.4, opposite angles of a parallelogram are _congruent_. So, $\angle S \cong \angle V$. The statement is _always_ true.

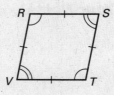

b. If rhombus *RSTV* is a _square_, then all four angles are congruent right angles. So $\angle T \cong \angle V$ if *RSTV* is a _square_. Because not all rhombuses are also _squares_, the statement is _sometimes_ true.

Example 2   *Classify special quadrilaterals*

Classify the special quadrilateral. *Explain* your reasoning.

The quadrilateral has four congruent _sides_. One of the angles is not a _right angle_, so the rhombus is not also a _square_. By the Rhombus Corollary, the quadrilateral is a _rhombus_.

✔ *Checkpoint* **Complete the following exercises.**

---

1. For any square *CDEF*, is it *always* or *sometimes* true that $\overline{CD} \cong \overline{DE}$? *Explain* your reasoning.

Always; a square has four congruent sides.

---

2. A quadrilateral has four congruent sides and four congruent angles. Classify the quadrilateral.

square

Your Notes

THEOREM 8.11

A parallelogram is a rhombus if and only if its diagonals are <u>perpendicular</u>.

▱ABCD is a rhombus if and only if $\overline{AC} \perp \overline{BD}$.

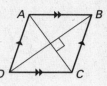

THEOREM 8.12

A parallelogram is a rhombus if and only if each diagonal bisects a pair of opposite angles.

▱ABCD is a rhombus if and only if $\overline{AC}$ bisects ∠ <u>BCD</u> and ∠ <u>BAD</u> and $\overline{BD}$ bisects ∠ <u>ABC</u> and ∠ <u>ADC</u>.

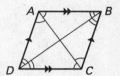

THEOREM 8.13

A parallelogram is a rectangle if and only if its diagonals are <u>congruent</u>.

▱ABCD is a rectangle if and only if $\overline{AC} \cong \overline{BD}$.

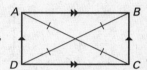

Example 3 · *List properties of special parallelograms*

Sketch rhombus *FGHJ*. List everything you know about it.

Solution

By definition, you need to draw a figure with the following properties:

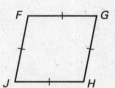

- The figure is a <u>parallelogram</u>.
- The figure has four congruent <u>sides</u>.

Because *FGHJ* is a parallelogram, it has these properties:

- Opposite sides are <u>parallel</u> and <u>congruent</u>.
- Opposite angles are <u>congruent</u>. Consecutive angles are <u>supplementary</u>.
- Diagonals <u>bisect</u> each other.

By Theorem 8.11, the diagonals of *FGHJ* are <u>perpendicular</u>. By Theorem 8.12, each diagonal bisects a pair of <u>opposite angles</u>.

Example 4 **Solve a real-world problem**

Framing You are building a frame for a painting. The measurements of the frame are shown at the right.

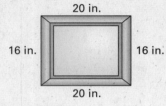
20 in.
16 in. 16 in.
20 in.

a. The frame must be a rectangle. Given the measurements in the diagram, can you assume that it is? *Explain.*

b. You measure the diagonals of the frame. The diagonals are about 25.6 inches. What can you conclude about the shape of the frame?

Solution

a. No, you cannot. The boards on opposite sides are the same length, so they form a _parallelogram_. But you do not know whether the angles are _right angles_.

b. By Theorem 8.13, the diagonals of a rectangle are _congruent_. The diagonals of the frame are _congruent_, so the frame forms a _rectangle_.

✔ *Checkpoint* **Complete the following exercises.**

3. Sketch rectangle *WXYZ*. List everything that you know about it.

W   X

Z   Y

WXYZ is a parallelogram with four right angles. Opposite sides are parallel and congruent. Opposite angles are congruent and consecutive angles are supplementary. The diagonals are congruent and bisect each other.

Homework

4. Suppose the diagonals of the frame in Example 4 are not congruent.

Could the frame still be a rectangle? *Explain.*

No; by Theorem 8.13, a rectangle must have congruent diagonals.

Use Properties of Trapezoids and Kites

Goal • Use properties of trapezoids and kites.

Your Notes

VOCABULARY

Trapezoid A trapezoid is a quadrilateral with exactly one pair of parallel sides.

Bases of a trapezoid The parallel sides of a trapezoid are the bases.

Base angles of a trapezoid A trapezoid has two pairs of base angles. Each pair shares a base as a side.

Legs of a trapezoid The nonparallel sides of a trapezoid are the legs.

Isosceles trapezoid An isosceles trapezoid is a trapezoid in which the legs are congruent.

Midsegment of a trapezoid The midsegment of a trapezoid is the segment that connects the midpoints of its legs.

Kite A kite is a quadrilateral that has two pairs of consecutive congruent sides, but opposite sides are not congruent.

Example 1   *Use a coordinate plane*

Show that *CDEF* is a trapezoid.

Solution

Compare the slopes of opposite sides.

Slope of $\overline{DE}$ = $\dfrac{4-3}{4-1}$ = $\dfrac{1}{3}$

Slope of $\overline{CF}$ = $\dfrac{2-0}{6-0}$ = $\dfrac{2}{6}$ = $\dfrac{1}{3}$

The slopes of $\overline{DE}$ and $\overline{CF}$ are the same, so $\overline{DE} \parallel \overline{CF}$.

Slope of $\overline{EF}$ = $\dfrac{2-4}{6-4}$ = $\dfrac{-2}{2}$ = $\underline{-1}$

Slope of $\overline{CD}$ = $\dfrac{3-0}{1-0}$ = $\dfrac{3}{1}$ = $\underline{3}$

The slopes of $\overline{EF}$ and $\overline{CD}$ are not the same, so $\overline{EF}$ is <u>not parallel</u> to $\overline{CD}$.

Because quadrilateral *CDEF* has exactly one pair of <u>parallel sides</u>, it is a trapezoid.

THEOREM 8.14

If a trapezoid is isosceles, then each pair of base angles is <u>congruent</u>.

If trapezoid *ABCD* is isosceles, then $\angle A \cong \angle \underline{D}$ and $\angle \underline{B} \cong \angle C$.

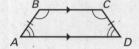

THEOREM 8.15

If a trapezoid has a pair of congruent <u>base angles</u>, then it is an isosceles trapezoid.

If $\angle A \cong \angle D$ (or if $\angle B \cong \angle C$), then trapezoid *ABCD* is isosceles.

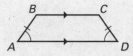

THEOREM 8.16

A trapezoid is isosceles if and only if its diagonals are <u>congruent</u>.

Trapezoid *ABCD* is isosceles if and only if $\overline{AC} \cong \overline{BD}$.

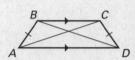

Example 2   *Use properties of isosceles trapezoids*

Kitchen A shelf fitting into a cupboard in the corner of a kitchen is an isosceles trapezoid. Find $m\angle N$, $m\angle L$, and $m\angle M$.

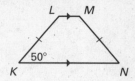

Solution

Step 1 Find $m\angle N$. *KLMN* is an __isosceles trapezoid__ , so $\angle N$ and $\angle$ _K_ are congruent base angles, and $m\angle N = m\angle$ _K_ = _50°_ .

Step 2 Find $m\angle L$. Because $\angle K$ and $\angle L$ are consecutive interior angles formed by $\overleftrightarrow{KL}$ intersecting two parallel lines, they are __supplementary__ . So, $m\angle L =$ _180°_ $-$ _50°_ = _130°_ .

Step 3 Find $m\angle M$. Because $\angle M$ and $\angle$ _L_ are a pair of base angles, they are congruent, and $m\angle M = m\angle$ _L_ = _130°_ .

So, $m\angle N =$ _50°_ , $m\angle L =$ _130°_ , and $m\angle M =$ _130°_ .

✔ *Checkpoint* **Complete the following exercises.**

1. In Example 1, suppose the coordinates of point *E* are (7, 5). What type of quadrilateral is *CDEF*? *Explain*.

   Parallelogram; opposite pairs of sides are parallel.

2. Find $m\angle C$, $m\angle A$, and $m\angle D$ in the trapezoid shown.

   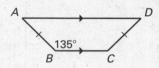

   $m\angle C = 135°$, $m\angle A = 45°$, $m\angle D = 45°$

THEOREM 8.17: MIDSEGMENT THEOREM FOR TRAPEZOIDS

The midsegment of a trapezoid is parallel to each base and its length is one half the sum of the lengths of the bases.

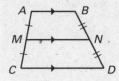

If $\overline{MN}$ is the midsegment of trapezoid $ABCD$, then

$\overline{MN} \parallel \underline{\ AB\ }$, $\overline{MN} \parallel \underline{\ DC\ }$, and $MN = \frac{1}{2}(\underline{\ AB\ } + \underline{\ CD\ })$.

Example 3 *Use the midsegment of a trapezoid*

In the diagram, $\overline{MN}$ is the midsegment of trapezoid $PQRS$. Find MN.

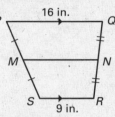

Solution

Use Theorem 8.17 to find MN.

$MN = \frac{1}{2}(\underline{\ PQ\ } + \underline{\ SR\ })$ Apply Theorem 8.17.

$\quad = \frac{1}{2}(\underline{\ 16\ } + \underline{\ 9\ })$ Substitute $\underline{\ 16\ }$ for PQ and $\underline{\ 9\ }$ for SR.

$\quad = \underline{\ 12.5\ }$ Simplify.

The length MN is $\underline{\ 12.5\ }$ inches.

✔ *Checkpoint* Complete the following exercise.

3. Find MN in the trapezoid at the right.

   $MN = 21$ ft

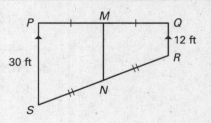

THEOREM 8.18

If a quadrilateral is a kite, then its diagonals are <u>perpendicular</u>.

If quadrilateral *ABCD* is a kite, then <u>$\overline{AC}$</u> ⊥ <u>$\overline{BD}$</u>.

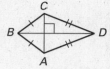

THEOREM 8.19

If a quadrilateral is a kite, then exactly one pair of opposite angles are congruent.

If quadrilateral *ABCD* is a kite and $\overline{BC} \cong \overline{BA}$, then ∠A <u>$\cong$</u> ∠C and ∠B <u>$\not\cong$</u> ∠D.

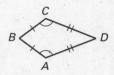

Example 4   *Apply Theorem 8.19*

Find *m*∠T in the kite shown at the right.

Solution

By Theorem 8.19, *QRST* has exactly one pair of <u>congruent</u> opposite angles. Because ∠Q $\not\cong$ ∠S, ∠<u>R</u> and ∠T must be congruent. So, *m*∠<u>R</u> = *m*∠T. Write and solve an equation to find *m*∠T.

$m∠T + m∠R +$ <u>70°</u> $+$ <u>88°</u> $=$ <u>360°</u>   **Corollary to Theorem 8.1**

$m∠T + m∠T +$ <u>70°</u> $+$ <u>88°</u> $=$ <u>360°</u>   **Substitute *m*∠T for *m*∠R.**

<u>2</u> $(m∠T) +$ <u>158°</u> $=$ <u>360°</u>   **Combine like terms.**

$m∠T =$ <u>101°</u>   **Solve for *m*∠T.**

Homework

✓ *Checkpoint* **Complete the following exercise.**

4. Find *m*∠G in the kite shown at the right.

$m∠G = 100°$

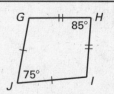

8.6 Identify Special Quadrilaterals

Goal • Identify special quadrilaterals.

Your Notes

Example 1 *Identify quadrilaterals*

Quadrilateral *ABCD* has both pairs of opposite sides congruent. What types of quadrilaterals meet this condition?

Solution

There are many possibilities.

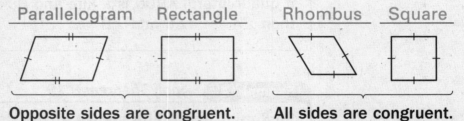

Parallelogram   Rectangle   Rhombus   Square

Opposite sides are congruent.   All sides are congruent.

✔ **Checkpoint** Complete the following exercise.

1. Quadrilateral *JKLM* has both pairs of opposite angles congruent. What types of quadrilaterals meet this condition?

   parallelogram, rectangle, square, rhombus

Example 2 *Identify a quadrilateral*

> In Example 2, *ABCD* is shaped like a square. But you must rely only on marked information when you interpret a diagram.

What is the most specific name for quadrilateral *ABCD*?

Solution

The diagram shows that both pairs of opposite sides are congruent. By Theorem 8.7, *ABCD* is a _parallelogram_ . All sides are congruent, so *ABCD* is a _rhombus_ by definition.

Squares are also rhombuses. However, there is no information given about the angle measures of *ABCD*. So, you cannot determine whether it is a _square_ .

Your Notes

Example 3 *Identify a quadrilateral*

Is enough information given in the diagram to show that quadrilateral FGHJ is an isosceles trapezoid? Explain.

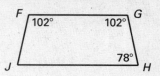

Solution

Step 1 **Show** that *FGHJ* is a _trapezoid_ . ∠*G* and ∠*H* are _supplementary_ but ∠*F* and ∠*G* are not. So, _FG_ ∥ _HJ_ , but *FJ* is not _parallel_ to *GH*. By definition, *FGHJ* is a _trapezoid_ .

Step 2 **Show** that trapezoid *FGHJ* is _isosceles_ . ∠*F* and ∠*G* are a pair of congruent _base angles_ . So, *FGHJ* is an _isosceles trapezoid_ by Theorem 8.15.

Yes, the diagram is sufficient to show that *FGHJ* is an isosceles trapezoid.

✔ **Checkpoint Complete the following exercises.**

2. **What is the most specific name for quadrilateral QRST? Explain your reasoning.**

Kite; there are two pairs of consecutive congruent sides.

3. **Is enough information given in the diagram to show that quadrilateral BCDE is a rectangle? Explain.**

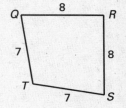

Yes; you know that *m∠D* = 90° by the Triangle Sum Theorem. Both pairs of opposite angles are congruent, so *BCDE* is a parallelogram by Theorem 8.8. By definition, *BCDE* is a rectangle.

Homework

Words to Review

Give an example of the vocabulary word.

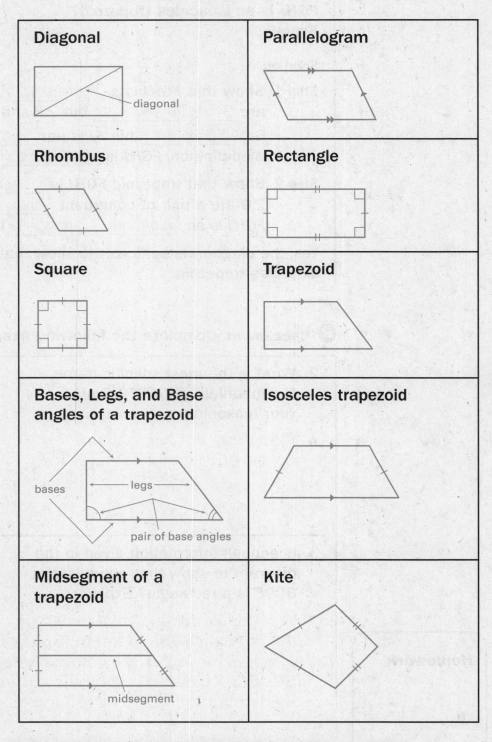

Diagonal	Parallelogram
diagonal	
Rhombus	**Rectangle**
Square	**Trapezoid**
Bases, Legs, and Base angles of a trapezoid	**Isosceles trapezoid**
bases legs pair of base angles	
Midsegment of a trapezoid	**Kite**
midsegment	

Review your notes and Chapter 8 by using the Chapter Review on pages 560–563 of your textbook.

9.1 Translate Figures and Use Vectors

Goal • Use a vector to translate a figure.

VOCABULARY

Image An image is a new figure produced from the transformation of a figure.

Preimage A preimage is the original figure in the transformation of a figure.

Isometry An isometry is a transformation that preserves length and angle measure.

Vector A vector is a quantity that has both direction and magnitude, or size.

Initial point The initial point of a vector is the starting point of the vector.

Terminal point The terminal point of a vector is the ending point of the vector.

Horizontal component The horizontal component describes the left and right direction of a vector.

Vertical component The vertical component describes the up and down direction of a vector.

Component form The component form of a vector combines the horizontal and vertical components.

> You can use *prime notation* to name an image. For example, if the preimage is △*ABC*, then its image is △*A'B'C'*, read as *"triangle A prime, B prime, C prime."*

Example 1   *Translate a figure in the coordinate plane*

Graph quadrilateral *ABCD* with vertices $A(-2, 6)$, $B(2, 4)$, $C(2, 1)$, and $D(-2, 3)$. Find the image of each vertex after the translation $(x, y) \rightarrow (x + 3, y - 3)$. Then graph the image using prime notation.

Solution

First, draw *ABCD*. Find the translation of each vertex by __adding__ 3 to its *x*-coordinate and __subtracting__ 3 from its *y*-coordinate. Then graph the image.

$$(x, y) \rightarrow (x + 3, y - 3)$$

$A(-2, 6) \rightarrow A'(\underline{\;1, 3\;})$

$B(2, 4) \rightarrow B'(\underline{\;5, 1\;})$

$C(2, 1) \rightarrow C'(\underline{\;5, -2\;})$

$D(-2, 3) \rightarrow D'(\underline{\;1, 0\;})$

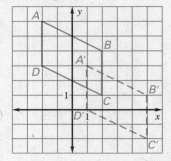

Example 2   *Write a translation rule and verify congruence*

Write a rule for the translation of △*ABC* to △*A'B'C'*. Then verify that the transformation is an isometry.

Solution

To go from *A* to *A'*, move 3 units __left__ and 2 units __up__. So, a rule for the translation is $(x, y) \rightarrow (\underline{\;x - 3, y + 2\;})$.

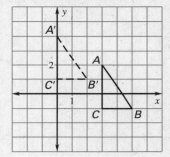

Use the SAS Congruence Postulate. Notice that $CB = C'B' = \underline{\;2\;}$, and $AC = A'C' = \underline{\;3\;}$. The slopes of $\overline{CB}$ and $\overline{C'B'}$ are __0__, and the slopes of $\overline{CA}$ and $\overline{C'A'}$ are __undefined__, so the sides are __perpendicular__. Therefore, $\angle C$ and $\angle C'$ are __congruent right angles__. So, △*ABC* $\cong$ △*A'B'C'*. The translation is an isometry.

THEOREM 9.1: TRANSLATION THEOREM

A translation is an isometry.

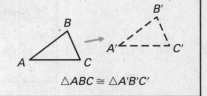

$$\triangle ABC \cong \triangle A'B'C'$$

✓ *Checkpoint* **Complete the following exercises.**

1. Draw △*PQR* with vertices *P*(4, 2), *Q*(6, 2), and
   R(4, −2). Find the image of each vertex after the
   translation (*x, y*) → (*x* − 4, *y* + 1). Graph the image
   using prime notation.

   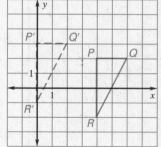

   P′(0, 3)

   Q′(2, 3)

   R′(0, −1)

2. In Example 2, write a rule to translate △*A′B′C′* back
   to △*ABC*.

   (*x, y*) → (*x* + 3, *y* − 2)

VECTORS

The diagram shows a vector named $\overrightarrow{FG}$, read as
"vector *FG*."

The initial point,
or starting
point, of the
vector is *F* .

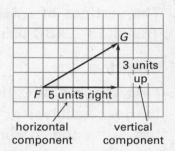

The terminal
point, or ending
point, of the
vector is *G* .

Use brackets
to write the
component form
of the vector ⟨*r, s*⟩.
Use parentheses
to write the
coordinates of the
point (*p, q*).

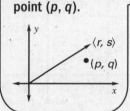

The component form of a vector combines the
horizontal and vertical components. So, the component
form of $\overrightarrow{FG}$ is ⟨5, 3⟩ .

Example 3 *Identify vector components*

Name the vector and write its component form.

a.

b.

Solution

a. The vector is $\overrightarrow{GH}$. From initial point _G_ to terminal point _H_ , you move _5_ units _right_ and _2_ units _down_ . So, the component form is $\langle 5, -2 \rangle$.

b. The vector is $\overrightarrow{RS}$. From initial point _R_ to terminal point _S_ , you move _7_ units _left_ and _0_ units _vertically_ . So, the component form is $\langle -7, 0 \rangle$.

✔ *Checkpoint* **Name the vector and write its component form.**

3.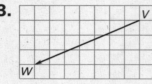

$\overrightarrow{VW}$; $\langle -7, -3 \rangle$

4.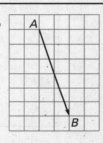

$\overrightarrow{AB}$; $\langle 2, -6 \rangle$

Example 4 *Use a vector to translate a figure*

The vertices of △*ABC* are *A*(0, 4), *B*(2, 3), and *C*(1, 0). Translate △*ABC* using the vector $\langle -4, 1 \rangle$.

> Notice that the vector can have different initial points. The vector describes only the direction and magnitude of the translation.

Solution

First, graph △*ABC*. Use $\langle -4, 1 \rangle$ to move each vertex _4_ units to the _left_ and _1_ unit _up_ . Label the image vertices. Draw △*A'B'C'*. Notice that the vectors drawn from preimage to image vertices are _parallel_ .

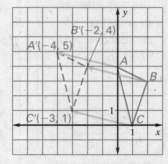

Example 5   *Solve a multi-step problem*

Construction A car heads out from point *A* toward point *D*. The car encounters construction at *B*, 8 miles east and 12 miles south of its starting point. The detour route leads the car to point *C*, as shown.

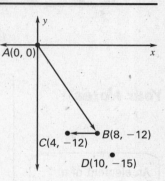

a. Write the component form of $\overrightarrow{AB}$.

b. Write the component form of $\overrightarrow{BC}$.

c. Write the component form of the vector that describes the straight line path from the car's current position *C* to its intended destination *D*.

a. The component form of the vector from *A*(0, 0) to *B*(8, −12) is
$$\overrightarrow{AB} = \underline{\langle 8 - 0, -12 - 0 \rangle} = \underline{\langle 8, -12 \rangle}.$$

b. The component form of the vector from *B*(8, −12) to *C*(4, −12) is
$$\overrightarrow{BC} = \underline{\langle 4 - 8, -12 - (-12) \rangle} = \underline{\langle -4, 0 \rangle}.$$

c. The car is currently at point *C* and needs to travel to *D*. The component form of the vector from *C*(4, −12) to *D*(10, −15) is
$$\overrightarrow{CD} = \underline{\langle 10 - 4, -15 - (-12) \rangle} = \underline{\langle 6, -3 \rangle}.$$

✔ *Checkpoint* **Complete the following exercises.**

5. The vertices of △*ABC* are *A*(−1, −1), *B*(0, 2), and *C*(1, −1). Translate △*ABC* using the vector ⟨5, 2⟩.

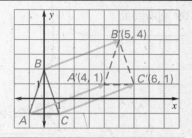

Homework

6. In Example 5, suppose there is no construction. Write the component form of the vector that describes the straight path from the car's starting point *A* to its final destination *D*.

⟨10, −15⟩

9.2 Use Properties of Matrices

Goal • Perform translations using matrix operations.

Your Notes

VOCABULARY

Matrix A matrix is a rectangular arrangement of numbers in rows and columns.

> An element of a matrix may also be called an *entry*.

Element Each number in a matrix is called an element.

Dimensions The dimensions of a matrix are the numbers of rows and columns.

Example 1   *Represent figures using matrices*

Write a matrix to represent the point or polygon.

a. Point *A*

b. Quadrilateral *ABCD*

Solution

a. Point matrix for *A*

$$\begin{bmatrix} -3 \\ 0 \end{bmatrix}$$ ← *x*-coordinate
← *y*-coordinate

> The columns in a polygon matrix follow the consecutive order of the vertices of the polygon.

b. Polygon matrix for *ABCD*

$$\begin{matrix} A & B & C & D \end{matrix}$$
$$\begin{bmatrix} -3 & 0 & 2 & -1 \\ 0 & 3 & 1 & -1 \end{bmatrix}$$ ← *x*-coordinates
← *y*-coordinates

✓ *Checkpoint* Complete the following exercise.

1. Write a matrix to represent △*RST* with vertices *R*(−5, −4), *S*(−1, 2), and *T*(3, 1).

$$\begin{matrix} R & S & T \end{matrix}$$
$$\begin{bmatrix} -5 & -1 & 3 \\ -4 & 2 & 1 \end{bmatrix}$$

Your Notes

Example 2 Add and subtract matrices

a. $\begin{bmatrix} 4 & -2 \\ 2 & -3 \end{bmatrix} + \begin{bmatrix} 1 & 2 \\ 5 & -6 \end{bmatrix} = \begin{bmatrix} 4+1 & -2+2 \\ 2+5 & -3+(-6) \end{bmatrix}$

$= \begin{bmatrix} 5 & 0 \\ 7 & -9 \end{bmatrix}$

b. $\begin{bmatrix} 7 & 4 & 5 \\ 1 & -2 & 8 \end{bmatrix} - \begin{bmatrix} 3 & -6 & 5 \\ 0 & 7 & 1 \end{bmatrix}$

$= \begin{bmatrix} 7-3 & 4-(-6) & 5-5 \\ 1-0 & -2-7 & 8-1 \end{bmatrix}$

$= \begin{bmatrix} 4 & 10 & 0 \\ 1 & -9 & 7 \end{bmatrix}$

Example 3 Represent a translation using matrices

The matrix $\begin{bmatrix} 2 & 3 & 4 \\ -3 & 2 & 0 \end{bmatrix}$ represents $\triangle ABC$. Find the image matrix that represents the translation of $\triangle ABC$ 4 units left and 1 unit down. Then graph $\triangle ABC$ and its image.

Solution

The translation matrix is $\begin{bmatrix} -4 & -4 & -4 \\ -1 & -1 & -1 \end{bmatrix}$.

Add this to the polygon matrix for the preimage to find the image matrix.

$\begin{bmatrix} -4 & -4 & -4 \\ -1 & -1 & -1 \end{bmatrix} + \begin{matrix} A & B & C \\ \begin{bmatrix} 2 & 3 & 4 \\ -3 & 2 & 0 \end{bmatrix} \end{matrix} = \begin{matrix} A' & B' & C' \\ \begin{bmatrix} -2 & -1 & 0 \\ -4 & 1 & -1 \end{bmatrix} \end{matrix}$

Translation matrix   **Polygon matrix**   **Image matrix**

> In order to add two matrices, they must have the same dimensions, so the translation matrix here must have three columns like the polygon matrix.

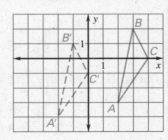

Copyright © McDougal Littell/Houghton Mifflin Company.

Lesson 9.2 • **Geometry Notetaking Guide**   **227**

Example 4   *Multiply matrices*

Multiply $\begin{bmatrix} 0 & 4 \\ 5 & 2 \end{bmatrix} \begin{bmatrix} -4 & 1 \\ 8 & -3 \end{bmatrix}$.

Solution

The matrices are both 2 × 2, so their product is defined. Use the following steps to find the elements of the product matrix.

Step 1 **Multiply** the numbers in the __first row__ of the first matrix by the numbers in the __first column__ of the second matrix. Put the result in the first row, first column of the product matrix.

$$\begin{bmatrix} 0 & 4 \\ 5 & 2 \end{bmatrix} \begin{bmatrix} -4 & 1 \\ 8 & -3 \end{bmatrix} = \begin{bmatrix} 0(-4) + 4(8) & ? \\ ? & ? \end{bmatrix}$$

Step 2 **Multiply** the numbers in the __first row__ of the first matrix by the numbers in the __second column__ of the second matrix. Put the result in the first row, second column of the product matrix.

$$\begin{bmatrix} 0 & 4 \\ 5 & 2 \end{bmatrix} \begin{bmatrix} -4 & 1 \\ 8 & -3 \end{bmatrix} = \begin{bmatrix} 0(-4) + 4(8) & 0(1) + 4(-3) \\ ? & ? \end{bmatrix}$$

Step 3 **Multiply** the numbers in the __second row__ of the first matrix by the numbers in the __first column__ of the second matrix. Put the result in the second row, first column of the product matrix.

$$\begin{bmatrix} 0 & 4 \\ 5 & 2 \end{bmatrix} \begin{bmatrix} -4 & 1 \\ 8 & -3 \end{bmatrix} = \begin{bmatrix} 0(-4) + 4(8) & 0(1) + 4(-3) \\ 5(-4) + 2(8) & ? \end{bmatrix}$$

Step 4 **Multiply** the numbers in the __second row__ of the first matrix by the numbers in the __second column__ of the second matrix. Put the result in the second row, second column of the product matrix.

$$\begin{bmatrix} 0 & 4 \\ 5 & 2 \end{bmatrix} \begin{bmatrix} -4 & 1 \\ 8 & -3 \end{bmatrix} = \begin{bmatrix} 0(-4) + 4(8) & 0(1) - 4(-3) \\ 5(-4) + 2(8) & 5(1) + 2(-3) \end{bmatrix}$$

Step 5 **Simplify** the product matrix.

$$\begin{bmatrix} 0 & 4 \\ 5 & 2 \end{bmatrix} \begin{bmatrix} -4 & 1 \\ 8 & -3 \end{bmatrix} = \begin{bmatrix} 32 & -12 \\ -4 & -1 \end{bmatrix}$$

✓ *Checkpoint* **Complete the following exercises.**

2. Subtract $\begin{bmatrix} 3 & -5 \\ 8 & -4 \end{bmatrix} - \begin{bmatrix} 9 & 7 \\ -3 & 1 \end{bmatrix}$.

$\begin{bmatrix} -6 & -12 \\ 11 & -5 \end{bmatrix}$

3. The matrix $\begin{bmatrix} -3 & -1 & 0 \\ -1 & 3 & 0 \end{bmatrix}$ represents $\triangle ABC$. Find the image matrix that represents the translation of $\triangle ABC$ 3 units right and 2 units up. Then graph $\triangle ABC$ and its image.

$\begin{bmatrix} 0 & 2 & 3 \\ 1 & 5 & 2 \end{bmatrix}$

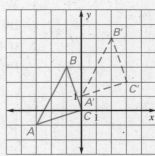

4. Multiply $\begin{bmatrix} 6 & 3 \\ 2 & -1 \end{bmatrix} \begin{bmatrix} 1 & 0 \\ 0 & -1 \end{bmatrix}$.

$\begin{bmatrix} 6 & -3 \\ 2 & 1 \end{bmatrix}$

Example 5 *Solve a real-world problem*

Hockey A men's hockey team *m* needs 7 sticks, 30 pucks, and 4 helmets. A women's team *w* needs 5 sticks, 25 pucks, and 5 helmets. A hockey stick costs $30, a puck costs $4, and a helmet costs $50. Use matrix multiplication to find the total cost of equipment for each team.

Solution

Write equipment needs and costs per item in matrix form. You will use matrix multiplication, so form the matrices so that the number of columns of the <u>equipment</u> matrix matches the number of rows of the <u>cost per item</u> matrix.

> You could solve this problem arithmetically, multiplying the number of sticks by the price of sticks, and so on, then adding the costs for each team.

$$\textbf{Equipment} \quad \cdot \quad \textbf{Cost} \;=\; \textbf{Total Cost}$$

$$
\begin{array}{c}
\text{Sticks Pucks Helmets} \\
\begin{array}{c} m \\ w \end{array}
\begin{bmatrix} 7 & 30 & 4 \\ 5 & 25 & 5 \end{bmatrix}
\end{array}
\cdot
\begin{array}{c}
\text{Dollars} \\
\begin{array}{c} \text{Stick} \\ \text{Puck} \\ \text{Helmet} \end{array}
\begin{bmatrix} 30 \\ 4 \\ 50 \end{bmatrix}
\end{array}
=
\begin{array}{c}
\text{Dollars} \\
\begin{array}{c} m \\ w \end{array}
\begin{bmatrix} ? \\ ? \end{bmatrix}
\end{array}
$$

You can find the total cost of equipment for each team by multiplying the equipment matrix by the cost per item matrix. The equipment matrix is <u>2</u> × <u>3</u> and the cost per item matrix is <u>3</u> × <u>1</u>, so their product is a <u>2</u> × <u>1</u> matrix.

$$
\begin{bmatrix} 7 & 30 & 4 \\ 5 & 25 & 5 \end{bmatrix}
\begin{bmatrix} 30 \\ 4 \\ 50 \end{bmatrix}
=
\begin{bmatrix} 7(30) + 30(4) + 4(50) \\ 5(30) + 25(4) + 5(50) \end{bmatrix}
=
\begin{bmatrix} 530 \\ 500 \end{bmatrix}
$$

The total cost of equipment for the men's team is <u>$530</u>, and the total cost for the women's team is <u>$500</u>.

✔ *Checkpoint* **Complete the following exercise.**

5. In Example 5, find the total costs if a stick costs $50, a puck costs $2, and a helmet costs $70.

Men's team: $690, Women's team: $650

Homework

Perform Reflections

Goal • Reflect a figure in any given line.

Your Notes

> **VOCABULARY**
> _____
>
> **Line of reflection** In a reflection, the mirror line is called the line of reflection.

Example 1 *Graph reflections in horizontal and vertical lines*

The vertices of △*ABC* are *A*(1, 2), *B*(3, 0), and *C*(5, 3). Graph the reflection of △*ABC* described.

a. In the line *n*: *x* = 2   **b.** In the line *m*: *y* = 3

Solution

a. Point *A* is 1 unit __left__ of *n*, so its reflection *A′* is 1 unit __right__ of *n* at (_3_ , _2_). Also, *B′* is 1 unit __left__ of *n* at (_1_ , _0_), and *C′* is 3 units __left__ of *n* at (_−1_ , _3_).

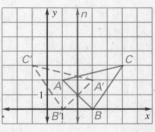

b. Point *A* is 1 unit __below__ *m*, so *A′* is 1 unit __above__ *m* at (_1_ , _4_). Also, *B′* is 3 units __above__ *m* at (_3_ , _6_). Because point *C* is on line *m*, you know that *C* = __C′__ .

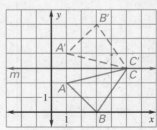

✔ *Checkpoint* Complete the following exercise.

> **1.** Graph the reflection of △*ABC* from Example 1 in the line *y* = 2.

Example 2   *Graph a reflection in y = x*

The endpoints of $\overline{CD}$ are C(−2, 2) and D(1, 2). Reflect the segment in the line y = x. Graph the segment and its image.

Solution

> The product of the slopes of perpendicular lines is −1.

The slope of y = x is ___1___ . The segment from C to its image, $\overline{CC'}$, is __perpendicular__ to the line of reflection y = x, so the slope of $\overline{CC'}$ will be __−1__ (because 1(−1) = __−1__). From C, move __2__ units right and __2__ units down to y = x. From that point, move __2__ units right and __2__ units down to locate C'(_2_ , _−2_).

The slope of $\overline{DD'}$ will also be __−1__ . From D, move __0.5__ units right and __0.5__ units down to y = x. Then move __0.5__ units right and __0.5__ units down to locate D'(_2_ , _1_).

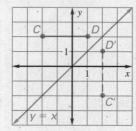

COORDINATE RULES FOR REFLECTIONS

- If (a, b) is reflected in the x-axis, its image is the point (_a_ , _−b_).

- If (a, b) is reflected in the y-axis, its image is the point (_−a_ , _b_).

- If (a, b) is reflected in the line y = x, its image is the point (_b_ , _a_).

- If (a, b) is reflected in the line y = −x, its image is the point (_−b_ , _−a_).

Example 3   *Graph a reflection in y = −x*

Reflect $\overline{CD}$ from Example 2 in the line $y = -x$. Graph $\overline{CD}$ and its image.

Solution

Use the coordinate rule for reflecting in the line $y = -x$.

$$(a, b) \rightarrow (-b, -a)$$

$C(-2, 2) \rightarrow C'(\ \underline{-2}\ ,\ \underline{2}\ )$

$D(1, 2) \rightarrow D'(\ \underline{-2}\ ,\ \underline{-1}\ )$

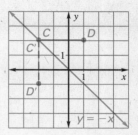

✔ **Checkpoint** The endpoints of $\overline{JK}$ are $J(-1, -2)$ and $K(1, -2)$. Reflect the segment in the given line. Graph the segment and its image.

2. $y = x$

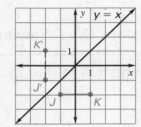

3. $y = -x$

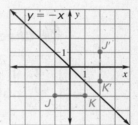

THEOREM 9.2: REFLECTION THEOREM

A reflection is an isometry.

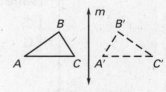

$$\triangle ABC \cong \triangle A'B'C'$$

Example 4   *Find a minimum distance*

Tools Workers are retrieving tools that they need for a project. One will enter the building at point *A* and the other at point *B*. Where should they park on driveway *m* to minimize the distance they will walk?

Solution

Reflect *B* in line *m* to obtain *B'*. Then draw $\overline{AB'}$. Label the __intersection__ of $\overline{AB'}$ and *m* as *C*. Because $\overline{AB'}$ is the __shortest__ distance between *A* and *B'* and BC = __B'C__ , park at point __C__ to minimize the combined distance, *AC* + *BC*, they have to walk.

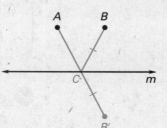

✔ ***Checkpoint*** **Complete the following exercise.**

4. In Example 4, reflect *A* in line *m*. What do you notice?

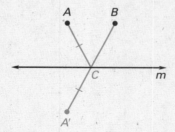

You obtain the same point *C* at which to park.

REFLECTION MATRICES

Reflection in the *x*-axis.

$$\begin{bmatrix} 1 & 0 \\ 0 & -1 \end{bmatrix}$$

Reflection in the *y*-axis.

$$\begin{bmatrix} -1 & 0 \\ 0 & 1 \end{bmatrix}$$

Example 5 *Use matrix multiplication to reflect a polygon*

The vertices of △*DEF* are *D*(1, 2), *E*(2, 3), and *F*(4, 1). Find the reflection of △*DEF* in the *y*-axis using matrix multiplication. Graph △*DEF* and its image.

Solution

Step 1 **Multiply** the polygon matrix by the matrix for a reflection in the *y*-axis.

$$\underset{\substack{\text{Reflection} \\ \text{matrix}}}{\longrightarrow} \begin{bmatrix} -1 & 0 \\ 0 & 1 \end{bmatrix} \overset{\begin{matrix} D & E & F \end{matrix}}{\begin{bmatrix} 1 & 2 & 4 \\ 2 & 3 & 1 \end{bmatrix}} \underset{\substack{\text{Polygon} \\ \text{matrix}}}{\longleftarrow}$$

$$= \begin{bmatrix} -1(1) + 0(2) & -1(2) + 0(3) & -1(4) + 0(1) \\ 0(1) + 1(2) & 0(2) + 1(3) & 0(4) + 1(1) \end{bmatrix}$$

$$= \overset{\begin{matrix} D' & E' & F' \end{matrix}}{\begin{bmatrix} -1 & -2 & -4 \\ 2 & 3 & 1 \end{bmatrix}}$$

Step 2 **Graph** △*DEF* and △*D'E'F'*.

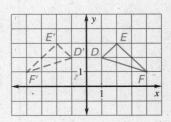

✔ **Checkpoint** **Complete the following exercise.**

5. The vertices of △*QRS* are *Q*(−1, 4), *R*(0, 1), and *S*(2, 3). Find the reflection of △*QRS* in the *x*-axis using matrix multiplication.

   Q'(−1, −4), *R'*(0, −1), *S'*(2, −3)

Homework

Goal • Rotate figures about a point.

Your Notes

VOCABULARY

Center of rotation In a rotation, a figure is turned about a fixed point called the center of rotation.

Angle of rotation In a rotation, rays drawn from the center of rotation to a point and its image form the angle of rotation.

Example 1 *Draw a rotation*

Draw a 150° rotation of △*ABC* about *P*.

Solution

Step 1 **Draw** a segment from *A* to *P*.

Step 2 **Draw** a ray to form a 150° angle with $\overline{PA}$.

Step 3 **Draw** *A′* so that *PA′* = *PA*.

Step 4 **Repeat** Steps 1–3 for each vertex. Draw △*A′B′C′*.

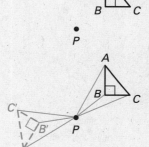

✔ *Checkpoint* **Complete the following exercise.**

1. Draw a 60° rotation of △*GHJ* about *P*.

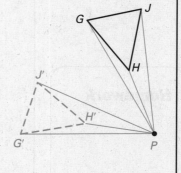

COORDINATE RULES FOR ROTATIONS ABOUT THE ORIGIN

When a point (a, b) is rotated counterclockwise about the origin, the following are true:

1. For a rotation of 90°,
$(a, b) \rightarrow (\underline{-b}, \underline{a})$.

2. For a rotation of 180°,
$(a, b) \rightarrow (\underline{-a}, \underline{-b})$.

3. For a rotation of 270°,
$(a, b) \rightarrow (\underline{b}, \underline{-a})$.

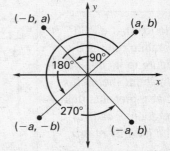

Example 2   *Rotate a figure using the coordinate rules*

Graph quadrilateral *KLMN* with vertices *K*(3, 2), *L*(4, 2), *M*(4, −3), and *N*(2, −1). Then rotate the quadrilateral 270° about the origin.

Solution

Graph *KLMN*. Use the coordinate rule for a 270° rotation to find the images of the vertices.

$(a, b) \rightarrow (b, -a)$

$K(3, 2) \rightarrow K'(\underline{2}, \underline{-3})$

$L(4, 2) \rightarrow L'(\underline{2}, \underline{-4})$

$M(4, -3) \rightarrow M'(\underline{-3}, \underline{-4})$

$N(2, -1) \rightarrow N'(\underline{-1}, \underline{-2})$

Graph the image *K'L'M'N'*.

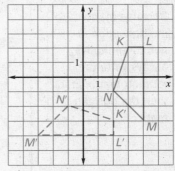

✔ *Checkpoint* **Complete the following exercise.**

2. Graph *KLMN* in Example 2. Then rotate the quadrilateral 90° about the origin.

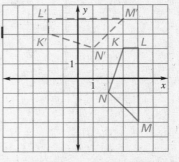

Your Notes

ROTATION MATRICES (COUNTERCLOCKWISE)

90° rotation	180° rotation
$\begin{bmatrix} 0 & -1 \\ 1 & 0 \end{bmatrix}$ 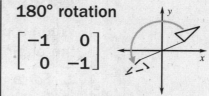	$\begin{bmatrix} -1 & 0 \\ 0 & -1 \end{bmatrix}$ 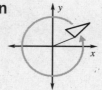
270° rotation	360° rotation
$\begin{bmatrix} 0 & 1 \\ -1 & 0 \end{bmatrix}$	$\begin{bmatrix} 1 & 0 \\ 0 & 1 \end{bmatrix}$

> Notice that a 360° rotation returns the figure to its original position. The matrix that represents this rotation is called the *identity matrix*.

Example 3 *Use matrices to rotate a figure*

Trapezoid *DEFG* has vertices *D*(−1, 3), *E*(1, 3), *F*(2, 1), and *G*(1, 0). Find the image matrix for a 180° rotation of *DEFG* about the origin. Graph *DEFG* and its image.

Solution

Step 1 Write the polygon matrix:
$$\begin{array}{cccc} D & E & F & G \end{array}$$
$$\begin{bmatrix} -1 & 1 & 2 & 1 \\ 3 & 3 & 1 & 0 \end{bmatrix}$$

Step 2 Multiply by the matrix for a 180° rotation.

$$\underset{\substack{\text{Rotation}\\\text{matrix}}}{\begin{bmatrix} -1 & 0 \\ 0 & -1 \end{bmatrix}} \underset{\substack{\text{Polygon}\\\text{matrix}}}{\begin{bmatrix} -1 & 1 & 2 & 1 \\ 3 & 3 & 1 & 0 \end{bmatrix}} = \underset{\substack{\text{Image}\\\text{matrix}}}{\begin{bmatrix} 1 & -1 & -2 & -1 \\ -3 & -3 & 1 & 0 \end{bmatrix}}$$

(over the columns: D E F G ... D' E' F' G')

> Because matrix multiplication is not commutative, always write the rotation matrix first, then the polygon matrix.

Step 3 Graph the preimage *DEFG*.
Graph the image *D'E'F'G'*.

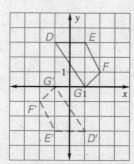

238 Lesson 9.4 • *Geometry Notetaking Guide*

Copyright © McDougal Littell/Houghton Mifflin Company.

⬤

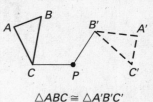

THEOREM 9.3: ROTATION THEOREM

A rotation is an isometry.

$\triangle ABC \cong \triangle A'B'C'$

Example 4 *Find side lengths in a rotation*

The quadrilateral is rotated about *P*.
Find the value of *y*.

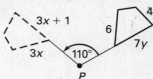

Solution

By Theorem 9.3, the rotation is an __isometry__ , so
corresponding side lengths are __equal__ . Then $3x =$ __6__ ,
so $x =$ __2__ . Now set up an equation to solve for *y*.

__7__ $y =$ __$3x + 1$__	Corresponding lengths in an isometry are equal.
__7__ $y =$ __$3(2) + 1$__	Substitute __2__ for *x*.
$y =$ __1__	Solve for *y*.

✔ **Checkpoint** Complete the following exercises.

---

3. Use the quadrilateral in Example 3. Find the image
matrix after a 270° rotation about the origin.

$$\begin{array}{cccc} D' & E' & F' & G' \end{array}$$
$$\begin{bmatrix} 3 & 3 & 1 & 0 \\ 1 & -1 & -2 & -1 \end{bmatrix}$$

⬤

Homework

4. The triangle is rotated about *P*.
Find the value of *b*.

$b = 4$

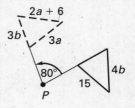

⬤

Apply Compositions of Transformations

Goal • Perform combinations of two or more transformations.

Your Notes

> ## VOCABULARY
>
> **Glide reflection** A glide reflection is a transformation in which every point P is mapped to a point P'' by the following steps:
> (1) A translation maps P onto P'.
> (2) A reflection in a line k parallel to the direction of the translation maps P' to P''.
>
> ---
>
> **Composition of transformations** When two or more transformations are combined to form a single transformation, the result is a composition of transformations.

Example 1 *Find the image of a glide reflection*

The vertices of $\triangle ABC$ are $A(2, 1)$, $B(5, 3)$, and $C(6, 2)$. Find the image of $\triangle ABC$ after the glide reflection.

Translation: $(x, y) \rightarrow (x - 8, y)$
Reflection: in the x-axis

> The line of reflection must be parallel to the direction of the translation to be a glide reflection.

Solution

Begin by graphing $\triangle ABC$. Then graph $\triangle A'B'C'$ after a translation 8 units <u>left</u>. Finally, graph $\triangle A''B''C''$ after a reflection in the x-axis.

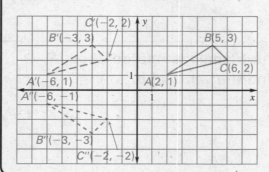

THEOREM 9.4: COMPOSITION THEOREM

The composition of two (or more) isometries is an isometry.

Example 2   *Find the image of a composition*

The endpoints of $\overline{CD}$ are C(−2, 6) and D(−1, 3). Graph the image of $\overline{CD}$ after the composition.

Reflection: in the *y*-axis
Rotation: 90° about the origin

> Unless you are told otherwise, do the transformations in the order given.

Solution

Step 1 Graph $\overline{CD}$.

Step 2 Reflect $\overline{CD}$ in the *y*-axis. $\overline{C'D'}$ has endpoints C'(2 , 6) and D'(1 , 3).

Step 3 Rotate $\overline{C'D'}$ 90° about the origin. $\overline{C''D''}$ has endpoints C''(−6 , 2) and D''(−3 , 1).

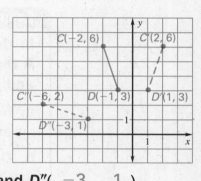

✔ *Checkpoint* **Complete the following exercises.**

1. Suppose △ABC in Example 1 is translated 5 units down, then reflected in the *y*-axis. What are the coordinates of the vertices of the image?

   A''(−2, −4), B''(−5, −2), C''(−6, −3)

---

2. Graph $\overline{CD}$ from Example 2. Do the rotation first, followed by the reflection.

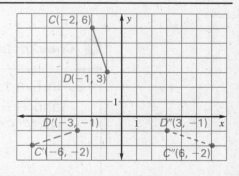

THEOREM 9.5: REFLECTIONS IN PARALLEL LINES THEOREM

If lines k and m are parallel, then a reflection in line k followed by a reflection in line m is the same as a ___translation___ .

If P'' is the image of P, then:

1. $\overline{PP''}$ is perpendicular to k and m, and

2. $PP'' = 2d$, where d is the distance between k and m.

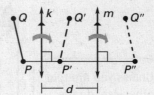

Example 3   *Use Theorem 9.5*

In the diagram, a reflection in line k maps $\overline{GF}$ to $\overline{G'F'}$. A reflection in line m maps $\overline{G'F'}$ to $\overline{G''F''}$. Also, $FA = 6$ and $DF'' = 3$.

a. Name any segments congruent to each segment: $\overline{GF}$, $\overline{FA}$, and $\overline{GB}$.

b. Does $AD = BC$? *Explain*.

c. What is the length of $\overline{GG''}$?

a. $\overline{GF} \cong \underline{\overline{G'F'}}$, and $\overline{GF} \cong \underline{\overline{G''F''}}$. $\overline{FA} \cong \underline{\overline{F'A}}$. $\overline{GB} \cong \underline{\overline{G'B}}$.

b. ___Yes___ ; AD ___=___ BC because $\overline{GG''}$ and $\overline{FF''}$ are ___perpendicular___ to both k and m, so $\overline{BC}$ and $\overline{AD}$ are opposite sides of a ___rectangle___ .

c. By the properties of reflections, $F'A = \underline{6}$ and $F'D = \underline{3}$. Theorem 9.5 implies that $GG'' = FF'' = \underline{2} \cdot \underline{AD}$, so the length of $\overline{GG''}$ is $\underline{2}(\underline{6} + \underline{3})$, or ___18___ units.

✔ *Checkpoint* **Complete the following exercise.**

3. In Example 3, suppose you are given that $BC = 10$ and $G'F' = 6$. What is the perimeter of quadrilateral $GG''F''F$?

   52 units

THEOREM 9.6: REFLECTIONS IN INTERSECTING LINES THEOREM

If lines *k* and *m* intersect at point *P*, then a reflection in *k* followed by a reflection in *m* is the same as a _rotation_ about _P_.

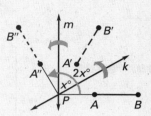

The angle of rotation is 2*x*°, where *x*° is the measure of the acute or right angle formed by *k* and *m*.

Example 4   *Use Theorem 9.6*

In the diagram, the figure is reflected in line *k*. The image is then reflected in line *m*. Describe a single transformation that maps *F* to *F*".

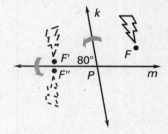

Solution

The measure of the acute angle formed between lines *k* and *m* is _80°_. So, by Theorem 9.6, a single transformation that maps *F* to *F*" is a _160°_ rotation about _point P_.

You can check that this is correct by tracing lines *k* and *m* and point *F*, then rotating the point _160°_.

☑ **Checkpoint** Complete the following exercise.

4. In the diagram below, the preimage is reflected in line *k*, then in line *m*. Describe a single transformation that maps *G* to *G*".

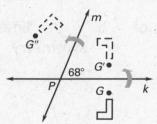

136° rotation about point *P*

Homework

9.6 Identify Symmetry

Goal • Identify line and rotational symmetries of a figure.

Your Notes

VOCABULARY

Line symmetry A figure in the plane has line symmetry if the figure can be mapped onto itself by a reflection in a line.

Line of symmetry In line symmetry, a line of reflection is called a line of symmetry.

Rotational symmetry A figure in a plane has rotational symmetry if the figure can be mapped onto itself by a rotation of 180° or less about the center of the figure.

Center of symmetry In rotational symmetry, the center of a figure is called the center of symmetry.

| Example 1 | *Identify lines of symmetry* |

How many lines of symmetry does the figure have?

a. [rectangle]   b. [pentagon]   c. [pentagon]

Solution

a. __Two__ lines of symmetry

b. __Five__ lines of symmetry

c. __One__ line of symmetry

> Notice that the lines of symmetry are also lines of reflection.

Your Notes

Example 2 *Identify rotational symmetry*

Does the figure have rotational symmetry? If so, *describe* any rotations that map the figure onto itself.

a. Square   **b.** Regular hexagon   **c.** Kite

Solution

a. The square __has__ rotational symmetry. The center is the intersection of the diagonals. Rotations of __90°__ or __180°__ about the center map the square onto itself.

b. The regular hexagon __has__ rotational symmetry. The center is the intersection of the diagonals. Rotations of __60°__, __120°__, or __180°__ about the center all map the hexagon onto itself.

c. The kite __does not have__ rotational symmetry because no rotation of __180°__ or less maps the kite onto itself.

Example 3 *Identify symmetry*

Identify the line symmetry and rotational symmetry of the figure at the right.

Solution

The figure __has__ line symmetry. __Two__ lines of symmetry can be drawn for the figure.

For a figure with s lines of symmetry, the smallest rotation that maps the figure onto itself has the measure $\dfrac{360°}{s}$. So, the figure has $\dfrac{360°}{2}$, or __180°__ rotational symmetry.

Your Notes

✓ *Checkpoint* **How many lines of symmetry does the figure have?**

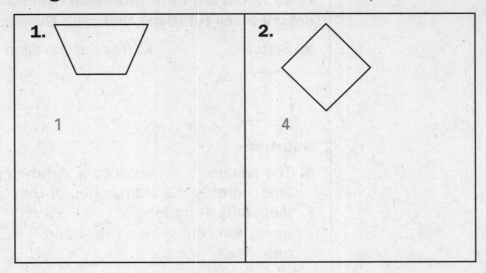

1.

1

2.

4

In Exercises 3 and 4, does the figure have rotational symmetry? If so, *describe* any rotations that map the figure onto itself.

3.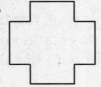

yes; 90° or 180° about the center

4.

no

5. Describe the lines of symmetry and rotational symmetry of the figure at the right.

8 lines of symmetry, 4 through the convex vertices and 4 through the concave vertices; 45°, 90°, 135°, or 180° about the center

Homework

Identify and Perform Dilations

Goal • Use drawing tools and matrices to draw dilations.

Your Notes

> **VOCABULARY**
>
> **Scalar multiplication** Scalar multiplication is the process of multiplying each element of a matrix by a real number or *scalar*.

Example 1 *Identify dilations*

Find the scale factor of the dilation. Then tell whether the dilation is a *reduction* or an *enlargement*.

a.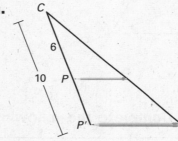

b.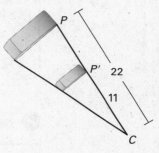

Solution

a. Because $\dfrac{CP'}{CP} = \dfrac{10}{6}$, the scale factor is $k = \dfrac{5}{3}$.
   The image P' is an __enlargement__ .

b. Because $\dfrac{CP'}{CP} = \dfrac{11}{22}$, the scale factor is $k = \dfrac{1}{2}$.
   The image P' is a __reduction__ .

✓ *Checkpoint* **Complete the following exercise.**

> **1.** In a dilation, $CP' = 4$ and $CP = 20$. Tell whether the dilation is a *reduction* or an *enlargement* and find its scale factor.
>
> reduction; $\dfrac{1}{5}$

Example 2   *Draw a dilation*

Draw and label □*LMNP*. **Then construct a dilation of** □*LMNP* **with point** *L* **as the center of dilation and a scale factor of** $\frac{1}{2}$.

Solution

Step 1   **Draw** *LMNP*. **Draw rays from** *L* **through vertices** *M*, *N*, **and** *P*.

Step 2   **Open** the compass to the length of $\overline{LM}$. Locate *M′* on $\overrightarrow{LM}$ so $LM' = \frac{1}{2}(LM)$. Locate *N′* and *P′* the same way.

Step 3   **Add** a second label *L′* to point *L*. Draw the sides of *L′M′N′P′*.

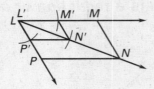

✔ Checkpoint   **Complete the following exercise.**

2. Draw and label △*PQR*. Then construct a dilation of △*PQR* with *P* as the center of dilation and a scale factor of **2**.

Sample answer:

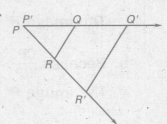

Example 3 *Scalar multiplication*

Simplify the product: $3\begin{bmatrix} 0 & 5 & 4 \\ 2 & -2 & -1 \end{bmatrix}$.

Solution

$3\begin{bmatrix} 0 & 5 & 4 \\ 2 & -2 & -1 \end{bmatrix} = \begin{bmatrix} \underline{3(0)} & \underline{3(5)} & \underline{3(4)} \\ \underline{3(2)} & \underline{3(-2)} & \underline{3(-1)} \end{bmatrix}$ Multiply each element in the matrix by $\underline{3}$.

$= \begin{bmatrix} \underline{0} & \underline{15} & \underline{12} \\ \underline{6} & \underline{-6} & \underline{-3} \end{bmatrix}$ Simplify.

✔ **Checkpoint** Simplify the product.

3. $4\begin{bmatrix} -6 & 3 & 2 \\ 5 & -1 & 4 \end{bmatrix}$

$\begin{bmatrix} -24 & 12 & 8 \\ 20 & -4 & 16 \end{bmatrix}$

4. $-3\begin{bmatrix} 5 & -1 & -2 \\ -2 & 0 & 4 \end{bmatrix}$

$\begin{bmatrix} -15 & 3 & 6 \\ 6 & 0 & -12 \end{bmatrix}$

Example 4 *Use scalar multiplication in a dilation*

The vertices of quadrilateral *ABCD* are *A*(−3, 0), *B*(0, 6), *C*(3, 6), and *D*(3, 3). Use scalar multiplication to find the image of *ABCD* after a dilation with its center at the origin and a scale factor of $\frac{1}{3}$. Graph *ABCD* and its image.

Solution

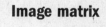

$$\frac{1}{3} \begin{array}{cccc} A & B & C & D \\ \begin{bmatrix} -3 & 0 & 3 & 3 \\ 0 & 6 & 6 & 3 \end{bmatrix} \end{array} = \begin{array}{cccc} A' & B' & C' & D' \\ \begin{bmatrix} -1 & 0 & 1 & 1 \\ 0 & 2 & 2 & 1 \end{bmatrix} \end{array}$$

Scale factor   Polygon matrix   Image matrix

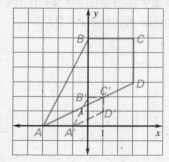

Example 5   *Find the image of a composition*

The vertices of △*KLM* are *K*(−3, 0), *L*(−2, 1), and *M*(−1, −1). Find the image of △*KLM* after the given composition.

Translation: $(x, y) \rightarrow (x + 4, y + 2)$
Dilation: centered at the origin with a scale factor of 2

Solution

Step 1 **Graph** the preimage △*KLM* in the coordinate plane.

Step 2 **Translate** △*KLM* 4 units to the __right__ and 2 units __up__ . Label it △*K′L′M′*.

Step 3 **Dilate** △*K′L′M′* using the __origin__ as the center and a scale factor of 2 to find △*K″L″M″*.

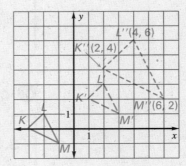

✔ Checkpoint **Complete the following exercises.**

5. The vertices of △*RST* are *R*(−4, 3), *S*(−1, −2), and *T*(2, 1). Use scalar multiplication to find the vertices of △*R′S′T′* after a dilation with its center at the origin and a scale factor of 2.

   R′(−8, 6), *S′*(−2, −4), *T′*(4, 2)

---

6. A segment has the endpoints *C*(−2, 2) and *D*(2, 2). Find the image of $\overline{CD}$ after a 90° rotation about the origin followed by a dilation with its center at the origin and a scale factor of 2.

   C″(−4, −4), *D″*(−4, 4)

Homework

Words to Review

Give an example of the vocabulary word.

Image  image	**Preimage** 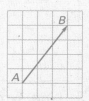 preimage
Isometry 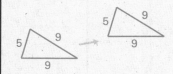	**Vector** 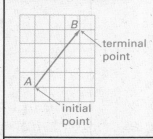
Initial point, Terminal point 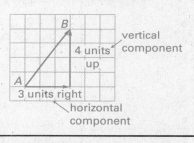 terminal point / initial point	**Horizontal component, Vertical component** 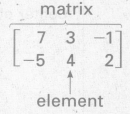 vertical component / 4 units up / 3 units right / horizontal component
Component form 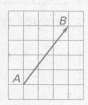 The component form of $\overline{AB}$ is $\langle 3, 4 \rangle$.	**Matrix, Element** matrix $$\begin{bmatrix} 7 & 3 & -1 \\ -5 & 4 & 2 \end{bmatrix}$$ element
Dimensions $$\begin{bmatrix} 7 & 3 & -1 \\ -5 & 4 & 2 \end{bmatrix}$$ The dimensions of the matrix are 2×3.	**Line of reflection** 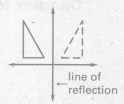 line of reflection

Center of rotation	Angle of rotation
The origin is the center of rotation.	The angle of rotation is 90°.
Glide reflection	**Composition of transformations**
First translate, then reflect.	First reflect, then reflect again.
Line symmetry, Line of symmetry	**Rotational symmetry**
k	180°
The figure has line symmetry. The line of symmetry is *k*.	The figure has 180° rotational symmetry.
Center of symmetry	**Scalar multiplication**
180° center of symmetry	$2\begin{bmatrix} -1 & 3 \\ 4 & -2 \end{bmatrix} = \begin{bmatrix} -2 & 6 \\ 8 & -4 \end{bmatrix}$

Review your notes and Chapter 9 by using the Chapter Review on pages 636–639 of your textbook.

Goal • Use properties of a tangent to a circle.

Your Notes

VOCABULARY

Circle A circle is the set of all points in a plane that are equidistant from a given point.

Center The center of a circle is the point from which all points of the circle are equidistant.

Radius A segment from the center of a circle to any point on the circle is a radius.

Chord A chord is a segment whose endpoints are on a circle.

Diameter A diameter is a chord that contains the center of the circle.

Secant A secant is a line that intersects a circle in two points.

Tangent A tangent is a line in the plane of a circle that intersects the circle in exactly one point.

Example 1 *Identify special segments and lines*

Tell whether the line, ray, or segment is best described as a *radius*, *chord*, *diameter*, *secant*, or *tangent* of $\odot C$.

a. $\overline{BC}$ **b.** $\overleftrightarrow{EA}$ **c.** $\overrightarrow{DE}$

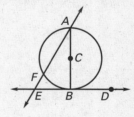

Solution

a. $\overline{BC}$ is a ___radius___ because C is the center and B is a point on the circle.

b. $\overleftrightarrow{EA}$ is a ___secant___ because it is a line that intersects the circle in two points.

c. $\overrightarrow{DE}$ is a ___tangent___ ray because it is contained in a line that intersects the circle at only one point.

Example 2   *Find lengths in circles in a coordinate plane*

Use the diagram to find the given lengths.

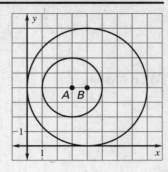

a. Radius of ⊙A

b. Diameter of ⊙A

c. Radius of ⊙B

d. Diameter of ⊙B

Solution

a. The radius of ⊙A is __2__ units.

b. The diameter of ⊙A is __4__ units.

c. The radius of ⊙B is __4__ units.

d. The diameter of ⊙B is __8__ units.

✔ *Checkpoint* **Complete the following exercises.**

1. In Example 1, tell whether $\overline{AB}$ is best described as a *radius, chord, diameter, secant,* or *tangent. Explain.*

$\overline{AB}$ is a diameter because it is a chord that contains the center *C*.

---

2. Use the diagram to find (a) the radius of ⊙C and (b) the diameter of ⊙D.

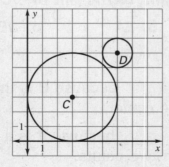

(a) The radius of ⊙C is 3 units.
(b) The diameter of ⊙D is 2 units.

Your Notes

Example 3   *Draw common tangents*

Tell how many common tangents the circles have and draw them.

a.   b.   c.

Solution

a. __3__ common tangents   b. __2__ common tangents   c. __1__ common tangent

✔ *Checkpoint* Tell how many common tangents the circles have and draw them.

3. no common tangents	4. 4 common tangents

THEOREM 10.1

In a plane, a line is tangent to a circle if and only if the line is __perpendicular__ to a radius of the circle at its endpoint on the circle.

Example 4   *Verify a tangent to a circle*

In the diagram, $\overline{RS}$ is a radius of $\odot R$.
Is $\overline{ST}$ tangent to $\odot R$?

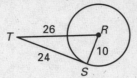

Solution

Use the Converse of the Pythagorean Theorem. Because
$10^2 + 24^2 = 26^2$, $\triangle RST$ is a __right triangle__ and
$\overline{RS} \perp$ __$\overline{ST}$__ . So, __$\overline{ST}$__ is perpendicular to a radius of $\odot R$
at its endpoint on $\odot R$. By __Theorem 10.1__ , $\overline{ST}$ is tangent
to $\odot R$.

✔ **Checkpoint** $\overline{RS}$ is a radius of $\odot R$. Is $\overline{ST}$ tangent to $\odot R$?

5.

R 8 T
5 12
S

Yes

6.

S 16
12 T
R 7

No

Example 5   *Find the radius of a circle*

In the diagram, *B* is a point of
tangency. Find the radius *r* of $\odot C$.

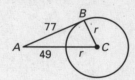

Solution

You know from Theorem 10.1 that $\overline{AB} \perp \overline{BC}$, so $\triangle ABC$ is a
__right triangle__ . You can use the Pythagorean Theorem.

$$AC^2 = BC^2 + AB^2$$ Pythagorean
                                Theorem

$$(r + 49)^2 = r^2 + 77^2$$ Substitute.

$$r^2 + \underline{98}\,r + \underline{2401} = r^2 + \underline{5929}$$ Multiply.

$$\underline{98}\,r = \underline{3528}$$ Subtract from
                      each side.

$$r = \underline{36}$$ Divide each side
                  by __98__ .

THEOREM 10.2

Tangent segments from a common external point are <u>congruent</u> .

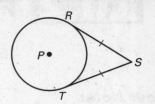

Example 6   *Use Theorem 10.2*

$\overline{QR}$ is tangent to $\odot C$ at R and $\overline{QS}$ is tangent to $\odot C$ at S. Find the value of x.

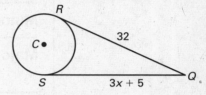

Solution

$QR = QS$	Tangent segments from the same point are congruent.
<u>32</u> = <u>$3x + 5$</u>	Substitute.
<u>9</u> = x	Solve for x.

✓ **Checkpoint** **Complete the following exercises.**

7. In the diagram, *K* is a point of tangency. Find the radius *r* of $\odot L$.

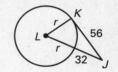

$r = 33$

8. $\overline{RS}$ is tangent to $\odot C$ at *S* and $\overline{RT}$ is tangent to $\odot C$ at *T*. Find the value(s) of *x*.

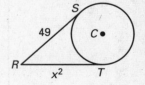

$x = \pm 7$

Homework

10.2 Find Arc Measures

Goal • Use angle measures to find arc measures.

Your Notes

VOCABULARY

Central angle A central angle of a circle is an angle whose vertex is the center of the circle.

Minor arc Part of a circle measuring less than 180°.

Major arc Part of a circle measuring between 180° and 360°.

Semicircle A semicircle is an arc with endpoints that are the endpoints of a diameter.

Measure of a minor arc The measure of a minor arc is the measure of its central angle.

Measure of a major arc The measure of a major arc is the difference between 360° and the measure of the related minor arc.

Congruent circles Two circles are congruent circles if they have the same radius.

Congruent arcs Two arcs are congruent arcs if they have the same measure and they are arcs of the same circle or of congruent circles.

MEASURING ARCS

The measure of a minor arc is the measure of its central angle. The expression $m\overset{\frown}{AB}$ is read as "the measure of arc *AB*."

The measure of the entire circle is ___360°___ . The measure of a major arc is the difference between ___360°___ and the measure of the related minor arc.

The measure of a semicircle is ___180°___ .

$m\overset{\frown}{AB} = 50°$

$m\overset{\frown}{ADB} = 310°$

Your Notes

Example 1   *Find measures of arcs*

Find the measure of each arc of ⊙C, where $\overline{DF}$ is a diameter.

a. $\overarc{DE}$ **b.** $\overarc{DFE}$ **c.** $\overarc{DEF}$

a. $\overarc{DE}$ is a __minor__ arc, so $m\overarc{DE} = m\angle$ __DCE__ = __117°__ .

b. $\overarc{DFE}$ is a __major__ arc, so
$m\overarc{DFE} =$ __360°__ − __117°__ = __243°__ .

c. $\overline{DF}$ is a diameter, so $\overarc{DEF}$ is a __semicircle__ , and
$m\overarc{DEF} =$ __180°__ .

✔ **Checkpoint** Complete the following exercise.

1. Find $m\overarc{RTS}$ in the diagram at the right.
$m\overarc{RTS} = 315°$

POSTULATE 23: ARC ADDITION POSTULATE

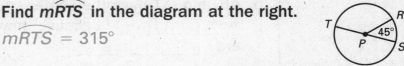

The measure of an arc formed by two adjacent arcs is the sum of the measures of the two arcs.

$m\overarc{ABC} = m$ _$\overarc{AB}$_ $+ m$ _$\overarc{BC}$_

Example 2   *Find measures of arcs*

Money You join a new bank and divide your money several ways, as shown in the circle graph at the right. Find the indicated arc measures.

a. $m\overarc{BD}$ **b.** $m\overarc{BCD}$

Checking B
55°
A
Money Market 140°
Savings 105°
Bonds 60° C
D

Solution

a. $m\overarc{BD} = m\overarc{BA} + m\overarc{AD}$
= __55°__ + __105°__
= __160°__

b. $m\overarc{BCD} = 360° − m\overarc{BD}$
= 360° − __160°__
= __200°__

> The measure of a minor arc is less than 180°. The measure of a major arc is greater than 180°.

Example 3   *Identify congruent arcs*

Tell whether the given arcs are congruent. *Explain* **why or why not.**

a. $\overset{\frown}{BC}$ and $\overset{\frown}{DE}$ **b.** $\overset{\frown}{AB}$ and $\overset{\frown}{CD}$ **c.** $\overset{\frown}{FG}$ and $\overset{\frown}{HJ}$

    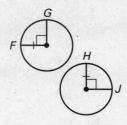

Solution

a. $\overset{\frown}{BC}$ ≅ $\overset{\frown}{DE}$ because they are in <u>the same circle</u>
   and $m\overset{\frown}{BC}$ = $m\overset{\frown}{DE}$.

b. $\overset{\frown}{AB}$ and $\overset{\frown}{CD}$ have the same <u>measure</u>, but they are
   <u>not congruent</u> because they are arcs of circles that
   are <u>not congruent</u>.

c. $\overset{\frown}{FG}$ ≅ $\overset{\frown}{HJ}$ because they are in <u>congruent circles</u>
   and $m\overset{\frown}{FG}$ = $m\overset{\frown}{HJ}$.

✔ *Checkpoint* **Complete the following exercises.**

2. In Example 2, find (a) $m\overset{\frown}{BCA}$ **and (b)** $m\overset{\frown}{ABC}$**.**
   (a) $m\overset{\frown}{BCA}$ = 305°, (b) $m\overset{\frown}{ABC}$ = 195°

3. In the diagram at the right, is
   $\overset{\frown}{PQ}$ ≅ $\overset{\frown}{SR}$**?** *Explain* **why or why not.**

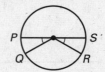

   $\overset{\frown}{PQ}$ ≅ $\overset{\frown}{SR}$ because they are in the
   same circle and $m\overset{\frown}{PQ}$ = $m\overset{\frown}{SR}$.

Homework

10.3 Apply Properties of Chords

Goal • Use relationships of arcs and chords in a circle.

Your Notes

THEOREM 10.3

In the same circle, or in congruent circles, two minor arcs are congruent if and only if their corresponding chords are congruent.

$\overset{\frown}{AB} \cong \overset{\frown}{CD}$ if and only if $\overline{AB} \cong \overline{CD}$.

Example 1   *Use congruent chords to find an arc measure*

In the diagram, $\odot A \cong \odot D$, $\overline{BC} \cong \overline{EF}$, and $m\overset{\frown}{EF} = 125°$. Find $m\overset{\frown}{BC}$.

Solution

Because $\overline{BC}$ and $\overline{EF}$ are congruent __chords__ in congruent __circles__, the corresponding minor arcs $\overset{\frown}{BC}$ and $\overset{\frown}{EF}$ are __congruent__.

So, $m\overset{\frown}{BC} = m\overset{\frown}{EF} = $ __125°__.

THEOREM 10.4

If one chord is a perpendicular bisector of another chord, then the first chord is a diameter.

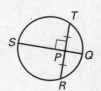

If $\overline{QS}$ is a perpendicular bisector of $\overline{TR}$, then __QS__ is a diameter of the circle.

THEOREM 10.5

If a diameter of a circle is perpendicular to a chord, then the diameter bisects the chord and its arc.

If $\overline{EG}$ is a diameter and $\overline{EG} \perp \overline{DF}$, then $\overline{HD} \cong \overline{HF}$ and __$\overset{\frown}{GD}$__ $\cong$ __$\overset{\frown}{GF}$__.

Example 2 **Use perpendicular bisectors**

Journalism A journalist is writing a
a story about three sculptures,
arranged as shown at the right.
Where should the journalist place
a camera so that it is the same
distance from each sculpture?

Solution

Step 1 **Label** the sculptures *A*, *B*, and *C*. Draw segments
$\overline{AB}$ and $\overline{BC}$.

Step 2 **Draw** the _perpendicular bisectors_ of $\overline{AB}$ and
$\overline{BC}$. By _Theorem 10.4_, these are diameters of
the circle containing *A*, *B*, and *C*.

Step 3 **Find** the point where these bisectors _intersect_.
This is the center of the circle through *A*, *B*, and *C*,
and so it is _equidistant_ from each point.

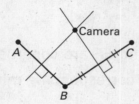

Example 3 **Use a diameter**

Use the diagram of $\odot E$ to find the length
of $\overline{BD}$. Tell what theorem you use.

Solution

Diameter $\overline{AC}$ is _perpendicular_ to $\overline{BD}$. So, by
Theorem 10.5, $\overline{AC}$ _bisects_ $\overline{BD}$, and $BF =$ _DF_.
Therefore, $BD = 2(\underline{DF}) = 2(\underline{6}) = \underline{12}$.

THEOREM 10.6

In the same circle, or in
congruent circles, two chords
are congruent if and only if
they are equidistant from
the center.

$\overline{AB} \cong \overline{CD}$ if and only
if _EF_ = _EG_.

Example 4 **Use Theorem 10.6**

In the diagram of ⊙*F*, *AB = CD =* **12.**
Find *EF*.

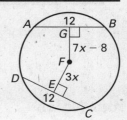

Solution

Chords $\overline{AB}$ and $\overline{CD}$ are congruent, so by
Theorem 10.6 they are equidistant
from *F*. Therefore, *EF =* GF .

EF = GF	**Use Theorem 10.6.**
$3x =$ 7x − 8	**Substitute.**
$x =$ 2	**Solve for x.**

So, $EF = 3x = 3($ 2 $) =$ 6 .

✔ *Checkpoint* **Complete the following exercises.**

1. If $m\widehat{TV} = 121°$, find $m\widehat{RS}$.

   $m\widehat{RS} = 121°$

2. Find the measures of $\widehat{CB}$, $\widehat{BE}$,
   and $\widehat{CE}$.

   $m\widehat{CB} = 64°$, $m\widehat{BE} = 64°$,
   $m\widehat{CE} = 128°$

3. In the diagram in Example 4, suppose *AB =* 27 and
   EF = GF = 7. Find *CD*.

   $CD = 27$

10.4 Use Inscribed Angles and Polygons

Goal • Use inscribed angles of circles.

Your Notes

VOCABULARY

Inscribed angle An inscribed angle is an angle whose vertex is on a circle and whose sides contain chords of the circle.

Intercepted arc The arc that lies in the interior of an inscribed angle and has endpoints on the angle is called the intercepted arc of the angle.

Inscribed polygon A polygon is an inscribed polygon if all of its vertices lie on a circle.

Circumscribed circle A circumscribed circle is a circle that contains the vertices of an inscribed polygon.

THEOREM 10.7: MEASURE OF AN INSCRIBED ANGLE THEOREM

The measure of an inscribed angle is one half the measure of its intercepted arc.

$$m\angle ADB = \frac{1}{2} \underline{\ m\overset{\frown}{AB}\ }$$

Example 1 *Use inscribed angles*

Find the indicated measure in $\odot P$.

a. $m\angle S$ b. $m\overset{\frown}{RQ}$

Solution

a. $m\angle S = \frac{1}{2} \underline{\ m\overset{\frown}{RT}\ } = \frac{1}{2}(\underline{\ 60°\ }) = \underline{\ 30°\ }$

b. $m\overset{\frown}{QS} = 2m\angle\ \underline{R}\ = 2 \cdot \underline{\ 37°\ } = \underline{\ 74°\ }$.

    Because $\overset{\frown}{RQS}$ is a semicircle,

    $m\overset{\frown}{RQ} = 180° - \underline{\ m\overset{\frown}{QS}\ } = 180° - \underline{\ 74°\ } = \underline{\ 106°\ }$.

Example 2 *Find the measure of an intercepted arc*

Find $m\overgroup{HJ}$ and $m\angle HGJ$. What do you
notice about $\angle HGJ$ and $\angle HFJ$?

Solution

From Theorem 10.7, you know that

$m\overgroup{HJ} = 2m\angle$ *HFJ* $= 2($ 39° $) =$ 78° .

Also, $m\angle HGJ = \dfrac{1}{2}$ $m\overgroup{HJ}$ $= \dfrac{1}{2}($ 78° $) =$ 39° .

So $\angle HGJ$ ≅ $\angle HFJ$.

THEOREM 10.8

If two inscribed angles of a circle
intercept the same arc, then the
angles are congruent.

$\angle ADB \cong \angle$ *ACB*

Example 3 *Use Theorem 10.8*

Name two pairs of congruent angles
in the figure.

Solution

Notice that $\angle QRP$ and $\angle$ *QSP* intercept the
same arc, and so $\angle QRP \cong \angle$ *QSP* by Theorem 10.8.
Also, $\angle RQS$ and $\angle$ *RPS* intercept the same arc, so
$\angle RQS \cong \angle$ *RPS* .

✔ *Checkpoint* **Find the indicated measure.**

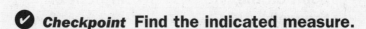

1. $m\angle GHJ$	**2.** $m\overgroup{CD}$	**3.** $m\angle RTS$

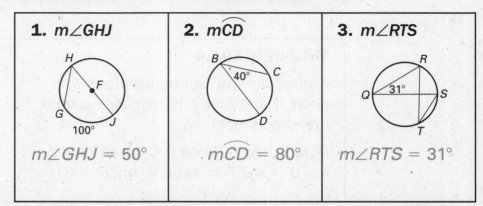

$m\angle GHJ = 50°$	$m\overgroup{CD} = 80°$	$m\angle RTS = 31°$

THEOREM 10.9

If a right triangle is inscribed in a circle, then the hypotenuse is a diameter of the circle. Conversely, if one side of an inscribed triangle is a diameter of the circle, then the triangle is a right triangle and the angle opposite the diameter is the right angle.

$m\angle ABC = 90°$ if and only if $\underline{AC}$ is a diameter of the circle.

Example 4 **Use a circumscribed circle**

Security A security camera rotates 90° and needs to be able to view the width of a wall. The camera is placed in a spot where the only thing viewed when rotating is the wall. You want to change the camera's position. Where else can it be placed so that the wall is viewed in the same way?

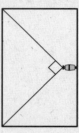

Solution

From Theorem 10.9, you know that if a right triangle is inscribed in a circle, then the hypotenuse of the triangle is a _diameter_ of the circle. So, draw the circle that has the width of the wall as a _diameter_. The wall fits perfectly with your camera's 90° rotation from any point on the _semicircle_ in front of the wall.

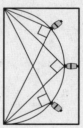

THEOREM 10.10

A quadrilateral can be inscribed in a circle if and only if its opposite angles are supplementary.

D, E, F, and G lie on $\odot C$ if and only if $m\angle D + m\angle F = m\angle E + m\angle G = \underline{180°}$.

Example 5   *Use Theorem 10.10*

Find the value of each variable.

a.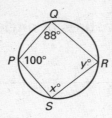

b.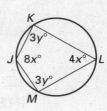

Solution

a. *PQRS* is inscribed in a circle, so opposite angles are <u>supplementary</u> .

$m\angle P + m\angle R =$ <u>180°</u> $m\angle Q + m\angle S =$ <u>180°</u>

$100° + y° =$ <u>180°</u> $88° + x° =$ <u>180°</u>

$y =$ <u>80</u> $x =$ <u>92</u>

b. *JKLM* is inscribed in a circle, so opposite angles are <u>supplementary</u> .

$m\angle J + m\angle L =$ <u>180°</u> $m\angle K + m\angle M =$ <u>180°</u>

$8x° + 4x° =$ <u>180°</u> $3y° + 3y° =$ <u>180°</u>

$12x =$ <u>180</u> $6y =$ <u>180</u>

$x =$ <u>15</u> $y =$ <u>30</u>

✓ *Checkpoint* **Complete the following exercises.**

4. **A right triangle is inscribed in a circle. The radius of the circle is 5.6 centimeters. What is the length of the hypotenuse of the right triangle?**

   11.2 centimeters

Homework

5. **Find the values of *a* and *b*.**

   $a = 18$, $b = 21$

   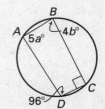

10.5 Apply Other Angle Relationships in Circles

• Find the measures of angles inside or outside a circle.

Your Notes

THEOREM 10.11

If a tangent and a chord intersect at a point on a circle, then the measure of each angle formed is one half the measure of its intercepted arc.

$$m\angle 1 = \tfrac{1}{2} \underline{\ m\overset{\frown}{AB}\ }$$

$$m\angle 2 = \tfrac{1}{2} \underline{\ m\overset{\frown}{BCA}\ }$$

Example 1 *Find angle and arc measures*

Line *m* is tangent to the circle. Find the indicated measure.

a. $m\angle 1$

b. $m\overset{\frown}{EFD}$

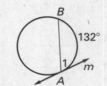

Solution

a. $m\angle 1 = \dfrac{1}{2}(132°) = \underline{\ 66°\ }$

b. $m\overset{\frown}{EFD} = \underline{\ 2\ }(110°) = \underline{\ 220°\ }$

THEOREM 10.12: ANGLES INSIDE THE CIRCLE THEOREM

If two chords intersect *inside* a circle, then the measure of each angle is one half the *sum* of the measures of the arcs intercepted by the angle and its vertical angle.

$$m\angle 1 = \tfrac{1}{2}(m\underline{\ \overset{\frown}{DC}\ } + m\underline{\ \overset{\frown}{AB}\ })$$

$$m\angle 2 = \tfrac{1}{2}(m\underline{\ \overset{\frown}{AD}\ } + m\underline{\ \overset{\frown}{BC}\ })$$

THEOREM 10.13: ANGLES OUTSIDE THE CIRCLE THEOREM

If a tangent and a secant, two tangents, or two secants intersect *outside* a circle, then the measure of the angle formed is one half the *difference* of the measures of the intercepted arcs.

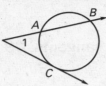 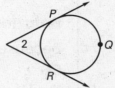

$$m\angle 1 = \frac{1}{2}(m\overset{\frown}{BC} - m\overset{\frown}{AC}) \qquad m\angle 2 = \frac{1}{2}(m\overset{\frown}{PQR} - m\overset{\frown}{PR})$$

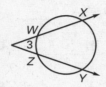

$$m\angle 3 = \frac{1}{2}(m\overset{\frown}{XY} - m\overset{\frown}{WZ})$$

Example 2   *Find an angle measure inside a circle*

Find the value of x.

The chords $\overline{FH}$ and $\overline{GJ}$ intersect inside the circle.

$x° = \frac{1}{2}(m\ \underline{FJ}\ + m\ \underline{HG}\ )$ **Use Theorem 10.12.**

$x° = \frac{1}{2}(\ \underline{112°}\ + \ \underline{140°}\ )$ **Substitute.**

$x = \underline{126}$ **Simplify.**

Example 3   *Find an angle measure outside a circle*

Find the value of x.

The tangent $\overrightarrow{GF}$ and the secant $\overrightarrow{GJ}$ intersect outside the circle.

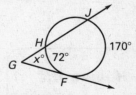

$m\angle FGH = \frac{1}{2}(m\ \underline{FJ}\ - m\ \underline{FH}\ )$ **Use Theorem 10.13.**

$x° = \frac{1}{2}(\ \underline{170°}\ - \ \underline{72°}\ )$ **Substitute.**

$x = \underline{49}$ **Simplify.**

Example 4 **Solve a real-world problem**

Airplane You are flying in an airplane about 5 miles above the ground. What is the measure of arc *BD*, the part of Earth that you can see? (Earth's radius is about 4000 miles.)

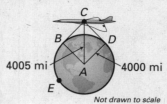

4005 mi   4000 mi

Not drawn to scale

Solution

> Because the value for $m\angle BCD$ is an approximation, use the symbol $\approx$ instead of $=$.

Because $\overline{CB}$ and $\overline{CD}$ are tangents, $\overline{CB} \perp \underline{\ AB\ }$ and $\overline{CD} \perp \underline{\ AD\ }$. Also, $\overline{BC} \cong \underline{\ DC\ }$. So, $\triangle ABC \cong \underline{\ \triangle ADC\ }$ by the HL Congruence Theorem, and $\angle BCA \cong \underline{\ \angle DCA\ }$.

Solve right triangle *CBA* to find that $m\angle BCA \approx \underline{\ 87.1°\ }$.

So, $m\angle BCD \approx 2(\underline{\ 87.1°\ }) = \underline{\ 174.2°\ }$. Let $\overset{\frown}{mBD} = x°$.

$m\angle BCD = \frac{1}{2}(m\ \underline{\overset{\frown}{DEB}} - m\ \underline{\overset{\frown}{BD}}\ )$ **Use Theorem 10.13.**

$\underline{174.2°} \approx \frac{1}{2}[(\underline{\ 360° - x°\ }) - \underline{\ x°\ }]$ **Substitute.**

$x \approx \underline{\ 5.8\ }$ **Solve for x.**

From the airplane, you can see an arc of about $\underline{\ 5.8°\ }$.

✔ *Checkpoint* **Find the indicated measure or the value of the variable.**

1. $\overset{\frown}{mACB}$ 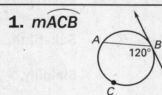 $\overset{\frown}{mACB} = 240°$	**2.** 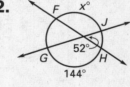 $x = 112$
3. 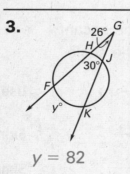 $y = 82$	**4.** 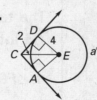 $a \approx 263.6$

Homework

10.6 Find Segment Lengths in Circles

Goal • Find segment lengths in circles.

Your Notes

VOCABULARY

Segments of a chord When two chords intersect in the interior of a circle, each chord is divided into two segments called segments of the chord.

Secant segment A secant segment is a segment that contains a chord of a circle, and has exactly one endpoint outside the circle.

External segment An external segment is the part of a secant segment that is outside the circle.

THEOREM 10.14: SEGMENTS OF CHORDS THEOREM

If two chords intersect in the interior of a circle, then the product of the lengths of the segments of one chord is equal to the product of the lengths of the segments of the other chord.

$EA \cdot \underline{EB} = EC \cdot \underline{ED}$

Example 1 Find lengths using Theorem 10.14

Find *ML* and *JK*.

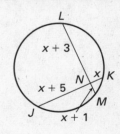

$NK \cdot NJ = \underline{NL} \cdot \underline{NM}$

$x \cdot (x + 5) = (\ \underline{x + 3}\ ) \cdot (\ \underline{x + 1}\ )$

$x^2 + 5x = \underline{x^2 + 4x + 3}$

$x = \underline{3}$

Find *ML* and *JK* by substitution.

$ML = (\ \underline{x + 1}\ ) + (\ \underline{x + 3}\ )$ $JK = \underline{x}\ + (\ \underline{x + 5}\ )$

$\quad = \underline{3} + \underline{1} + \underline{3} + \underline{3}$ $\quad = \underline{3} + \underline{3} + \underline{5}$

$\quad = \underline{10}$ $\quad = \underline{11}$

THEOREM 10.15: SEGMENTS OF SECANTS THEOREM

If two secant segments share the same endpoint outside a circle, then the product of the lengths of one secant segment and its external segment equals the product of the lengths of the other secant segment and its external segment.

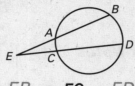

$EA \cdot \underline{EB} = EC \cdot \underline{ED}$

Example 2   **Use Theorem 10.15**

Find the value of *x*.

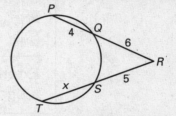

Solution

$$RQ \cdot RP = RS \cdot RT \qquad \text{Use Theorem } \underline{10.15}.$$

$$\underline{6} \cdot (\underline{6} + \underline{4}) = \underline{5} \cdot (x + \underline{5}) \qquad \text{Substitute.}$$

$$\underline{60} = \underline{5}\,x + \underline{25} \qquad \text{Simplify.}$$

$$\underline{7} = x \qquad \text{Solve for } x.$$

✔ **Checkpoint** Find the value of *x*.

1.

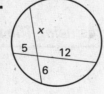

$x = 10$

2.

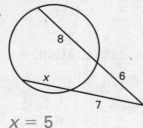

$x = 5$

THEOREM 10.16: SEGMENTS OF SECANTS AND TANGENTS THEOREM

If a secant segment and a tangent segment share an endpoint outside a circle, then the product of the lengths of the secant segment and its external segment equals the square of the length of the tangent segment.

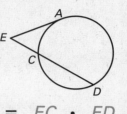

$EA^2 = \underline{EC} \cdot \underline{ED}$

Example 3 Find lengths using Theorem 10.16

Use the figure at the right to find *RS*.

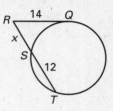

Solution

$RQ^2 = RS \cdot RT$ Use Theorem $\underline{10.16}$.

$\underline{14}^2 = x \cdot (x + \underline{12})$ Substitute.

$\underline{196} = x^2 + \underline{12}x$ Simplify.

$0 = x^2 + \underline{12}x - \underline{196}$ Write in standard form.

$x = \dfrac{-12 \pm \sqrt{\underline{12}^2 - 4(\underline{1})(\underline{-196})}}{2(\underline{1})}$ Use quadratic formula.

$x = \underline{-6 \pm 2\sqrt{58}}$ Simplify.

Lengths cannot be $\underline{negative}$, so use the $\underline{positive}$ solution.

So, $x = \underline{-6 + 2\sqrt{58}} \approx \underline{9.23}$, and $RS \approx \underline{9.23}$.

✔ Checkpoint Complete the following exercise.

3. Use the figure at the right to find *JK*.

    $JK = -3 + \sqrt{73}$

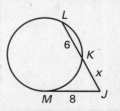

Example 4   *Solve a real-world problem*

Fountain You are standing at point *C*, 45 feet from the Point State Park fountain in Pittsburgh, PA. The distance from you to a point of tangency on the fountain is 105 feet. Find the distance *CA* between you and your friend at point *A*.

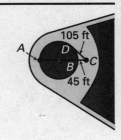

Solution

$\underline{CB} \cdot CA = \underline{CD^2}$ **Use Theorem 10.16.**

$\underline{45} \cdot CA = \underline{105^2}$ **Substitute.**

$CA = \underline{245}$ **Solve for *CA*.**

You are $\underline{245}$ feet from your friend.

✔ *Checkpoint* **Complete the following exercise.**

4. In Example 4, suppose $\overline{AB}$ is a diameter of the fountain. Use the diagram below and Theorem 10.16 to find the radius of the fountain.

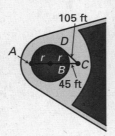

100 ft

Homework

10.7 Write and Graph Equations of Circles

Goal • Write equations of circles in the coordinate plane.

Your Notes

VOCABULARY

Standard equation of a circle The standard equation of a circle with center (h, k) and radius r is
$(x - h)^2 + (y - k)^2 = r^2$.

Example 1 *Write an equation of a circle*

Write the equation of the circle shown.

Solution

The radius is __2__ and the center is at __the origin__.

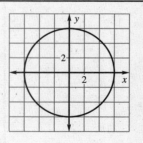

$x^2 + y^2 = $ __r__ ^{2} **Equation of circle**

$x^2 + y^2 = $ __2__ ^{2} **Substitute.**

$x^2 + y^2 = $ __4__   **Simplify.**

The equation of the circle is $x^2 + y^2 = $ __4__.

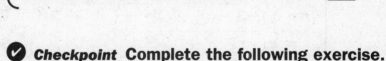 **Checkpoint** Complete the following exercise.

1. Write an equation of the circle shown.

$x^2 + y^2 = 36$

STANDARD EQUATION OF A CIRCLE

The standard equation of a circle with center (h, k) and radius r is:

$$(x - h)^2 + (y - k)^2 = r^2$$

Example 2   *Write the standard equation of a circle*

Write the standard equation of a circle with center $(0, -5)$ and radius 3.7.

$$(x - h)^2 + (y - k)^2 = r^2 \qquad \text{Standard equation of a circle}$$

$$(x - \underline{0})^2 + (y - (\underline{-5}))^2 = \underline{3.7}^{\,2} \qquad \text{Substitute.}$$

$$x^2 + (y + \underline{5})^2 = \underline{13.69} \qquad \text{Simplify.}$$

Example 3   *Write the standard equation of a circle*

The point $(-3, 4)$ is on a circle with center $(-1, 2)$. Write the standard equation of the circle.

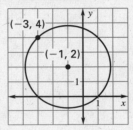

Solution

To write the standard equation, you need to know the values of h, k, and r. To find r, find the distance between the <u>center</u> and the point $(-3, 4)$ on the circle.

$$r = \sqrt{[-3 - (\underline{-1})]^2 + (\underline{4} - 2)^2} \qquad \text{Distance formula}$$

$$= \sqrt{(\underline{-2})^2 + \underline{2}^{\,2}} \qquad \text{Simplify.}$$

$$= \underline{2\sqrt{2}} \qquad \text{Simplify.}$$

Substitute $(h, k) = (-1, 2)$ and $r = \underline{2\sqrt{2}}$ into the standard equation of a circle.

$$(x - h)^2 + (y - k)^2 = r^2 \qquad \text{Standard equation of a circle}$$

$$(x - (\underline{-1}))^2 + (y - \underline{2})^2 = (\underline{2\sqrt{2}})^2 \qquad \text{Substitute.}$$

$$(x + \underline{1})^2 + (y - \underline{2})^2 = \underline{8} \qquad \text{Simplify.}$$

The standard equation of the circle is $(x + \underline{1})^2 + (y - \underline{2})^2 = \underline{8}$.

Example 4 *Graph a circle*

The equation of a circle is $(x - 2)^2 + (y + 3)^2 = 16$. Graph the circle.

If you know the equation of a circle, you can graph the circle by identifying its center and radius.

Solution

Rewrite the equation to find the center and radius.

$$(x - 2)^2 + (y + 3)^2 = 16$$

$$(x - 2)^2 + [y - (\underline{-3})]^2 = \underline{4^2}$$

The center is (\underline{2} , \underline{-3}) and the radius is \underline{4} . Use a compass to graph the circle.

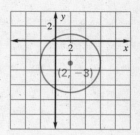

✔ *Checkpoint* **Complete the following exercises.**

2. Write the standard equation of a circle with center $(-3, -5)$ and radius 6.1.

   $(x + 3)^2 + (y + 5)^2 = 37.21$

3. The point $(-1, 2)$ is on a circle with center $(3, -3)$. Write the standard equation of the circle.

   $(x - 3)^2 + (y + 3)^2 = 41$

4. The equation of a circle is $(x + 2)^2 + (y - 1)^2 = 9$. Graph the circle.

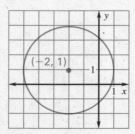

Example 5   *Use graphs of circles*

Time Capsule You bury a time capsule and use a grid to write directions for finding it. Use the following measurements to find the burial location of the time capsule.

- The capsule is about 11 feet from the oak tree at A(0, 0).
- The capsule is 8 feet from the flagpole at B(0, 8).
- The capsule is 4 feet from the mailbox at C(−12, 8).

Solution

The set of all points equidistant from a given point is a circle, so the burial location is located on each of the following circles.

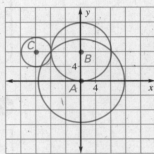

⊙A with center (_0_ , _0_) and radius __11__

⊙B with center (_0_ , _8_) and radius _8_

⊙C with center (_−12_ , _8_) and radius _4_

To find the burial location, graph the circles on a graph where units are measured in feet. Estimate the point of __intersection__ of all three circles.

The burial location is at about (_−8_ , _8_).

✔ **Checkpoint** Complete the following exercise.

5. In Example 4, suppose the mailbox is at C(12, 8) and the time capsule is 4 feet away. Find the burial location of the time capsule.

(8, 8)

Homework

Words to Review

Give an example of the vocabulary word.

Circle 	**Center, radius, diameter of a circle** 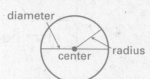
Chord 	**Secant**
Tangent 	**Central angle** 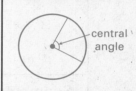
Minor arc, Major arc $\overset{\frown}{AB}$ is a minor arc. $\overset{\frown}{ACB}$ is a major arc.	**Semicircle** 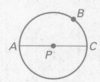 $\overset{\frown}{ABC}$ is a semicircle.
Measure of a minor arc $m\overset{\frown}{AB} = 92°$	**Measure of a major arc** $m\overset{\frown}{ACB} = 268°$

Congruent circles	Congruent arcs
	$\overset{\frown}{AB} \cong \overset{\frown}{BC}$
Inscribed angle	Intercepted arc
inscribed angle	intercepted arc
Inscribed polygon	Circumscribed circle
inscribed polygon	circumscribed circle
Segments of a chord	Secant segment
segments of a chord	secant segment
External segment	Standard equation of a circle
external segment	$(x - h)^2 + (y - k)^2 = r^2$ where the center of the circle is (h, k) and the radius is r.

Review your notes and Chapter 10 by using the Chapter Review on pages 708–711 of your textbook.

Areas of Triangles and Parallelograms

Goal • Find areas of triangles and parallelograms.

Your Notes

VOCABULARY

Bases of a parallelogram Either pair of parallel sides of a parallelogram are bases.

Height of a parallelogram The shortest distance between bases of a parallelogram is the height.

POSTULATE 24: AREA OF A SQUARE POSTULATE

The area of a square is the __square__ of the length of its side.

POSTULATE 25: AREA CONGRUENCE POSTULATE

If two polygons are __congruent__, then they have the same area.

POSTULATE 26: AREA ADDITION POSTULATE

The area of a region is the __sum__ of the areas of its nonoverlapping parts.

THEOREM 11.1: AREA OF A RECTANGLE

The area of a rectangle is the product of its __base__ and __height__.

THEOREM 11.2: AREA OF A PARALLELOGRAM

The area of a parallelogram is the product of a __base__ and its corresponding __height__.

THEOREM 11.3: AREA OF A TRIANGLE

The area of a triangle is __one half__ the product of a __base__ and its corresponding __height__.

Your Notes

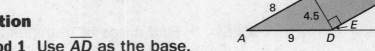
Example 1   *Use a formula to find area*

Find the area of □ABCD.

Solution

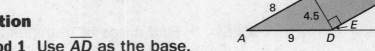

Method 1 Use $\overline{AD}$ as the base.
The base is extended to measure the
height _CF_ . So, $b =$ _9_ and $h =$ _4_ .

Area $= bh =$ _9_ (_4_) $=$ _36_ square units

Method 2 Use $\overline{AB}$ as the base.
Then the height is _BE_ . So, $b =$ _8_ and
$h =$ _4.5_ .

Area $= bh =$ _8_ (_4.5_) $=$ _36_ square units

✔ **Checkpoint** Find the area of the polygon.

1.
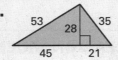
53   28   35
45   21

924 square units

2.
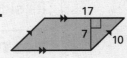
17
7   10

119 square units

Example 2   *Solve for unknown measures*

**The base of a triangle is four times its height. The
area of the triangle is 50 square inches. Find the
base and height.**

Solution

Let h represent the height of the triangle.
Then the base is _4h_ .

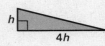
h
$4h$

$A = \frac{1}{2}bh$ .... **Write formula.**

_50_ $= \frac{1}{2}($ _4h_ $)(h)$ .... **Substitute** _50_ **for A and** _4h_ **for b.**

_50_ $=$ _2_ h^2 .... **Simplify.**

_25_ $= h^2$ .... **Divide each side by** _2_ .

_5_ $= h$ .... **Find positive square root of each side.**

The height of the triangle is _5_ inches, and the base is
4 · _5_ $=$ _20_ inches.

> Note that there are
> other ways you can
> draw the triangle in
> Example 2.
>
>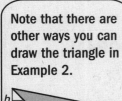
> h
> $4h$

Example 3   *Solve a multi-step problem*

Vacuum A robotic vacuum cleaner can clean 2 square meters of carpet in 8 minutes. About how long does it take for it to clean a carpet covering a room with the dimensions shown at the right?

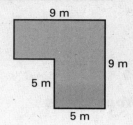

Solution

Step 1 Find the area of the carpet.

Area = Area of rectangle + Area of square

= 4(9) + 5(5) = 61 m^2

Step 2 Determine how long it takes the robotic vacuum to clean the carpet.

61 m^2 · $\dfrac{8 \text{ min}}{2 \text{ m}^2}$ = 244 minutes   **Use unit analysis.**

It takes 244 minutes, or about 4 hours for the robotic vacuum to clean the carpet.

✓ *Checkpoint* **Complete the following exercises.**

3. A parallelogram has an area of 133 square feet and a height of 19 feet. What is the length of the base?

7 feet

---

4. In Example 3, suppose there are 4 sections of carpet measuring 1 meter by 2 meters that are covered and cannot be swept. About how many hours does it take for the robotic vacuum to clean the carpet?

about 3.5 hours

Homework

11.2 Areas of Trapezoids, Rhombuses, and Kites

Goal • Find areas of other types of quadrilaterals.

VOCABULARY

Height of a trapezoid The height of a trapezoid is the perpendicular distance between its bases.

THEOREM 11.4: AREA OF A TRAPEZOID

The area of a trapezoid is one half the product of the height and the sum of the lengths of the bases.

$$A = \frac{1}{2} \underline{\;h\;} (\underline{\;b_1\;} + \underline{\;b_2\;})$$

Example 1 *Find the area of a trapezoid*

Beavers To prevent beavers from damming a drainage pipe, the trapezoid-shaped fence shown is placed at the pipe. Approximate the area enclosed by the fence.

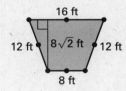

Solution

The height of the trapezoid is $\underline{\;8\sqrt{2}\;}$ feet. The lengths of the bases are $\underline{\;16\;}$ feet and $\underline{\;8\;}$ feet.

$A = \frac{1}{2}h(b_1 + b_2)$ **Formula for area of a trapezoid**

$\quad = \frac{1}{2}(\underline{\;8\sqrt{2}\;})(\underline{\;16\;} + \underline{\;8\;})$ **Substitute.**

$\quad \approx \underline{\;136\;}$ **Approximate.**

The area enclosed by the fence is about $\underline{\;136\;}$ square feet.

THEOREM 11.5: AREA OF A RHOMBUS

The area of a rhombus is one half the product of the lengths of its diagonals.

$$A = \frac{1}{2} \underline{d_1 d_2}$$

THEOREM 11.6: AREA OF A KITE

The area of a kite is one half the product of the lengths of its diagonals.

$$A = \frac{1}{2} \underline{d_1 d_2}$$

Example 2 **Find the area of a rhombus**

Find the area of the rhombus.

Solution

Step 1 **Find** the length of each diagonal. The diagonals of a rhombus __bisect__ each other, so $QT = \underline{\ TS\ }$ and $PT = \underline{\ TR\ }$.

$QS = QT + \underline{\ TS\ } = 8 + \underline{\ 8\ } = \underline{\ 16\ }$ cm

$PR = \underline{\ PT\ } + TR = \underline{\ 11\ } + 11 = \underline{\ 22\ }$ cm

Step 2 **Find** the area of the rhombus. Let d_1 represent QS and d_2 represent PR.

$A = \frac{1}{2}d_1 d_2$ **Formula for area of a rhombus**

$= \frac{1}{2}(\underline{\ 16\ })(\underline{\ 22\ })$ **Substitute.**

$= \underline{\ 176\ }$ **Simplify.**

The area of the rhombus is __176__ square centimeters.

✓ **Checkpoint** **Find the area of the figure.**

1.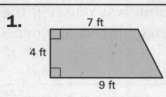

7 ft

4 ft

9 ft

32 ft²

2.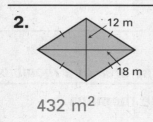

12 m

18 m

432 m²

| Example 3 | **Solve for unknown measures** |

One diagonal of a kite is two times as long as the other diagonal. The area of the kite is 56.25 square inches. What are the lengths of the diagonals?

Solution

Draw and label a diagram. Let x be the length of one diagonal. The other diagonal is twice as long, so label it ___2x___. Use the formula for the area of a kite to find the value of x.

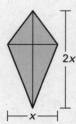

2x

x

$$A = \frac{1}{2}d_1d_2 \qquad \text{Formula for area of a kite}$$

$\underline{\quad 56.25 \quad} = \frac{1}{2}(\underline{\ x\ })(\underline{\ 2x\ })$ **Substitute.**

$\underline{\quad 56.25 \quad} = \underline{\ x^2\ }$ **Simplify.**

$\underline{\quad 7.5 \quad} = x$ **Find positive square root of each side.**

The lengths of the diagonals are __7.5__ inches and 2(__7.5__) = __15__ inches.

Your Notes

Example 4   *Find an area in the coordinate plane*

Yard You have a diagram of your backyard. Each square represents a 3 meter by 3 meter square. Find the area of your backyard.

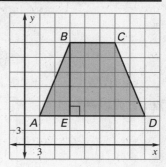

Solution

Step 1 Find the lengths of the bases and the height of trapezoid *ABCD*.

$$b_1 = BC = |\ \underline{18}\ -\ \underline{9}\ | = \underline{9}\ \text{m}$$
$$b_2 = AD = |\ \underline{24}\ -\ \underline{3}\ | = \underline{21}\ \text{m}$$
$$h = BE = |\ \underline{21}\ -\ \underline{6}\ | = \underline{15}\ \text{m}$$

Step 2 Find the area of *ABCD*.

$$A = \frac{1}{2}h(b_1 + b_2) = \frac{1}{2}(\underline{15})(\underline{9} + \underline{21}) = \underline{225}$$

The area of your backyard is __225__ square meters.

✔ *Checkpoint* **Complete the following exercises.**

3. One diagonal of a kite is three times as long as the other diagonal. The area of the kite is 73.5 square yards. What are the lengths of the diagonals?

7 yards and 21 yards

---

4. Find the area of a rhombus with vertices *M*(2, 4), *N*(5, 6), *P*(8, 4), and *Q*(5, 2).

12 square units

Homework

Perimeter and Area of Similar Figures

Goal • Use ratios to find areas of similar figures.

Your Notes

> **THEOREM 11.7: AREAS OF SIMILAR POLYGONS**
>
> If two polygons are similar with the lengths of corresponding sides in the ratio of $a:b$, then the ratio of their areas is $\underline{a^2} : \underline{b^2}$.
>
> $\dfrac{\text{Side length of Polygon I}}{\text{Side length of Polygon II}} = \dfrac{a}{b}$
>
> $\dfrac{\text{Area of Polygon I}}{\text{Area of Polygon II}} = \dfrac{a^2}{b^2}$
>
>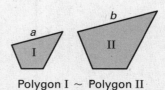
>
> Polygon I ~ Polygon II

Example 1 *Find ratios of similar polygons*

In the diagram, $\triangle ABC \sim \triangle DEF$.
Find the indicated ratio.

a. Ratio (shaded to unshaded) of the perimeters

b. Ratio (shaded to unshaded) of the areas

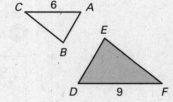

> You can also compare the measures with fractions. The perimeter of $\triangle DEF$ is three halves the perimeter of $\triangle ABC$. The area of $\triangle DEF$ is nine fourths the area of $\triangle ABC$.

Solution

The ratio of the lengths of corresponding sides is
$\dfrac{9}{6} = \dfrac{3}{2}$, or $\underline{3} : \underline{2}$.

a. By Theorem 6.1, the ratio of the perimeters is $\underline{3} : \underline{2}$.

b. By Theorem 11.7 above, the ratio of the areas is
$\underline{3^2} : \underline{2^2}$, or $\underline{9} : \underline{4}$.

Example 2 *Solve a real-world problem*

Windows You buy two rectangular pieces of aluminum window screening. One is 15 feet long and costs $135. The other is similar in shape and is 20 feet long. The screen is sold by the square foot. What is the cost of the longer roll?

Solution

The ratio of the length of the longer roll to the shorter roll is $\underline{20}$: $\underline{15}$, or $\underline{4}$: $\underline{3}$. So, the ratio of the areas is $\underline{4^2}$: $\underline{3^2}$, or $\underline{16}$: $\underline{9}$. This ratio is also the ratio of the screen costs. Let x be the cost of the longer roll.

$$\frac{16}{9} = \frac{x}{\boxed{135}}$$ ← Cost of longer roll
← Cost of shorter roll

$x = \underline{240}$ Solve for x.

It costs $\$\underline{240}$ for the longer roll.

✔ **Checkpoint** **Complete the following exercises.**

1. Given $\triangle ABC \sim \triangle DEF$, find the ratio (shaded to unshaded) of the perimeters and areas.

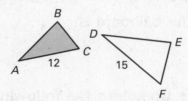

$4:5; \ 16:25$

2. In Example 2, suppose you decide to buy a different kind of screening but in the same dimensions. The longer roll costs $200. What is the cost of the shorter roll?

$112.50

Example 3 **Use a ratio of areas**

Billboards A large rectangular billboard is 12 feet high and 27 feet long. A smaller billboard is similar to the large billboard. The area of the smaller billboard is 144 square feet. Find the height of the smaller billboard.

Solution

First draw a diagram to represent the problem. Label dimensions and areas.

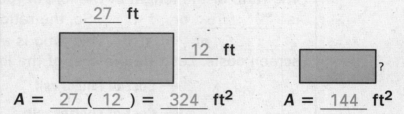

$A =$ __27__ (__12__) = __324__ ft^2 $A =$ __144__ ft^2

Then use Theorem 11.7. If the area ratio is $a^2 : b^2$, then the length ratio is __a__ : __b__ .

$$\frac{\text{area of smaller billboard}}{\text{area of large billboard}} = \frac{144}{324} = \frac{4}{9}$$

$$\frac{\text{length of smaller billboard}}{\text{length of large billboard}} = \frac{2}{3}$$

Any length in the smaller billboard is $\frac{2}{3}$ of the corresponding length in the large billboard. So, the height of the smaller billboard is $\frac{2}{3}$ (__12__ feet) = __8__ feet.

✔ *Checkpoint* **Complete the following exercise.**

3. In Example 3, suppose the area of the smaller billboard is 225 square feet. Find the height of the smaller billboard.

   10 ft

Example 4 *Solve a multi-step problem*

Stop sign A stop sign rug is a regular octagon. Each side is 2 feet and the area is about 19.3 square feet. You make a stop sign mat with a perimeter of 72 inches. Find the area of the mat to the nearest tenth of a square inch.

Solution

All regular octagons are similar, so the rug and mat are similar.

Step 1 **Find** the ratio of the lengths of the rug and mat by finding the ratio of the perimeters. Use the same units for both lengths in the ratio.

$$\frac{\text{Perimeter of rug}}{\text{Perimeter of mat}} = \frac{8(2 \text{ ft})}{72 \text{ in.}} = \frac{16 \text{ ft}}{6 \text{ ft}} = \frac{8}{3}$$

So, the ratio of corresponding lengths (rug to mat) is 8 : 3 .

Step 2 **Calculate** the area of the mat. Let x be this area.

$$\frac{(\text{length in rug})^2}{(\text{length in mat})^2} = \frac{\text{area of rug}}{\text{area of mat}}$$

$$\frac{8^2}{3^2} = \frac{19.3 \text{ ft}^2}{x \text{ ft}^2}$$

$$64 \, x = 173.7$$

$$x \approx 2.714 \text{ ft}^2$$

Step 3 **Convert** the area to square inches.

$$2.714 \text{ ft}^2 \cdot \frac{144 \text{ in.}^2}{1 \text{ ft}^2} \approx 390.8 \text{ in.}^2$$

The area of the mat is about 390.8 square inches.

✔ *Checkpoint* **Complete the following exercise.**

4. Rectangles I and II are similar. The perimeter of Rectangle I is 48 inches. Rectangle II is 30 inches by 18 inches. Find the area of Rectangle I.

135 in.^{2}

Goal • Find arc lengths and other measures.

Your Notes

VOCABULARY

Circumference The circumference of a circle is the distance around the circle.

Arc length An arc length is a portion of the circumference of a circle.

THEOREM 11.8: CIRCUMFERENCE OF A CIRCLE

The circumference C of a circle is $C = \underline{\pi d}$ or $C = \underline{2\pi r}$, where d is the diameter of the circle and r is the radius of the circle.

$C = \underline{\pi d} = \underline{2\pi r}$

Example 1   *Use the formula for circumference*

Find the indicated measure.

a. Circumference of a circle with radius 11 meters

b. Radius of a circle with circumference 18 yards

Solution

a. $C = 2\pi r$

$= 2 \cdot \pi \cdot \underline{11}$

$= \underline{22}\,\pi$

$\approx \underline{69.12}\ $ m

b. $C = 2\pi r$

$\underline{18} = 2\pi r$

$\dfrac{18}{2\pi} = r$

$\underline{2.86}\ $ yd $\approx r$

✔ *Checkpoint* **Complete the following exercise.**

1. Find the circumference of a circle with diameter 23 inches.

about 72.26 inches

Your Notes

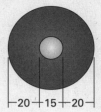

> Always pay attention to units. As in Example 2, you may need to convert units to get a correct answer.

Example 2   *Use circumference to find distance traveled*

Skateboarding The dimensions of the skateboard wheel shown at the right are in millimeters. To the nearest meter, how far does the wheel travel when it makes 35 revolutions?

−20 −15 −20

Solution

Step 1 **Find** the diameter of the wheel.

$$d = \underline{\ 15\ } + 2(\underline{\ 20\ }) = \underline{\ 55\ } \text{ mm}$$

Step 2 **Find** the circumference of the wheel.

$$C = \pi d = \pi(\underline{\ 55\ }) \approx \underline{\ 172.8\ } \text{ mm}$$

Step 3 **Find** the distance the wheel travels in 35 revolutions. In one revolution, the wheel travels a distance equal to its __circumference__. In 35 revolutions, the wheel travels a distance equal to __35__ times its circumference.

$$\frac{\text{Distance}}{\text{traveled}} = \frac{\text{Number of}}{\text{revolutions}} \cdot \text{Circumference}$$

$$\approx \underline{\ 35\ } \cdot \underline{\ 172.8\ } \text{ mm}$$

$$= \underline{\ 6048\ } \text{ mm}$$

Step 4 **Use** unit analysis. Change __6048__ millimeters to meters.

$$\underline{\ 6048\ } \text{ mm} \cdot \frac{1 \text{ m}}{1000 \text{ mm}} = \underline{\ 6.048\ } \text{ m}$$

The wheel travels about __6__ meters.

✔ *Checkpoint* **Complete the following exercise.**

> **2.** A skateboard wheel has a diameter of 56 millimeters. How many revolutions does the wheel make when traveling 3 meters?
>
> about 17 revolutions

ARC LENGTH COROLLARY

In a circle, the ratio of the length of a given arc to the circumference is equal to the ratio of the measure of the arc to 360°.

$$\frac{\text{Arc length of } \overset{\frown}{AB}}{2\pi r} = \frac{m\overset{\frown}{AB}}{360°}, \text{ or}$$

$$\text{Arc length of } \overset{\frown}{AB} = \frac{m\overset{\frown}{AB}}{360°} \cdot 2\pi r$$

Example 3   *Find and use arc lengths*

Find the indicated measure.

a. Arc length of $\overset{\frown}{AB}$ **b.** $m\overset{\frown}{RS}$

a. Arc length of $\overset{\frown}{AB} = \dfrac{88°}{360°} \cdot 2\pi(\underline{2}) \approx \underline{3.07}$ meters

b. $\dfrac{\text{Arc length of } \overset{\frown}{RS}}{2\pi r} = \dfrac{m\overset{\frown}{RS}}{360°}$ Write equation.

$\dfrac{\boxed{38}}{2\pi\boxed{12.3}} = \dfrac{m\overset{\frown}{RS}}{360°}$ Substitute.

$\underline{360°} \cdot \dfrac{\boxed{38}}{2\pi\boxed{12.3}} = m\overset{\frown}{RS}$ Multiply each side by $\underline{360°}$.

$\underline{177°} \approx m\overset{\frown}{RS}$ Use a calculator.

✔ *Checkpoint* Find the indicated measure.

3. Arc length of $\overset{\frown}{AB}$	**4.** Circumference of $\odot Z$
	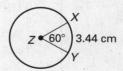
about 6.77 ft	20.64 cm

Example 4   *Use arc length to find distances*

Luggage A conveyor belt for luggage at an airport is shown at the right. The outer part of the belt forms a 180° arc at each end. For each arc, the radius is 8 feet. Approximate the distance around the belt for a coin on the outer portion. Round to the nearest foot.

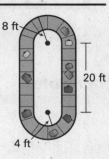

8 ft

20 ft

4 ft

Solution

The outer portion is made of two straight sections and two semicircles. To find the distance around the outer portion, find the sum of the lengths of each part.

$$\text{Distance} = 2 \cdot \begin{array}{c}\text{Length of each}\\\text{straight section}\end{array} + 2 \cdot \begin{array}{c}\text{Length of each}\\\text{semicircle}\end{array}$$

$$= 2(\underline{\ 20\ }) + 2 \cdot \left(\frac{1}{2} \cdot 2\pi \cdot 8\right)$$

$$\approx \underline{\ 90.27\ } \text{ feet}$$

The distance around the outer portion is about __90__ feet.

✔ *Checkpoint* **Complete the following exercise.**

5. In Example 4, the inner portion of the belt also has 180° arcs on each end. The radius of each arc is 4 feet. Find the distance around the belt for a coin on the inner portion. Round to the nearest foot.

   about 65 ft

Homework

11.5 Areas of Circles and Sectors

Goal • Find the areas of circles and sectors.

Your Notes

VOCABULARY

Sector of a circle A sector of a circle is the region bounded by two radii of the circle and their intercepted arc.

THEOREM 11.9: AREA OF A CIRCLE

The area of a circle is π times the square of the radius.

$A = \underline{\pi r^2}$

Example 1 *Use the formula for area of a circle*

Find the indicated measure.

a. Area

4.2 m

b. Diameter

$A = 201$ in.^{2}

Solution

a. $A = \pi r^2$ Write formula for the area of a circle.

$= \pi(\underline{\ 4.2\ })^2$ Substitute $\underline{4.2}$ for r.

$= \underline{17.64}\ \pi$ Simplify.

$\approx \underline{55.42}$ m^2 Use a calculator.

b. $A = \pi r^2$ Write formula for the area of a circle.

$\underline{201} = \pi r^2$ Substitute $\underline{201}$ for A.

$\dfrac{201}{\pi} = r^2$ Divide each side by $\underline{\pi}$.

$\underline{8}$ in. $\approx r$ Find the positive square root of each side.

The radius is about $\underline{8}$ inches, so the diameter is about $\underline{16}$ inches.

Your Notes

THEOREM 11.10: AREA OF A SECTOR

The ratio of the area of a sector of a circle to the area of the whole circle (πr^2) is equal to the ratio of the measure of the intercepted arc to 360°.

$$\frac{\text{Arc of sector } APB}{\boxed{\pi r^2}} = \frac{\boxed{m\overset{\frown}{AB}}}{360°}, \text{ or}$$

$$\text{Area of sector } APB = \frac{\boxed{m\overset{\frown}{AB}}}{360°} \cdot \underline{\pi r^2}$$

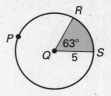

Example 2   *Find areas of sectors*

Find the areas of the sectors formed by ∠RQS.

Solution

Step 1 Find the measures of the minor and major arcs.

Because $m\angle RQS = \underline{63°}$, $m\overset{\frown}{RS} = \underline{63°}$ and $m\overset{\frown}{RPS} = 360° - \underline{63°} = \underline{297°}$.

Step 2 Find the areas of the small and large sectors.

$$\text{Area of small sector} = \frac{m\overset{\frown}{RS}}{360°} \cdot \pi r^2$$

$$= \frac{\boxed{63°}}{360°} \cdot \pi \cdot \underline{5}^{\,2}$$

$$\approx \underline{13.74}$$

$$\text{Area of large sector} = \frac{m\overset{\frown}{RPS}}{360°} \cdot \pi r^2$$

$$= \frac{\boxed{297°}}{360°} \cdot \pi \cdot \underline{5}^{\,2}$$

$$\approx \underline{64.80}$$

The areas of the small and large sectors are about __13.74__ square units and __64.80__ square units, respectively.

Your Notes

✓ **Checkpoint** In Exercises 1 and 2, use the diagram to find the indicated measure.

1. Area

9 cm

about 63.62 cm²

2. Radius

A = 154 ft²

about 7 ft

3. Find the areas of the sectors formed by ∠RQS.

small sector: about 74.93 ft²;
large sector: about 179.54 ft²

P R
Q 106°
9 ft
S

Example 3   *Use the Area of a Sector Theorem*

Use the diagram to find the area of ⊙C.

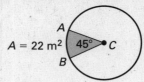

A = 22 m²   45°   C
B

Solution

Area of sector $ACB = \dfrac{m\widehat{AB}}{360°}$ • Area of ⊙C

$\dfrac{22}{} = \dfrac{\boxed{45°}}{360°}$ • Area of ⊙C

$\underline{176}$ = Area of ⊙C

The area of ⊙C is __176__ square meters.

Your Notes

Example 4 *Find an area*

Construction A contractor needs to cut a section out of a rectangular piece of wood as shown. To the nearest square inch, what is the area of the remaining wood?

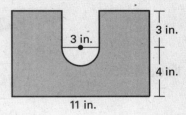

3 in.

3 in.

4 in.

11 in.

Solution

The area you need to find is the area of the rectangle minus the area of the cut-out section. The cut-out can be divided into a semicircle and a square.

Area of wood

$$= \boxed{\begin{array}{c}\text{Area of} \\ \text{rectangle}\end{array}} - \left[\begin{array}{c}\text{Area of} \\ \text{semicircle}\end{array} + \begin{array}{c}\text{Area of} \\ \text{square}\end{array}\right]$$

$$= \underline{11} \; (\; \underline{7}\;) - \left[\; \frac{180°}{360°} \cdot (\; \underline{\pi \cdot 1.5^2}\;) + \underline{3^2}\;\right]$$

$$= \underline{77} - [\; \underline{1.125\pi} + \underline{9}\;]$$

$$\approx \underline{64.47}$$

The area is about ___64.5___ square inches.

> Use the radius (1.5 in.) not the diameter (3 in.) when you calculate the area of the semicircle.

✔ *Checkpoint* **Complete the following exercises.**

4. Find the area of ⊙G.

28.8 yd²

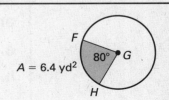

F

80°

G

A = 6.4 yd²

H

---

5. Find the area of the figure.

about 33.24 ft²

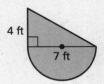

4 ft

7 ft

Homework

11.6 Areas of Regular Polygons

Goal • Find areas of regular polygons inscribed in circles.

Your Notes

VOCABULARY

Center of a polygon The center of a polygon is the center of its circumscribed circle.

Radius of a polygon The radius of a polygon is the radius of its circumscribed circle.

Apothem of a polygon The distance from the center to any side of the polygon is the apothem.

Central angle of a regular polygon A central angle of a regular polygon is an angle formed by two radii drawn to consecutive vertices of the polygon.

Example 1 *Find angle measures in a regular polygon*

In the diagram, *ABCDEF* is a regular hexagon inscribed in ⊙*G*. Find each angle measure.

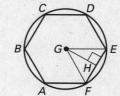

a. *m∠EGF*

b. *m∠EGH*

c. *m∠HEG*

Solution

a. ∠*EGF* is a central angle, so $m\angle EGF = \dfrac{360°}{6}$, or __60°__ .

b. $\overline{GH}$ is an apothem, which makes it an __altitude__ of isosceles △*EGF*. So, $\overline{GH}$ __bisects__ ∠*EGF* and
$m\angle EGH = \dfrac{1}{2}\, m\angle EGF =$ __30°__ .

c. The sum of the measures of right △*HEG* is 180°.
So, __90°__ + __30°__ + *m∠HEG* = 180°, and
m∠HEG = __60°__ .

THEOREM 11.11: AREA OF A REGULAR POLYGON

The area of a regular *n*-gon with side length *s* is half the product of the apothem *a* and the perimeter *P*, so

$A = \frac{1}{2}$ _aP_ , or $A = \frac{1}{2}$ _a_ • _ns_ .

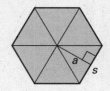

Example 2   *Find the area of a regular polygon*

Coaster A wooden coaster is a regular octagon with 3 centimeter sides and a radius of about 3.92 centimeters. What is the area of the coaster?

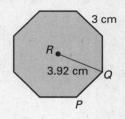

Solution

Step 1 **Find** the perimeter *P* of the coaster. An octagon has __8__ sides, so *P* = __8__ (__3__) = __24__ centimeters.

Step 2 **Find** the apothem *a*. The apothem is height __RS__ of △*PQR*. Because △*PQR* is isosceles, altitude $\overline{RS}$ __bisects__ $\overline{QP}$.

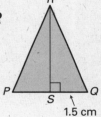

So, $QS = \frac{1}{2}(QP) = \frac{1}{2}(\,3\,)$

$= \underline{1.5}$ cm.

To find *RS*, use the Pythagorean Theorem for △*RQS*.

$a = RS$

$\approx \sqrt{\underline{3.92}\,^2 - \underline{1.5}\,^2} = \sqrt{\underline{13.1164}} \approx \underline{3.622}$

Step 3 **Find** the area *A* of the coaster.

> In general, your answer will be more accurate if you avoid rounding until the last step. Round your final answers to the nearest tenth unless you are told otherwise.

$A = \frac{1}{2}aP$ **Formula for area of regular polygon**

$\approx \frac{1}{2}(\,\underline{3.622}\,)(\,\underline{24}\,)$ **Substitute.**

$\approx \underline{43.5}$ **Simplify.**

The area of the coaster is about __43.5__ square centimeters.

Your Notes

✓ *Checkpoint* **Complete the following exercises.**

1. In the diagram, *FGHJ* is a square inscribed in ⊙*K*. Find *m∠FKJ* and *m∠KJF*.

   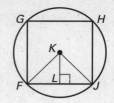

   m∠FKJ = 90°; *m∠KJF* = 45°

---

2. The radius of the regular pentagon is about 6.8 inches. Find the area to the nearest square inch.

   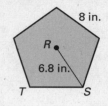

   about 110 in.^{2}

Example 3   *Find the perimeter and area of a regular polygon*

A regular nonagon is inscribed in a circle with radius 5 units. Find the perimeter *P* and area *A* of the nonagon.

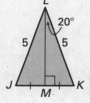

The measure of central ∠*JLK* is $\frac{360°}{9}$, or __40°__ .

Apothem $\overline{LM}$ bisects the central angle, so *m∠KLM* is __20°__ . To find the lengths of the legs, use trigonometric ratios for right △*KLM*.

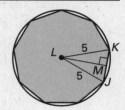

$\sin \underline{\ 20°\ } = \dfrac{MK}{5}$ $\cos \underline{\ 20°\ } = \dfrac{LM}{5}$

$\underline{\ 5\sin 20°\ } = MK$ $\underline{\ 5\cos 20°\ } = LM$

The regular nonagon has side lengths
$s = 2MK = 2(\underline{\ 5\sin 20°\ }) = \underline{\ 10\sin 20°\ }$
and apothem $a = LM = \underline{\ 5\cos 20°\ }$.

So,

$P = 9s = 9(\underline{\ 10\sin 20°\ }) = \underline{\ 90\sin 20°\ } \approx \underline{\ 30.8\ }$ units,

and

$A = \dfrac{1}{2}aP$

$\quad = \dfrac{1}{2}(\underline{\ 5\cos 20°\ })(\underline{\ 90\sin 20°\ }) \approx \underline{\ 72.3\ }$ square units.

✔ **Checkpoint** **Complete the following exercise.**

3. Find the perimeter and area of the equilateral triangle inscribed in ⊙*F*.

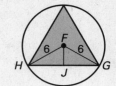

Perimeter: about 31.2 units; Area: about 46.8 square units

FINDING LENGTHS IN A REGULAR *N*-GON

To find the area of a regular *n*-gon with radius *r*, you may need to first find the apothem *a* or the side length *s*.

You can use . . .	. . . when you know *n* and . . .	. . . as in . . .
Pythagorean Theorem: $\left(\frac{1}{2}s\right)^2 + a^2 = r^2$	Two measures: *r* and *a*, or *r* and *s*	Example 2 and Checkpoint Ex. 2
Special Right Triangles	Any one measure: *r* or *a* or *s* **And** the value of *n* is 3, 4, or 6	Checkpoint Ex. 3
Trigonometry	Any one measure: *r* or *a* or *s*	Example 3 and Checkpoint Ex. 3

Homework

Use Geometric Probability

Goal • Use lengths and areas to find geometric probabilities.

Your Notes

VOCABULARY

Probability The probability of an event is a measure of the likelihood that the event will occur.

Geometric probability A geometric probability is a ratio that involves a geometric measure such as length or area.

PROBABILITY AND LENGTH

Let $\overline{AB}$ be a segment that contains the segment $\overline{CD}$. If a point K on $\overline{AB}$ is chosen at random, then the probability that it is on $\overline{CD}$ is the ratio of the length of $\overline{CD}$ to the length of $\overline{AB}$.

$$P(K \text{ is on } \overline{CD}) = \frac{\text{Length of } \overline{CD}}{\text{Length of } \overline{AB}}$$

Example 1 *Use lengths to find a geometric probability*

Find the probability that a point chosen at random on $\overline{FJ}$ is on $\overline{GK}$.

F G   H   K J
—8 —6 —4 —2   0   2   4   6   8

> To apply the geometric probability formulas on this page and the next, you need to know that every point on the segment or in the region is *equally likely* to be chosen.

Solution

$$P(\text{Point is on } \overline{GK}) = \frac{\text{Length of } \boxed{GK}}{\text{Length of } \boxed{FJ}}$$

$$= \frac{\boxed{6 - (-3)}}{\boxed{7 - (-5)}}$$

$$= \frac{9}{12} = \frac{3}{4}, \underline{\ 0.75\ }, \text{ or } \underline{\ 75\ } \%$$

Your Notes

Example 2 *Use a segment to model a real-world probability*

Shuttle A shuttle to town runs every 10 minutes. The ride from your boarding location to town takes 13 minutes. One afternoon, you arrive at the boarding location at 2:41. You want to get to town by 2:57. What is the probability you will get there by 2:57?

Solution

Step 1 Find the longest you can wait for the shuttle and still get to town by 2:57. The ride takes 13 minutes, so you need to catch the shuttle no later than 13 minutes before 2:57, or __2:44__. The longest you can wait is __3__ minutes (__2:44__ − 2:41 = __3__ min).

Step 2 Model the situation. The shuttle runs every 10 minutes, so it will arrive in 10 minutes or less. You need it to arrive within __3__ minutes.

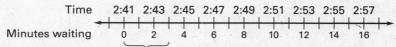

The shuttle needs to arrive within the first __3__ minutes.

Step 3 Find the probability.

$$P(\text{Get to town by 2:57}) = \frac{\text{Favorable waiting time}}{\text{Maximum waiting time}}$$

$$= \frac{3}{10}$$

The probability that you get to town by 2:57 is $\frac{3}{10}$, or __30__ %.

PROBABILITY AND AREA

Let *J* be a region that contains region *M*. If a point *K* in *J* is chosen at random, then the probability that it is in region *M* is the ratio of the area of *M* to the area of *J*.

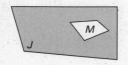

$$P(K \text{ is in region } M) = \frac{\text{Area of } M}{\text{Area of } J}$$

Example 3   *Use areas to find a geometric probability*

Golf A golf ball is hit and stops on the green. A prize is won if it stops in the painted circle. The diameters of the green and circle are shown at the right. If the ball is equally likely to stop on any point on the green, what is the probability that a prize is won?

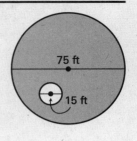
75 ft
15 ft

Solution

Find the ratio of the circle's area to the green's area.

> All circles are similar and the Area of Similar Polygons Theorem also applies to circles. The ratio of radii is 7.5 : 37.5, or 1 : 5, so the ratio of areas is $1^2 : 5^2$, or 1 : 25.

$P(\text{prize is won}) = \dfrac{\text{Area of painted circle}}{\text{Area of green}}$

$= \dfrac{\pi\left(\boxed{7.5}^{\,2}\right)}{\pi\left(\boxed{37.5}^{\,2}\right)} = \dfrac{\boxed{56.25}\,\pi}{\boxed{1406.25}\,\pi} = \dfrac{1}{25}$

The probability that a prize is won is $\dfrac{1}{25}$, or $\underline{\ 4\ }$%.

✓ **Checkpoint** Complete the following exercises.

1. Find the probability that a point chosen at random on $\overline{LP}$ is on $\overline{MN}$.

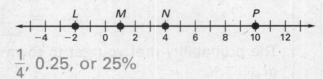

$\dfrac{1}{4}$, 0.25, or 25%

2. In Example 2, suppose you arrive at the pickup location at 2:38. What is the probability that you will get to town by 2:57?

60%

3. On the green in Example 3, the hole is 4.25 inches in diameter. Find the probability that your ball stops in the hole.

about 0.000022

Example 4   *Estimate area on a grid to find a probability*

Property A homeowner's property is shown in the scale drawing. If a deer is equally likely to be anywhere on the property, estimate the probability that it is on grass.

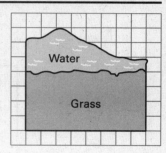

Solution

Step 1 **Find** the grass area. The shape is a rectangle, so the area is bh = __8__ • __4__ = __32__ square units.

Step 2 **Find** the total area of the property.

Count the squares that are fully covered. There are __32__ squares in the grass and __12__ in the water. So, there are __44__ full squares.

Make groups of partial squares so the area of each is about **1 square unit**. The total area of partial squares is about __3__ square units. So use __44__ + __3__ = __47__ square units for the total area.

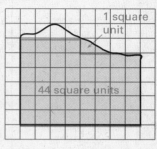

> The deer must be in the grass or in the water, so check that the probabilities in Example 4 and Checkpoint Exercise 4 add up to 100%.

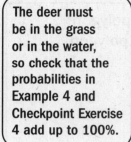

Step 3 **Write** a ratio of the areas to find the probability.

$$P(\text{deer on grass}) = \frac{\text{Area of grass}}{\text{Total area of property}} \approx \frac{32}{47}$$

The probability that the deer is on grass is about $\frac{32}{47}$, or about __68.1__ %.

✓ *Checkpoint* **Complete the following exercise.**

Homework

4. In Example 4, estimate the probability that the deer is in the water.

about 31.9%

Words to Review

Give an example of the vocabulary word.

Bases, height of a parallelogram base height base	**Height of a trapezoid** height
Circumference Circumference	**Arc length** Arc length of $\overset{\frown}{AB}$ A B
Sector of a circle A Sector B	**Center of a polygon, Radius of a polygon** center radius
Apothem of a polygon apothem	**Central angle of a regular polygon** Central angle
Probability The probability of an event is a measure of the likelihood that the event will occur.	**Geometric probability** A geometric probability is a ratio that involves a geometric measure such as length or area.

Review your notes and Chapter 11 by using the Chapter Review on pages 780–783 of your textbook.

12.1 Explore Solids

Goal • Identify solids.

Your Notes

VOCABULARY

Polyhedron A polyhedron is a solid that is bounded by polygons that enclose a single region of space.

Face The faces of a polyhedron are polygons.

Edge An edge of a polyhedron is a line segment formed by the intersection of two faces.

Vertex A vertex of a polyhedron is a point where three or more edges meet.

Base A base is a polygon that is used to name the polyhedron.

Regular polyhedron A regular polyhedron is a polyhedron whose faces are all congruent regular polygons.

Convex polyhedron A convex polyhedron is a polyhedron such that any two points on its surface can be connected by a line segment that lies entirely inside or on the polyhedron.

> Notice that the names of four of the Platonic solids end in "hedron." *Hedron* is Greek for "side" or "face." Sometimes a cube is called a regular *hexahedron*.

Platonic solids A Platonic solid is one of five regular polyhedra: a regular tetrahedron, a cube, a regular octahedron, a regular dodecahedron, and a regular icosahedron.

Cross section A cross section is the intersection of a plane and a solid.

TYPES OF SOLIDS

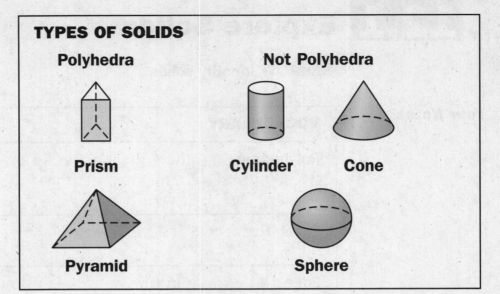

Polyhedra	Not Polyhedra
Prism	Cylinder Cone
Pyramid	Sphere

Example 1   *Identify and name polyhedra*

Tell whether the solid is a polyhedron. If it is, name the polyhedron and find the number of faces, vertices, and edges.

a.
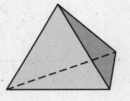

b.
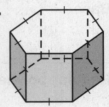

c.
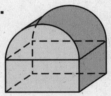

Solution

a. This is a polyhedron. It has __4__ faces so it is a ___tetrahedron___ . It has __4__ vertices and __6__ edges.

b. This is a polyhedron. The two bases are congruent hexagons, so it is a __hexagonal prism__ . It has __8__ faces, __12__ vertices, and __18__ edges.

c. This is not a polyhedron. The solid has a curved surface.

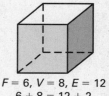

THEOREM 12.1: EULER'S THEOREM

The number of faces (*F*), vertices (*V*), and edges (*E*) of a polyhedron are related by the formula

$F + V = E +$ <u>2</u>.

$F = 6$, $V = 8$, $E = 12$
$6 + 8 = 12 + 2$

Example 2   *Use Euler's Theorem*

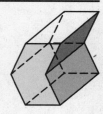

Find the number of faces, vertices, and edges of the polyhedron shown. Check your answers using Euler's Theorem.

The polyhedron has <u>8</u> faces, <u>12</u> vertices, and <u>18</u> edges.

Use Euler's Theorem to check.

$F + V = E + 2$	Euler's Theorem
<u>8</u> + <u>12</u> = <u>18</u> + 2	Substitute.
<u>20</u> = <u>20</u>	Check.

Example 3   *Describe cross sections*

Describe the shape formed by the intersection of the plane and the solid.

a.

b.
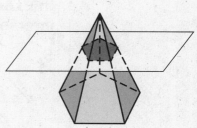

c.
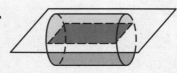

Solution

a. The cross section is a <u>circle</u>.

b. The cross section is a <u>pentagon</u>.

c. The cross section is a <u>rectangle</u>.

✔ *Checkpoint* **Complete the following exercises.**

In Exercises 1–3, tell whether the solid is a polyhedron. If it is, name the polyhedron and find the number of faces, vertices, and edges.

1. 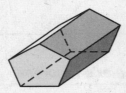 This is a polyhedron. Its bases are congruent pentagons, so it is a pentagonal prism. It has 7 faces, 10 vertices, and 15 edges.

2. 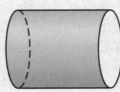 This is not a polyhedron. The solid has a curved surface.

3. 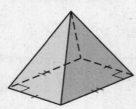 This is a polyhedron. Its base is a rectangle, so it is a rectangular pyramid. It has 5 faces, 5 vertices, and 8 edges.

4. Is it possible for a polyhedron to have 16 faces, 34 vertices, and 50 edges? *Explain.*

No; Using Euler's Theorem $F + V = E + 2$, $16 + 34 \neq 50 + 2$.

In Exercises 5–7, *describe* the shape formed by the intersection of the plane and the solid.

5. 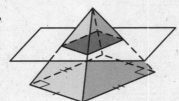 rectangle

6.  pentagon

7.  triangle

Homework

Surface Area of Prisms and Cylinders

Goal • Find the surface areas of prisms and cylinders.

Your Notes

VOCABULARY

Prism A prism is a polyhedron with two congruent faces, called bases, that lie in parallel planes.

Lateral faces The lateral faces of a prism are parallelograms formed by connecting the corresponding vertices of the bases.

Lateral edges The lateral edges of a prism are the segments connecting the corresponding vertices of the bases.

Surface area The surface area of a polyhedron is the sum of the areas of its faces.

Lateral area The lateral area of a polyhedron is the sum of the areas of its lateral faces.

Net A net of a polyhedron is a two-dimensional representation of the faces of a polyhedron.

Right prism In a right prism, each lateral edge is perpendicular to both bases.

Oblique prism An oblique prism is a prism with lateral edges that are not perpendicular to the bases.

Cylinder A cylinder is a solid with congruent circular bases that lie in parallel planes.

Right cylinder In a right cylinder, the segment joining the centers of the bases is perpendicular to the bases.

> Remember, the *apothem* of a polygon is the distance from the center to any side of the polygon.

THEOREM 12.2: SURFACE AREA OF A RIGHT PRISM

The surface area S of a right prism is

$$S = 2B + \underline{\ Ph\ } = aP + \underline{\ Ph\ },$$

where a is the apothem of the base, B is the area of a base, P is the perimeter of a base, and h is the height.

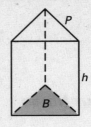

Example 1 *Find the surface area of a right prism*

Find the surface area of the right prism.

Solution

Each base is an equilateral triangle with a side length s of $\underline{\ 6\ }$ inches. Using the formula for the area of an equilateral triangle, the area of each base is

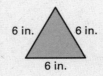

$$B = \tfrac{1}{4}\sqrt{3}\,(s^2)$$

$$= \tfrac{1}{4}\sqrt{3}\,(\underline{\ 6\ }^2) = \underline{\ 9\ }\sqrt{3}\text{ in.}^2$$

The perimeter of each base is $P = \underline{\ 18\ }$ in. and the height is $h = \underline{\ 8\ }$ in.

$S = 2B + Ph$ **Surface area of a right prism**

$\quad = 2(\underline{\ 9\ }\sqrt{3}) + \underline{\ 18\ }(\underline{\ 8\ })$ **Substitute.**

$\quad \approx \underline{\ 175.18\ }$ **Simplify.**

The surface area is about $\underline{\ 175.18\ }$ square inches.

✔ **Checkpoint** Complete the following exercise.

1. Find the surface area of a right rectangular prism with height 5 feet, length 11 feet, and width 4 feet.

   238 ft^2

THEOREM 12.3: SURFACE AREA OF A RIGHT CYLINDER

The surface area S of a right cylinder is

$S = 2B + Ch = $ <u>$2\pi r^2 + 2\pi rh$</u> ,

where B is the area of a base, C is the circumference of a base, r is the radius of a base, and h is the height.

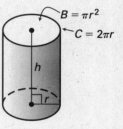

$B = \pi r^2$
$C = 2\pi r$

Example 2 *Find the surface area of a cylinder*

Find the surface area of the right cylinder.

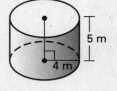

5 m
4 m

Solution

Each base has a radius of <u>4</u> meters, and the cylinder has a height of <u>5</u> meters.

$S = 2\pi r^2 + 2\pi rh$	**Surface area of a cylinder**
$= 2\pi(\underline{4}^2) + 2\pi(\underline{4})(\underline{5})$	**Substitute.**
$= \underline{32}\,\pi + \underline{40}\,\pi$	**Simplify.**
$= \underline{72}\,\pi$	**Add.**
$\approx \underline{226.19}$	**Use a calculator.**

The surface area is about <u>226.19</u> square meters.

✓ **Checkpoint** Complete the following exercise.

2. Find the surface area of a right cylinder with height 9 centimeters and radius 6 centimeters. Round your answer to two decimal places.

   565.49 cm²

Example 3	*Find the height of a cylinder*

Find the height of the right cylinder shown, which has a surface area of 198.8 square millimeters.

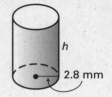

h

2.8 mm

Solution

Substitute known values in the formula for the surface area of a right cylinder and solve for the height *h*.

$$S = 2\pi r^2 + 2\pi rh$$ **Surface area of a cylinder**

$$\underline{198.8} = 2\pi(\underline{2.8}^2) + 2\pi(\underline{2.8})h$$ **Substitute.**

$$\underline{198.8} = \underline{15.68}\,\pi + \underline{5.6}\,\pi h$$ **Simplify.**

$$\underline{198.8} - \underline{15.68}\,\pi = \underline{5.6}\,\pi h$$ **Subtract** $\underline{15.68}\,\pi$ **from each side.**

$$\underline{149.54} \approx \underline{5.6}\,\pi h$$ **Simplify. Use a calculator.**

$$\underline{8.5} \approx h$$ **Divide each side by** $\underline{5.6}\,\pi$.

The height of the cylinder is about $\underline{8.5}$ millimeters.

✔ *Checkpoint* **Complete the following exercise.**

3. Find the radius of a right cylinder with height 5 inches and surface area 168π square inches.

7 in.

Homework

12.3 Surface Area of Pyramids and Cones

Goal • Find the surface areas of pyramids and cones.

Your Notes

> Pyramids are classified by the shapes of their bases.

VOCABULARY

Pyramid A pyramid is a polyhedron in which the base is a polygon and the lateral faces are triangles with a common vertex.

Vertex of a pyramid The vertex of a pyramid is the common vertex of the lateral faces of a pyramid.

Regular pyramid A regular pyramid has a regular polygon for a base and the segment joining the vertex and the center of the base is perpendicular to the base. The lateral faces of a regular pyramid are congruent isosceles triangles.

Slant height The slant height of a regular pyramid is the height of a lateral face of the regular pyramid.

Cone A cone has a circular base and a vertex that is not in the same plane as the base.

Vertex of a cone The vertex of a cone is the point on the cone that is located at a perpendicular distance from the base, called the height of the cone.

Right cone In a right cone, the segment joining the vertex and the center of the base is perpendicular to the base and the slant height is the distance between the vertex and a point on the base edge.

Lateral surface The lateral surface of a cone consists of all segments that connect the vertex with points on the base edge.

Example 1   *Find the area of a lateral face of a pyramid*

Find the area of each lateral face of the regular square pyramid.

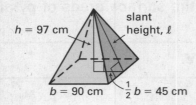

$h = 97$ cm   slant height, ℓ

$b = 90$ cm $\frac{1}{2}b = 45$ cm

Solution

Use the Pythagorean Theorem to find the slant height ℓ.

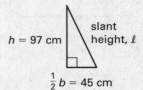

slant height, ℓ

$h = 97$ cm

$\frac{1}{2}b = 45$ cm

$\ell^2 = h^2 + \left(\frac{1}{2}b\right)^2$ **Write formula.**

$\ell^2 = \underline{\;97\;}^2 + \underline{\;45\;}^2$ **Substitute for h and $\frac{1}{2}b$.**

$\ell^2 = \underline{\;11{,}434\;}$ **Simplify.**

$\ell = \underline{\;\pm\sqrt{11{,}434}\;}$ **Take the square root of each side.**

$\ell \approx \underline{\;106.93\;}$ **Find the positive square root.**

Find the area of each triangular face.

$A = \frac{1}{2}b\ell$ **Write formula.**

$\approx \frac{1}{2}(\underline{\;90\;})(\underline{\;106.93\;})$ **Substitute for b and ℓ.**

$\approx \underline{\;4811.85\;}$ **Simplify.**

The area of each lateral face is about $\underline{\;4811.85\;}$ square centimeters.

THEOREM 12.4: SURFACE AREA OF A REGULAR PYRAMID

The surface area S of a regular pyramid is

$S = B + \underline{\;\frac{1}{2}P\ell\;}$,

where B is the area of the base, P is the perimeter of the base, and ℓ is the slant height.

Example 2   *Find the surface area of a pyramid*

Find the surface area of the regular hexagonal pyramid.

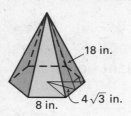

18 in.

8 in. $4\sqrt{3}$ in.

> Remember, the *apothem* of a polygon is the distance from the center to any side of the polygon.

Solution

First, find the area of the base using the formula for the area of a regular polygon, $\frac{1}{2}aP$. The apothem a of the hexagon is __$4\sqrt{3}$__ inches and the perimeter P is $6 \cdot$ __8__ $=$ __48__ inches.

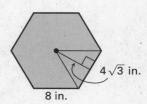

$4\sqrt{3}$ in.

8 in.

So, the area of the base B is $\frac{1}{2}($ __$4\sqrt{3}$__ $)($ __48__ $) =$ __$96\sqrt{3}$__ square inches. Then, find the surface area.

$$S = B + \frac{1}{2}P\ell$$ Surface area of regular pyramid

$$= \underline{96\sqrt{3}} + \frac{1}{2}(\underline{48})(\underline{18})$$ Substitute.

$$= \underline{96\sqrt{3}} + \underline{432}$$ Simplify.

$$\approx \underline{598.3}$$ Use a calculator.

The surface area of the regular hexagonal pyramid is about __598.3__ square inches.

THEOREM 12.5: SURFACE AREA OF A RIGHT CONE

The surface area S of a right cone is

$$S = B + \frac{1}{2}C\ell = \underline{\pi r^2 + \pi r\ell},$$

where B is area of the base, C is the circumference of the base, r is the radius of the base, and ℓ is the slant height.

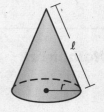

ℓ

| **Example 3** | *Find the surface area of a right cone* |

Find the surface area of the right cone.

Solution

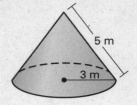

The base has a radius of __3__ meters, and the cone has a slant height of __5__ meters.

$$S = \pi r^2 + \pi r \ell$$ **Surface area of right cone**

$$= \pi(\underline{\,3\,}^2) + \pi(\underline{\,3\,})(\underline{\,5\,})$$ **Substitute.**

$$= \underline{\,9\,}\pi + \underline{\,15\,}\pi$$ **Simplify.**

$$= \underline{\,24\,}\pi$$ **Add.**

$$\approx \underline{\,75.4\,}$$ **Use a calculator.**

The surface area of the right cone is about __75.4__ square meters.

✔ *Checkpoint* **Complete the following exercises.**

1. Find (a) the area of each lateral face and (b) the surface area of the regular square pyramid.

   a. 300 mm²   b. 1600 mm²

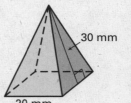

2. Find the surface area of the right cone. Round your answer to two decimal places.

   301.59 ft²

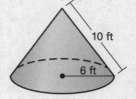

Homework

12.4 Volume of Prisms and Cylinders

Goal • Find volumes of prisms and cylinders.

Your Notes

VOCABULARY

Volume The volume of a solid is the number of cubic units contained in its interior.

POSTULATE 27: VOLUME OF A CUBE POSTULATE

The volume of a cube is the cube of the length of its side.

$V = \underline{s^3}$

POSTULATE 28: VOLUME CONGRUENCE POSTULATE

If two polyhedra are congruent, then <u>they have the same volume</u>.

POSTULATE 29: VOLUME ADDITION POSTULATE

The volume of a solid is the <u>sum</u> of the volumes of all its nonoverlapping parts.

THEOREM 12.6: VOLUME OF A PRISM

The volume V of a prism is $V = \underline{Bh}$, where B is the area of the base and h is the height.

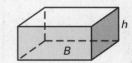

THEOREM 12.7: VOLUME OF A CYLINDER

The volume V of a cylinder is $V = Bh = \underline{\pi r^2 h}$, where B is the area of a base, h is the height, and r is the radius of a base.

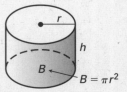

$B = \pi r^2$

Example 1   *Find volumes of prisms and cylinders*

Find the volume of the solid.

a. Right triangular prism   **b.** Right cylinder

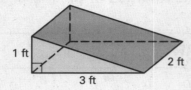 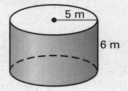

Solution

a. The area of the base is $\frac{1}{2}(\underline{\ 1\ })(\underline{\ 3\ }) = \underline{\frac{3}{2}}$ ft^2 and $h = 2$ ft.

$V = Bh = \underline{\frac{3}{2}} \cdot \underline{\ 2\ } = \underline{\ 3\ }$ ft^3

b. The area of the base is $\pi \cdot \underline{\ 5\ }^2$, or $\underline{\ 25\ } \pi$ m^2. Use $h = 6$ to find the volume.

$V = Bh = \underline{\ 25\ } \pi(\underline{\ 6\ }) = \underline{\ 150\ } \pi \approx \underline{\ 471.24\ }$ m^3

Example 2   *Use volume of a right cylinder*

The volume of the right cylinder shown is 1253 cubic centimeters. Find the value of x.

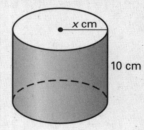

Solution

The area of the base is πx^2 square meters.

$V = Bh$	Formula for volume of a cylinder
$\underline{\ 1253\ } = \pi x^2(\underline{\ 10\ })$	Substitute.
$\underline{\ 1253\ } = \underline{\ 10\ } \pi x^2$	Rewrite.
$\dfrac{\boxed{1253}}{\boxed{10}\ \pi} = x^2$	Divide each side by $\underline{\ 10\ } \pi$.
$\underline{\ 39.88\ } \approx x^2$	Simplify.
$\underline{\ 6.32\ } \approx x$	Find the positive square root.

The radius of the cylinder is about $\underline{\ 6.32\ }$ centimeters.

THEOREM 12.8: CAVALIERI'S PRINCIPLE

If two solids have the same height and the same cross-sectional area at every level, then they have the same _volume_ .

Example 3 *Find the volume of an oblique cylinder*

Find the volume of the oblique cylinder.

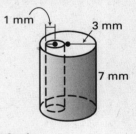

5 in.

8 in.

Solution

Cavalieri's Principle tells you that the volume formulas work for oblique prisms and cylinders.

Cavalieri's Principle allows you to use Theorem 12.7 to find the volume of the oblique cylinder.

$V = \pi r^2 h$ **Formula for volume of a cylinder**

$= \pi(\underline{\ 5\ }^2)(\underline{\ 8\ })$ **Substitute.**

$= \underline{\ 200\ }\ \pi$ **Simplify.**

$\approx \underline{\ 628.32\ }$ **Use a calculator.**

The volume of the oblique cylinder is about _628.32_ in.^{3}

Example 4 *Find the volume of a composite solid*

Find the volume of the solid.

1 mm

3 mm

7 mm

Solution

The area of the base B can be found by subtracting the area of the small circle from the area of the large circle.

B = Area of large circle − Area of small circle

$= \pi(\underline{\ 3\ }^2) - \pi(\underline{\ 1\ }^2) = \underline{\ 8\ }\ \pi \approx \underline{\ 25.13\ }$ mm^2

Use the formula for volume of a cylinder.

$V = Bh$ **Formula for volume of a cylinder**

$= (\underline{\ 25.13\ })(\underline{\ 7\ })$ **Substitute.**

$= \underline{\ 175.91\ }$ **Use a calculator.**

The volume of the solid is about _175.91_ cubic millimeters.

✔ *Checkpoint* **Complete the following exercises.**

In Exercises 1 and 2, find the volume of the solid. Round your answer to two decimal places, if necessary.

1. Right rectangular prism

220 m³

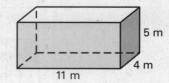

5 m
4 m
11 m

2. Right cylinder

1017.88 ft³

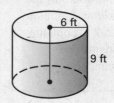

6 ft
9 ft

3. The volume of the right cylinder is 200π cubic centimeters. Find the value of x.

10 cm

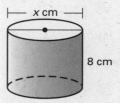

x cm
8 cm

In Exercises 4 and 5, find the volume of the solid. Round your answer to two decimal places.

4. Oblique cylinder

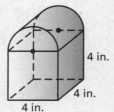

12 mm
18 mm
60°

1763.01 mm³

5. Composite solid

4 in.
4 in.
4 in.
4 in.

89.13 in.³

Homework

12.5 Volume of Pyramids and Cones

• Find volumes of pyramids and cones.

Your Notes

THEOREM 12.9: VOLUME OF A PYRAMID

The volume V of a pyramid is

$V = \underline{\frac{1}{3}Bh}$,

where B is the area of the base and h is the height.

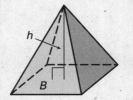

Example 1   *Find the volume of a pyramid*

Find the volume of the pyramid with the regular base.

Solution

First, find the area of the base using the formula for the area of a regular polygon, $\frac{1}{2}aP$. The apothem a of the hexagon is

$\underline{2\sqrt{3}}$ inches and the perimeter P is

$6 \cdot \underline{4} = \underline{24}$ inches.

So, the area of the base B is

$\frac{1}{2}(\underline{2\sqrt{3}})(\underline{24}) = \underline{24\sqrt{3}}$ in.^{2}.

Then, find the volume.

> The formula given in Theorem 12.9 applies to both right and oblique pyramids. This follows from Cavalieri's Principle.

$V = \frac{1}{3}Bh$ **Formula for volume of a pyramid**

$= \frac{1}{3}\underline{24\sqrt{3}}(\underline{10})$ **Substitute.**

$= \underline{80\sqrt{3}}$ **Simplify.**

$\approx \underline{138.56}$ **Use a calculator.**

The volume of the pyramid is about $\underline{138.56}$ cubic inches.

THEOREM 12.10: VOLUME OF A CONE

The volume V of a cone is

$$V = \frac{1}{3}Bh = \frac{1}{3}\pi r^2 h,$$

where B is area of the base, h is the height, and r is the radius of the base.

Example 2   *Find volumes of cones*

Find the volume of the cone.

a. Right cone

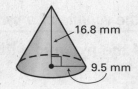

16.8 mm

9.5 mm

b. Oblique cone

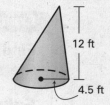

12 ft

4.5 ft

Solution

a. Use the formula for volume of a cone.

$$V = \frac{1}{3}\pi r^2 h \qquad \text{Formula for volume of a cone}$$

$$= \frac{1}{3}\pi(\underline{\,9.5\,}^2)(\underline{\,16.8\,}) \qquad \text{Substitute.}$$

$$= \underline{\,505.4\,}\,\pi \qquad \text{Simplify.}$$

$$\approx \underline{\,1587.8\,} \qquad \text{Use a calculator.}$$

The volume of the right cone is about __1587.8__ mm^3.

b. Use the formula for volume of a cone.

$$V = \frac{1}{3}\pi r^2 h \qquad \text{Formula for volume of a cone}$$

$$= \frac{1}{3}\pi(\underline{\,4.5\,}^2)(\underline{\,12\,}) \qquad \text{Substitute.}$$

$$= \underline{\,81\,}\,\pi \qquad \text{Simplify.}$$

$$\approx \underline{\,254.5\,} \qquad \text{Use a calculator.}$$

The volume of the oblique cone is about __254.5__ ft^3.

> The formula given in Theorem 12.10 applies to both right and oblique cones. This follows from Cavalieri's Principle.

Example 3 — *Use trigonometry to find the volume of a cone*

Find the volume of the right cone.

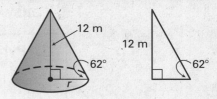

12 m

62°

12 m

62°

Solution

To find the radius *r* of the base, use trigonometry.

$$\underline{\tan}\ 62° = \frac{\text{opp.}}{\text{adj.}}$$ **Write ratio.**

$$\tan 62° = \frac{12}{r}$$ **Substitute.**

$$r = \frac{\boxed{12}}{\boxed{\tan 62°}} \approx \underline{6.38}$$ **Solve for *r*.**

Use the formula for the volume of a cone.

$$V = \frac{1}{3}(\pi r^2)h \approx \frac{1}{3}\pi(\underline{6.38}^{\ 2})(\underline{12}) \approx \underline{511.5}$$

The volume of the cone is about ___511.5___ cubic meters.

Example 4 — *Find volume of a composite solid*

Find the volume of the solid shown. The cone and the cylinder are right.

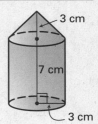

3 cm

7 cm

3 cm

Solution

Volume of solid $=$ Volume of ___cylinder___ $+$ Volume of ___cone___

$$= \pi r^2h + \frac{1}{3}\pi r^2h$$

$$= \pi(\underline{3}^{\ 2})(\underline{7}) + \frac{1}{3}\pi(\underline{3}^{\ 2})(\underline{3})$$ **Substitute.**

$$= \underline{63}\ \pi + \underline{9}\ \pi$$ **Simplify.**

$$= \underline{226.19}$$ **Use a calculator.**

The volume of the solid is about ___226.19___ cubic centimeters.

✓ *Checkpoint* **Find the volume of the solid. Round your answer to two decimal places.**

1. Pyramid with regular base

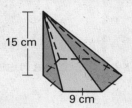

15 cm

9 cm

1052.22 cm³

2. Right cone

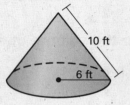

10 ft

6 ft

301.59 ft³

3. Right cone

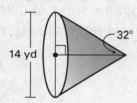

14 yd

32°

574.70 yd³

4. Composite solid

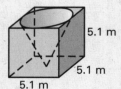

5.1 m

5.1 m

5.1 m

97.92 m³

Homework

12.6 Surface Area and Volume of Spheres

Goal • Find surface areas and volumes of spheres.

Your Notes

VOCABULARY

Sphere A sphere is the set of all points in space equidistant from a given point.

Center of a sphere The center of a sphere is the given point from which all points on the sphere are equidistant.

Radius of a sphere A radius of a sphere is a segment from the center to a point on the sphere.

Chord of a sphere A chord of a sphere is a segment whose endpoints are on the sphere.

Diameter of a sphere A diameter of a sphere is a chord that contains the center of the sphere.

Great circle A great circle is the intersection of a sphere and a plane that contains the center of the sphere.

Hemisphere A hemisphere is one of the congruent halves of a sphere.

THEOREM 12.11: SURFACE AREA OF A SPHERE

The surface area S of a sphere is

$S = \underline{4\pi r^2}$,

where r is the radius of the sphere.

Example 1   *Find the surface area of a sphere*

Find the surface area of the sphere.

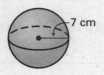

7 cm

Solution

$S = 4\pi r^2$	Formula for surface area of a sphere
$= 4\pi(\,\underline{7}\,^2)$	Substitute _7_ for *r*.
$= \underline{196}\ \pi$	Simplify.
$\approx \underline{615.75}$	Use a calculator.

The surface area of the sphere is about _615.75_ cm^2.

Example 2   *Find the diameter of a sphere*

The surface area of a sphere is 110.25π square feet. Find the diameter of the sphere.

Solution

$S = 4\pi r^2$	Formula for surface area of a sphere
$\underline{110.25\pi} = 4\pi r^2$	Substitute _110.25π_ for *S*.
$\underline{27.5625} = r^2$	Divide each side by _4π_ .
$\underline{5.25} = r$	Find the positive square root.

The diameter of the sphere is

$2r = 2 \cdot \underline{5.25} = \underline{10.5}$ feet.

> Be sure to multiply the value of *r* by 2 to find the diameter.

THEOREM 12.12: VOLUME OF A SPHERE

The volume V of a sphere is

$$V = \underline{\frac{4}{3}\pi r^3},$$

where r is the radius of the sphere.

Example 3 *Find the volume of a sphere*

Find the volume of the sphere.

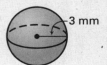

3 mm

Solution

$V = \frac{4}{3}\pi r^3$ Formula for volume of a sphere

$= \frac{4}{3}\pi(\underline{3}^3)$ Substitute $\underline{3}$ for r.

$\approx \underline{113.1}$ Use a calculator.

The volume of the sphere is about $\underline{113.1}$ cubic millimeters.

Example 4 *Find the volume of a composite solid*

Find the volume of the composite solid.

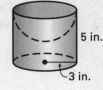

5 in.

3 in.

Solution

$$\begin{array}{l}\text{Volume of} \\ \text{solid}\end{array} = \begin{array}{l}\text{Volume of} \\ \underline{\text{cylinder}}\end{array} - \begin{array}{l}\text{Volume of} \\ \underline{\text{hemisphere}}\end{array}$$

$= \pi r^2 h - \frac{1}{2}\left(\frac{4}{3}\pi r^3\right)$ **Volume formulas**

$= \pi(\underline{3}^2)(\underline{5}) - \frac{1}{2}\left(\frac{4}{3}\pi(\underline{3}^3)\right)$ **Substitute.**

$= \underline{45}\,\pi - \underline{18}\,\pi$ **Simplify.**

$\approx \underline{84.82}$ **Use a calculator.**

The volume of the solid is about $\underline{84.82}$ cubic inches.

✓ *Checkpoint* **Complete the following exercises.**

1. The diameter of a sphere is $\dfrac{1}{\sqrt{\pi}}$ meter. Find the surface area of the sphere.

   1 m^2

2. The surface area of a sphere is 169π square inches. Find the radius of the sphere.

   6.5 in.

3. The radius of a sphere is 2.4 cm. Find the volume of the sphere. Round your answer to two decimal places.

   57.89 cm^3

4. Find the volume of the composite solid. Round your answer to two decimal places.

   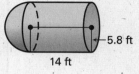
   5.8 ft
   14 ft

   1888.20 ft^3

Homework

12.7 Explore Similar Solids

Goal • Use properties of similar solids.

Your Notes

VOCABULARY

Similar solids Similar solids are two solids of the same type with equal ratios of corresponding linear measures, such as heights or radii.

Example 1 *Identify similar solids*

Tell whether the given right rectangular prism is similar to the right rectangular prism shown at the right.

a.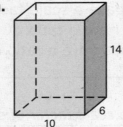

b.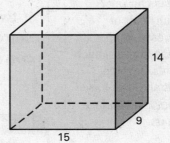

Solution

> To compare the ratios of corresponding side lengths, write the ratios as fractions in simplest form.

a. The prisms are similar because the ratios of corresponding linear measures are equal, as shown. The solids have a scale factor of __1__ : __2__ .

lengths: $\dfrac{\boxed{5}}{\boxed{10}} = \dfrac{1}{2}$

widths: $\dfrac{\boxed{3}}{\boxed{6}} = \dfrac{1}{2}$

heights: $\dfrac{\boxed{7}}{\boxed{14}} = \dfrac{1}{2}$

b. The prisms are not similar because the ratios of corresponding linear measures are not equal, as shown.

lengths: $\dfrac{\boxed{5}}{\boxed{15}} = \dfrac{1}{3}$

widths: $\dfrac{\boxed{3}}{\boxed{9}} = \dfrac{1}{3}$

heights: $\dfrac{\boxed{7}}{\boxed{14}} = \dfrac{1}{2}$

Your Notes

✔ *Checkpoint* **Tell whether the pair of solids is similar.** *Explain* **your reasoning.**

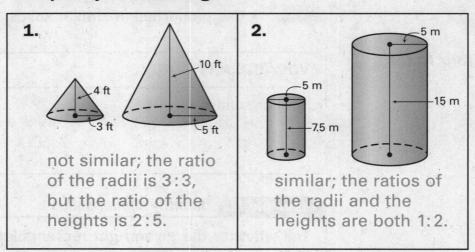

1.

not similar; the ratio of the radii is 3:3, but the ratio of the heights is 2:5.

2.

similar; the ratios of the radii and the heights are both 1:2.

> In Theorem 12.13, areas can refer to any pair of corresponding areas in the similar solids, such as lateral areas, base areas, and surface areas.

THEOREM 12.13: SIMILAR SOLIDS THEOREM

If two similar solids have a scale factor of $a:b$, then corresponding areas have a ratio of $\underline{\ a^2\ }:\underline{\ b^2\ }$, and corresponding volumes have a ratio of $\underline{\ a^3\ }:\underline{\ b^3\ }$.

Example 2   *Use the scale factor of similar solids*

Cylinders *A* and *B* are similar with a scale factor of 2:5. Find the surface area and volume of Cylinder *B* given that the surface area of Cylinder *A* is 96π square feet and the volume of Cylinder *A* is 128π cubic feet.

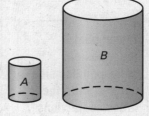

Solution

Use Theorem 12.13 to write and solve two proportions.

$$\frac{\text{Surface area of } A}{\text{Surface area of } B} = \frac{a^2}{b^2} \qquad \frac{\text{Volume of } A}{\text{Volume of } B} = \frac{a^3}{b^3}$$

$$\frac{96\pi}{\text{Surface area of } B} = \frac{4}{25} \qquad \frac{128\pi}{\text{Volume of } B} = \frac{8}{125}$$

Surface area of *B* = $\underline{\ 600\pi\ }$ Volume of *B* = $\underline{\ 2000\pi\ }$

The surface area of Cylinder *B* is $\underline{\ 600\pi\ }$ square feet, and the volume of Cylinder *B* is $\underline{\ 2000\pi\ }$ cubic feet.

Example 3   *Find the scale factor*

The two cones are similar.
Find the scale factor.

$V = 108\pi \text{ cm}^3$ $V = 256\pi \text{ cm}^3$

Use Theorem 12.13 to find the
ratio of the two volumes.

$\dfrac{a^3}{b^3} = \dfrac{108\pi}{256\pi}$ **Write ratio of volumes.**

$\dfrac{a^3}{b^3} = \dfrac{27}{64}$ **Simplify.**

$\dfrac{a}{b} = \dfrac{3}{4}$ **Find cube roots.**

The two cones have a scale factor of __3__ : __4__ .

✔ *Checkpoint* **Complete the following exercises.**

3. Cones A and B are similar with a scale factor of
   $5:2$. Find the surface area and volume of Cone B
   given that the surface area of Cone A is 2356.2
   square centimeters and the volume of Cone A is
   7450.9 cubic centimeters. Round your answers to
   two decimal places.

   376.99 cm^2; 476.86 cm^3

4. The two cylinders are similar.
   Find the scale factor of
   Cylinder I to Cylinder II.

   $3:2$

   $S = 288 \text{ in.}^2$ $S = 128 \text{ in.}^2$

Example 4 | *Compare similar solids*

A store sells balls of string in two different sizes. The diameter of the larger ball is 1.5 times the diameter of the smaller ball. If the balls of string cost $4.99 and $1.49, respectively, which ball of string is the better buy?

Step 1 Compute the ratio of volumes using the diameters.

$$\frac{\text{Volume of large ball}}{\text{Volume of small ball}} = \frac{1.5^3}{1^3} \approx \frac{3.38}{1},$$

or about 3.38 : 1

Step 2 Find the ratio of costs.

$$\frac{\text{Price of large ball}}{\text{Price of small ball}} = \frac{4.99}{1.49} \approx \frac{3.35}{1},$$

or about 3.35 : 1

Step 3 Compare the ratios in Steps 1 and 2.

If the ratios were the same, neither ball would be a better buy. Comparing the smaller ball to the larger one, the price increase is less than the volume increase. So, you get more string for your dollar if you buy the larger ball of string.

The larger ball of string is the better buy.

✔ **Checkpoint** Complete the following exercise.

5. A store sells birdseed in two sizes of cube-shaped blocks. The smaller block measures 3 in. on an edge and sells for $1.99. The larger block measures 5 in. on an edge and sells for $5.99. Which block of birdseed is the better buy?

   the larger block

Homework

Words to Review

Give an example of the vocabulary word.

Polyhedron, face, edge, vertex, base	**Regular, convex polyhedron**
Platonic solids	**Tetrahedron**
Cube	**Octahedron**
Dodecahedron	**Icosahedron**
Cross section	**Prism, lateral faces, lateral edges**

Surface area	Lateral area
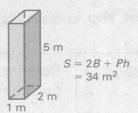 5 m $S = 2B + Ph$ $= 34\ m^2$ 2 m 1 m	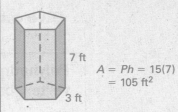 7 ft $A = Ph = 15(7)$ $= 105\ ft^2$ 3 ft

Net	Right prism
 net	

Oblique prism	Cylinder
	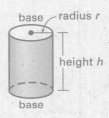 base — radius r height h base

Right cylinder	Pyramid
	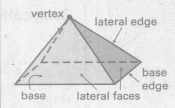 vertex — lateral edge base edge base — lateral faces

Vertex of a pyramid	Regular pyramid
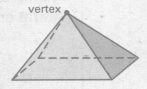 vertex	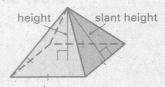 height — slant height

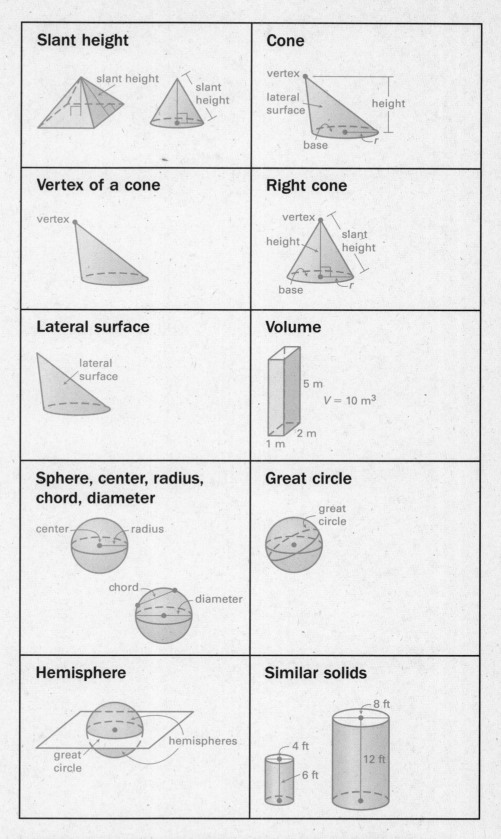

Slant height

slant height

slant height

Cone

vertex

lateral surface

height

base

r

Vertex of a cone

vertex

Right cone

vertex

height

slant height

base

r

Lateral surface

lateral surface

Volume

5 m

$V = 10 \text{ m}^3$

2 m

1 m

Sphere, center, radius, chord, diameter

center

radius

chord

diameter

Great circle

great circle

Hemisphere

hemispheres

great circle

Similar solids

8 ft

4 ft

12 ft

6 ft

Review your notes and Chapter 12 by using the Chapter Review on pages 857–860 of your textbook.